Math

Lesson Guide

2

Book Staff and Contributors

Lisa White *Lead Content Specialist*
Megan Simmons *Content Specialist*
Lauralyn Vaughn *Manager, Instructional Design*
Maria Galanou, Maureen Steddin *Text Editors*
Tricia Battipede *Senior Creative Manager*
Jayoung Cho *Senior Visual Designer*
Caitlin Gildrien, April Okano *Visual Designers*
Sheila Smith *Cover Designer*
Deborah Benton, Dana Crisafulli *Writers*
Amy Eward *Senior Manager, Writing and Editing*
Abhilasha Parakh *Senior Project Manager*

Doug McCollum *Senior Vice President, Product Development*
Kristin Morrison *Vice President, Design and Product Management*
Kelly Engel *Senior Director, Curriculum*
Christopher Frescholtz *Senior Director, Program Management*
Erica Castle *Senior Director, Creative Design*
Lisa Dimaio Iekel *Senior Production Manager*

Image Credits

All illustrations © Stride, Inc. unless otherwise noted.

Characters: Tommy DiGiovanni, Matt Fedor, Ben Gamache, Shannon Palmer

Cover Illustration: Helen Musselwhite

Interior Pattern: Pastel wallpaper patterns. © mxtama/iStock.

Interior Images: 1 Child playing hopscotch. © Nadezhda1906/iStock. **37** Lemonade stand. © jkbowers/iStock. **63** Cat looking at a math problem. © dtv2/iStock. **113** Three puppies looking over a fence. © dageldog/iStock. **129** Ruler measuring the depth of snow. © gchapel/iStock. **171** A young girl assembling a jigsaw puzzle. © nattrass/iStock. **209** Colorful bouncing balls. © Alexander Kirch/EyeEm/Getty Images. **211** Mother and daughter baking. © shapecharge/iStock. **243** King Penguins marching. © burroblando/iStock. **275** Dog tangram. © Freer Law/iStock. **297** Children picking up litter at a beach. © SolStock/iStock. **337** Cat sitting in a chair at a table. © 101cats/iStock. **367** Child touching an emoji. © fotosipsak/iStock. **397** Small boy makes a robot from discarded household items. © yulkapopkova/iStock.

At Stride, Inc. (NYSE: LRN)—formerly K12 Inc.—we are reimagining lifelong learning as a rich, deeply personal experience that prepares learners for tomorrow. Since its inception, Stride has been committed to removing barriers that impact academic equity and to providing high-quality education for anyone—particularly those in underserved communities. The company has transformed the teaching-and-learning experience for millions of people by providing innovative, high-quality, tech-enabled education solutions, curriculum, and programs directly to students, schools, the military, and enterprises in primary, secondary, and post-secondary settings. Stride is a premier provider of K–12 education for students, schools, and districts, including career-learning services through middle and high school curriculum. Providing a solution to the widening skills gap in the workplace and student loan crisis, Stride equips students with real-world skills for in-demand jobs with career learning. For adult learners, Stride delivers professional skills training in healthcare and technology, as well as staffing and talent development for Fortune 500 companies. Stride has delivered millions of courses over the past decade and serves learners in all 50 states and more than 100 countries. The company is a proud sponsor of Future of School, a nonprofit organization dedicated to closing the gap between the pace of technology and the pace of change in education. More information can be found at stridelearning.com, K12.com, destinationsacademy.com, galvanize.com, techelevator.com, and medcerts.com.

ISBN: 978-1-60153-607-5

Printed by Walsworth, Marceline, MO, USA, April 2022.

Table of Contents

Add and Subtract with Two Digits

Add More Than Two Numbers

Working with Length

Solve Story Problems with One Step

Mid-Year Project

Solve Story Problems

Numbers Through 1,000

Shapes

Add and Subtract within 1,000

Number Patterns

Data Displays

End-of-Year Project

Math 2

Welcome to Math 2! We're grateful for this opportunity to play a role in your students' math education. We've provided the following overview of the content and structure of the course so that you can best support your students. At any time, if you have questions or would like further clarification, never hesitate to reach out to us. Let's get started!

Math 2 encourages students to learn independently. As a Learning Coach, your role is to support and enhance the learning experience. Each lesson includes rich interactivity to ensure students build the depth of understanding they need to succeed. Online interactions provide a wealth of data, so teachers know exactly where students are struggling. Additionally, the offline practice, during which students write directly in the activity book, offers variety. With rich content designed to engage and motivate students, and enough practice to reinforce each concept, Math 2 includes the tools and technology that students need to succeed in math.

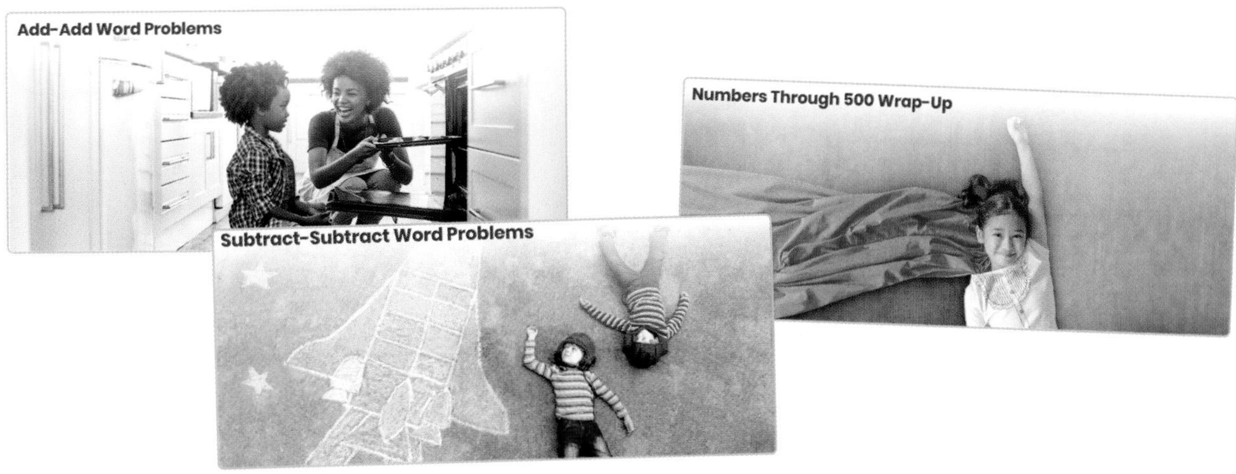

Course Components

Online Lessons

The online lessons provide the core instruction and multiple opportunities for practice in Math 2. The online lessons include

- A predictable lesson structure.
- Interactive problems and assessments that challenge students to use higher-order thinking skills.
- A carefully thought-out progression from guided to independent practice.
- Computer-scored practice with instant and meaningful feedback.
- Learning experiences that support struggling students.
- Explanations and exploratory interactions that support deep understanding, coupled with enough practice to build speed and accuracy.

- Frequent practice with math facts, including games to engage and motivate students.
- Student-friendly learning goals.

Lesson Guide

Each course is accompanied by a lesson guide that makes it quick and easy for Learning Coaches to understand each lesson at a glance—without logging in. The lesson guide provides an overview of a lesson's content, activities, and materials; answer keys for activity book pages; alerts when special Learning Coach attention is needed; and other features to aid the Learning Coach in supporting students.

Activity Book

Math 2 includes a consumable activity book, where students can put pencil to paper every instructional day. Key features include

- Full-color pages with adequate space for answers.
- Problems that require students to draw sketches, show problem-solving steps, evaluate answers, and write explanations.

Additional Supplied Materials

This course includes a base-10 blocks set, which is valuable for modeling place value and basic operations. Math 2 also includes a set of snap cubes, as well as 2-D and 3-D shapes. All manipulatives also have a PDF option that students can use in place of the physical manipulatives.

Also Needed

Students should obtain a binder or spiral notebook to use as their Math Notebook, in which they can work problems, make sketches, and take notes as they work through a lesson. Students should always have paper and a pencil handy.

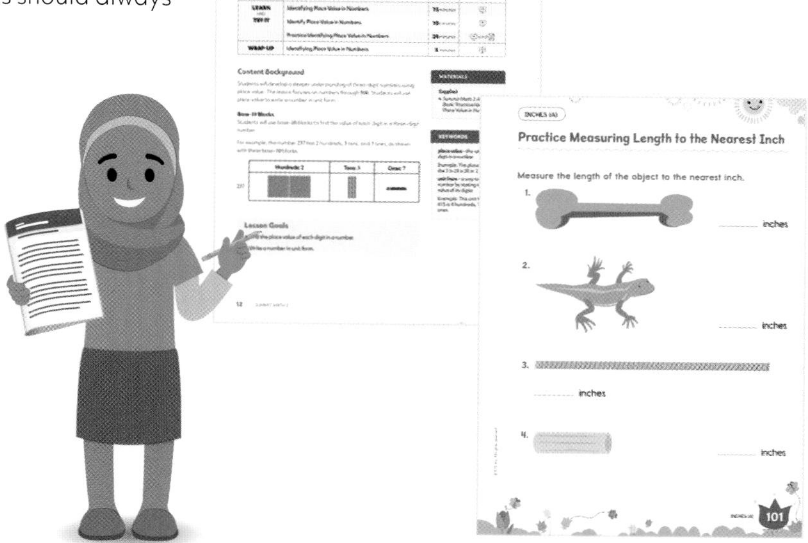

Course Structure

Math 2 is designed to lead students through a logical sequence of concepts based on current state standards. The material is structured to fit within a typical 180-day school year, but it can also be easily adapted to fit individual needs.

Math 2 is divided into units. A typical unit is divided into a series of related concepts, which are divided into daily lessons. Each lesson ends with a quick, nongraded exit ticket assessment. The final lesson in each concept includes a review of the concept and a nongraded concept assessment. A graded unit assessment appears at the end of each unit.

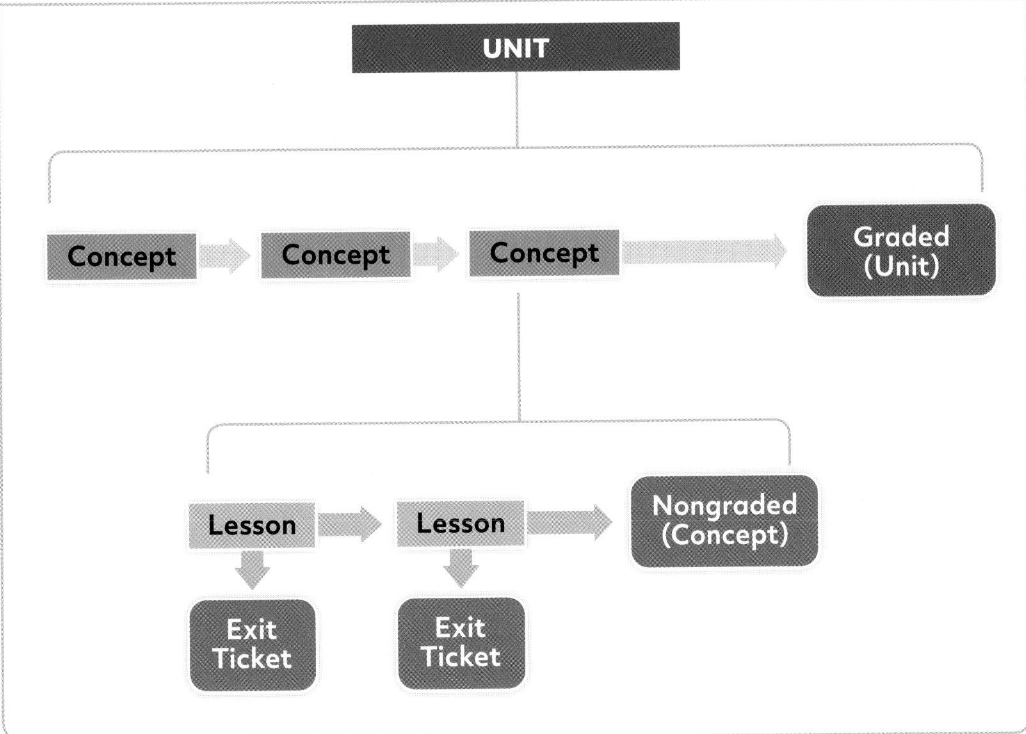

Lesson Model Overview

Concepts in Math 2 follow a multiday learning cycle consisting of an **initial lesson**, one or more **middle lessons**, and a **final lesson**, each of which follows a consistent, predictable instructional formula.

INITIAL AND MIDDLE DAYS

During the initial and middle days, students learn and practice the core content. As students work through these lessons, they are asked to work more and more independently. They progress from concrete explorations and explicit instruction, through guided practice, to independent practice and application.

FINAL DAY

The final day of each concept includes practice problems and a nongraded assessment based on the key objectives in the concept. The results of the concept assessment do not count toward the student's grade, but they are made available to the teacher. Students will also have an opportunity to practice in Stride Skills Arcade on final days.

	Initial Day	Middle Days	Final Day
GET READY			
Get Ready activities introduce and orient students to the lesson content.	Lesson Introduction Look Back	Lesson Introduction Math Facts	Lesson Introduction
LEARN AND TRY IT			
Learn and **Try It** activities include multiple cycles of bite-sized instruction coupled with guided practice. The multiple cycles are followed by independent practice problems.	**LEARN** **TRY IT** Guided **TRY IT** Independent	**LEARN** **TRY IT** Guided **TRY IT** Independent	**TRY IT** Review
WRAP-UP			
Wrap-Up activities include formative assessments at both the lesson and concept levels.	**WRAP-UP** Exit Ticket	**WRAP-UP** Exit Ticket	**WRAP-UP** Nongraded Concept Assessment Stride Skills Arcade

Activity Descriptions

This table briefly describes specific activity types in Math 2.

GET READY	Description
Lesson Introduction	The Lesson Introduction is the first activity in every lesson. It introduces the content of the lesson within an engaging context. It also presents the objectives as student-friendly goals and lists the relevant state standards covered in the lesson.
Look Back	The Look Back is a quick review of the prerequisite objectives that are essential to understanding the new concept. Students who struggle with the Look Back should seek additional help before proceeding.
Math Facts	A Math Facts practice provides independent practice of math facts. Students build speed and accuracy through interactive online questions and games.
LEARN AND TRY	**Description**
Learn	All initial and middle days include one or more bite-sized Learn and Try It cycles. These activities include a variety of approaches. Some Learn activities use guided explorations in which students explore and discover mathematical concepts by playing with interactive sliders or virtual manipulatives. Other Learn activities use explicit instruction. In these activities, students may view a video and then work through audio-enhanced example problems.

LEARN AND TRY	Description
Try It (Guided)	Each Learn activity is followed by a short, guided Try It that allows students to immediately apply the concepts they have just learned. These problems provide significant support with step-by-step explanations. All problems include feedback based on student answers as well as complete solutions. The guided Try Its prepare students for the independent practice.
Try It (Independent)	All initial and middle days include an independent Try It. The independent practice has two parts: an online part and an offline part. The independent online practice problems are similar to the types of problems students will encounter in the graded unit assessment. These online problems include feedback and solutions. The offline problems are found in the activity book.
Try It (Practice Concept)	The final day of each concept includes a Try It that reviews key objectives in the concept. The review includes online interactive problems.

WRAP-UP	Description
Nongraded Assessments	Initial and middle days of concepts end with a short nongraded exit ticket. Final days end with a formative concept assessment. The questions are designed to gauge the students' understanding as they complete lessons and concepts. Although the questions are not graded, the results are available to teachers.
Stride Skills Arcade	Final days end with independent practice in Stride Skills Arcade.
Graded Assessment	The final lesson in a unit has a graded unit assessment. All unit assessments have online computer-scored items. Four units also include offline, teacher-graded assessments.

A Balance of Online and Offline Time

Math 2 online activities make up about 75 percent of the core lesson time. However, equally critical to learning is that students practice working out math calculations by hand. Math 2 incorporates a daily offline activity in a predictable place within each lesson sequence. In the last Try It activity of each lesson day, after completing online practice in which instant feedback can help address any misunderstandings, students work out related problems in the activity book.

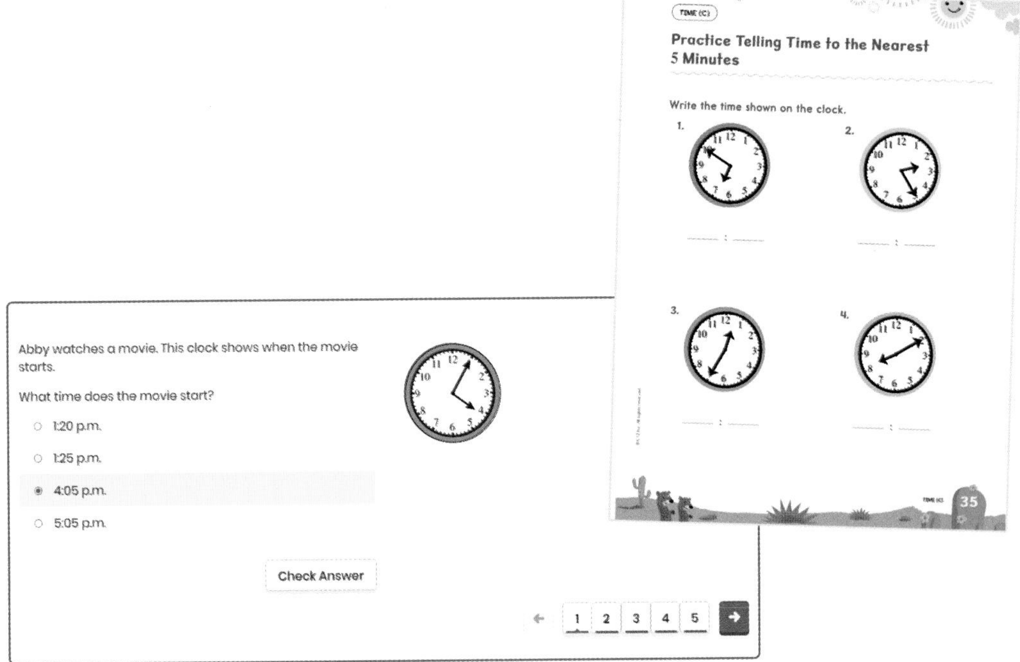

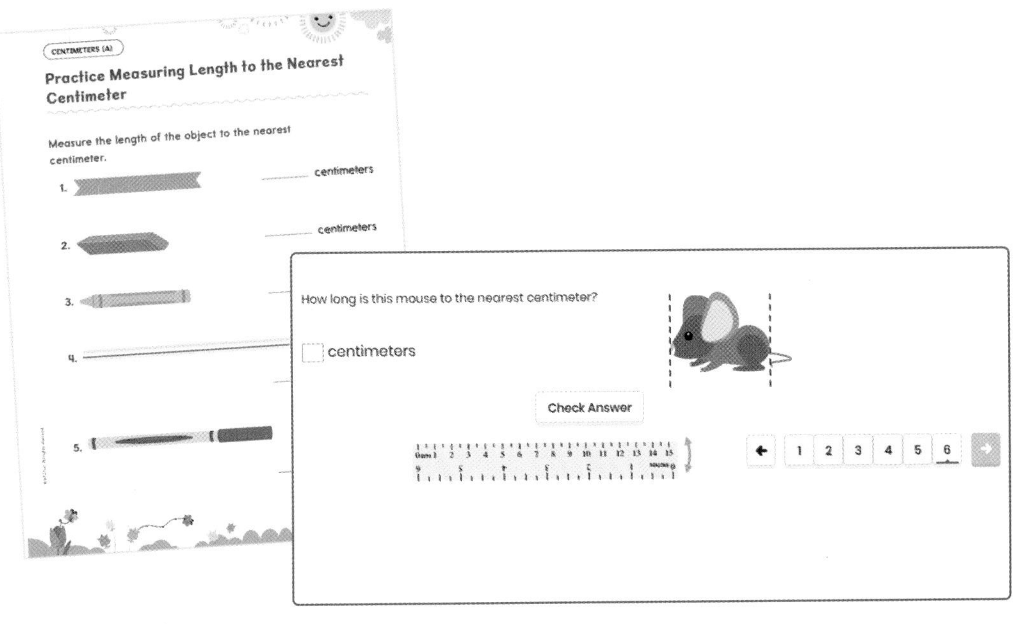

Special Features

In addition to the standard units and lessons, the Math 2 course has these special features.

Mini-Projects

Mini-Projects occur at the end of each semester. In these projects, students complete a small, creative project designed to tie together concepts and skills that they encounter across units. These small projects are designed to emphasize real-world scenarios that connect mathematics to other subjects, including science, technology, engineering, art, and history.

Virtual Manipulatives

Virtual manipulatives allow students to play with and explore mathematical concepts. These virtual manipulatives are placed in strategic spots within the online lessons. Virtual manipulatives provided in Math 2 include

- Base-10 blocks.
- Centimeter and inch rulers.
- Manipulative sandboxes.

All explorations with virtual manipulatives are followed by direct explanations to ensure that students grasp the critical concepts. Printable or tactile manipulatives are available for students who need or prefer an offline version.

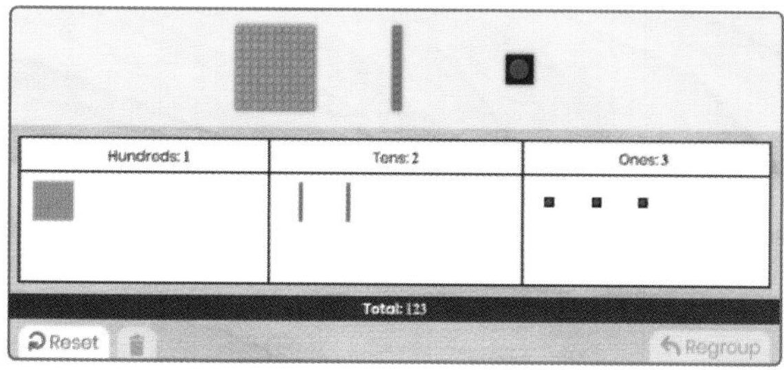

Base-10 Blocks

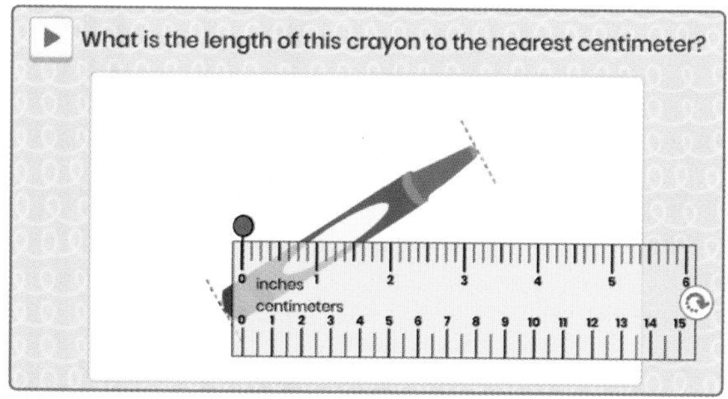

Ruler

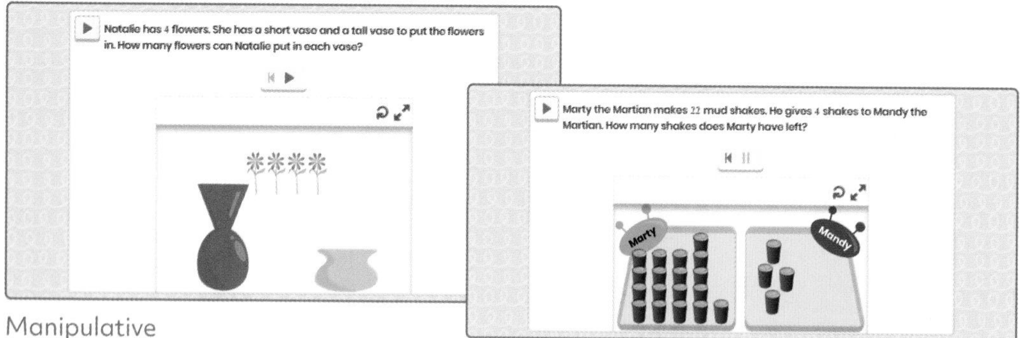

Manipulative Sandboxes

Audio and Video Support

Math 2 provides video support, designed and delivered by expert teachers, for physical and virtual manipulatives.

In addition, the core instruction includes audio to support early readers, as well as video for especially difficult concepts.

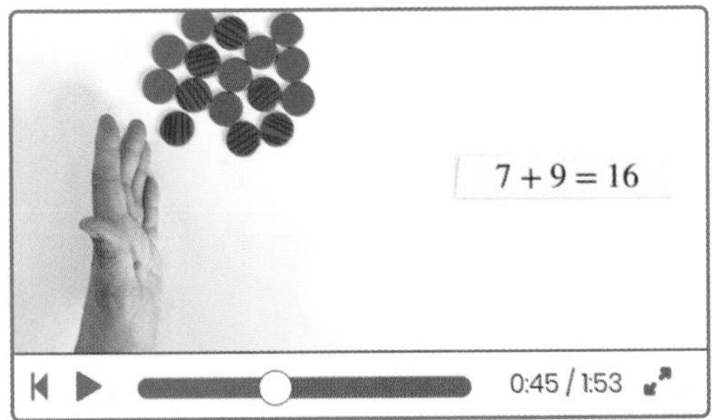

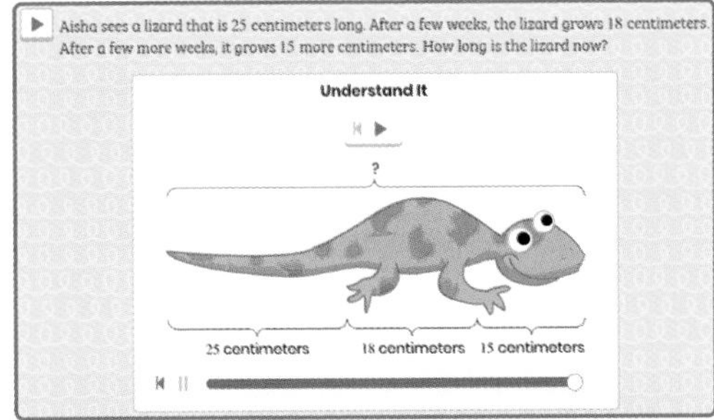

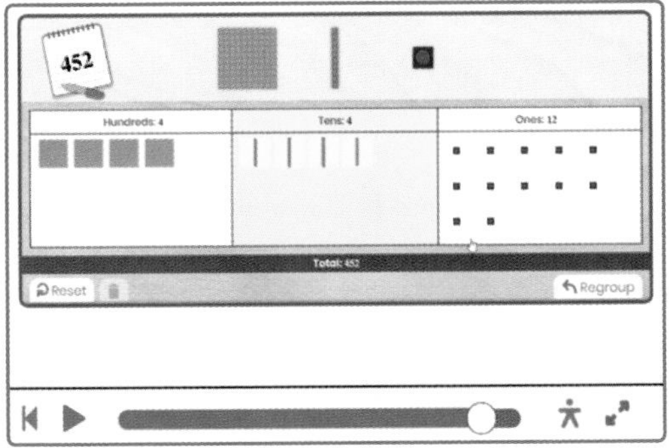

Instant Recall: Facts Fluency Practice

Students need to be able to recall addition and subtraction facts quickly and accurately. Math 2 includes cycles of practice that look at specific sets of facts. There are three types of math facts practice.

1. Matching problems to provide scaffolding as students build familiarity
2. A set of fill-in-the-blank problems for students to build mastery
3. A game for students to continue to practice automatic recall of facts in a fun way

Game-Like Embedded Practice

Repetition is an important part of building speed and accuracy. However, students must be motivated to practice in a variety of ways. Built-in games engage students to spend sufficient time practicing until key math tasks become natural and automatic.

Assessment Overview

To ensure students can show what they have learned and to support high academic outcomes, students need exposure to the types of questions they will see on state assessments.

Online Interactive Questions

Online interactive questions provide powerful opportunities for students to demonstrate deep understanding. For this reason, a variety of online question types, including drag and drop and fill in the blank, are used throughout Math 2.

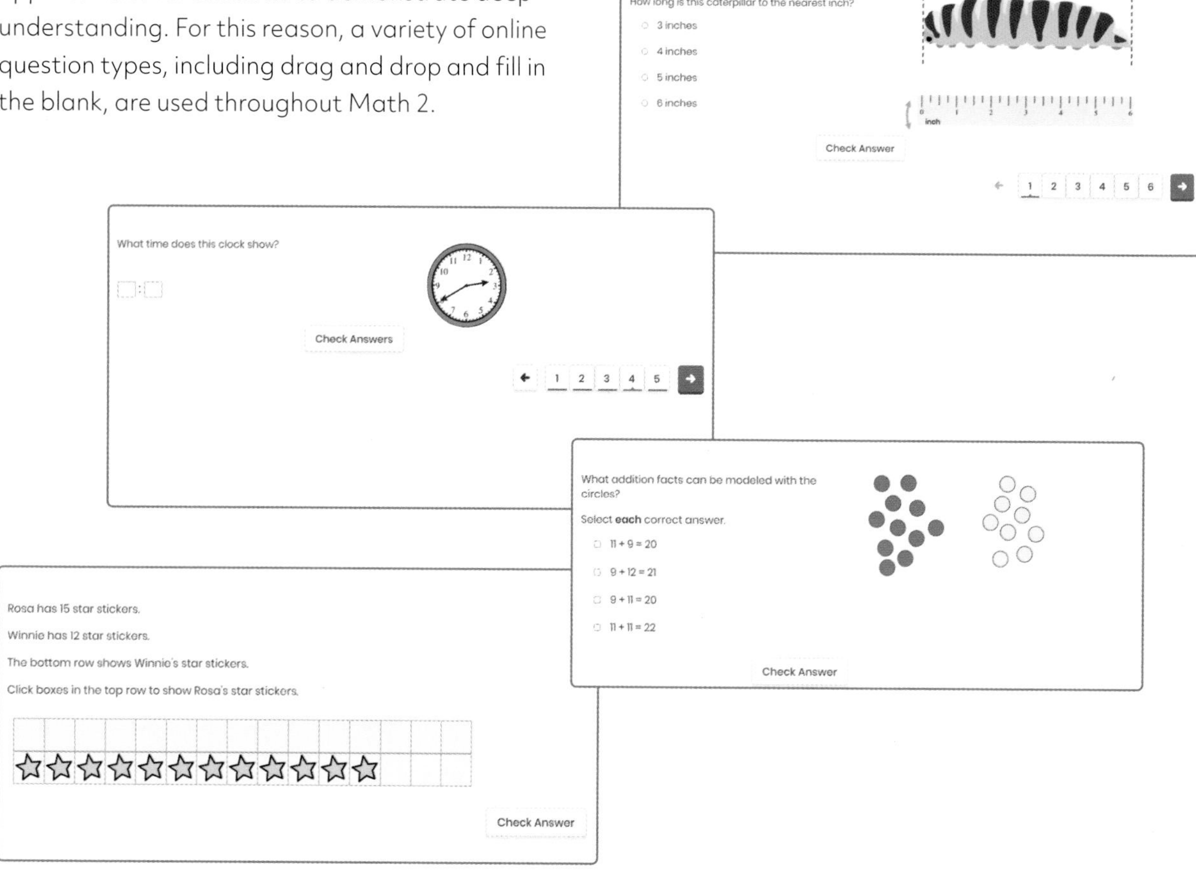

Graded Assessments

Math 2 includes a computer-scored graded assessment at the end of each unit. Four units will also include a teacher-graded assessment.

Students will complete a teacher-graded mini-project at the end of each semester.

Assessment Type	How Many in Math 2
Unit assessment, computer-scored	12
Unit assessment, teacher-graded	4
Mini-project, teacher-graded	2

Instructional Approach

Building Balanced Understanding and Efficiency

For a long period of time, most math instruction focused strictly on how—not why—to perform calculations. Math 2 balances conceptual instruction and exploration to explain the why, with procedural practice designed to move students toward speed and accuracy. As you look across a lesson, a concept, and even a unit, you will see a careful progression in which students first use models to grasp why the math works and then move toward more efficient methods of solving problems.

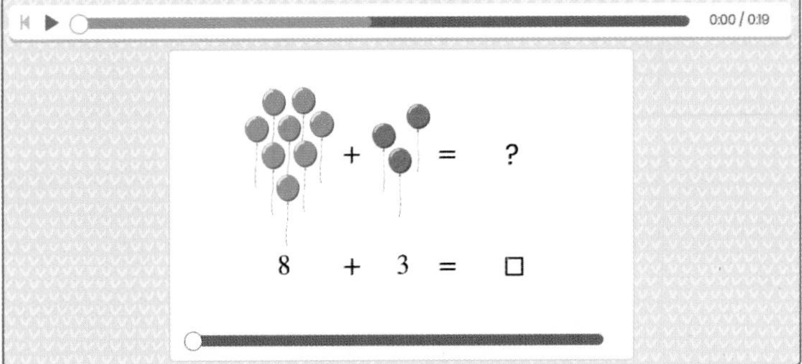

Conceptual Explorations

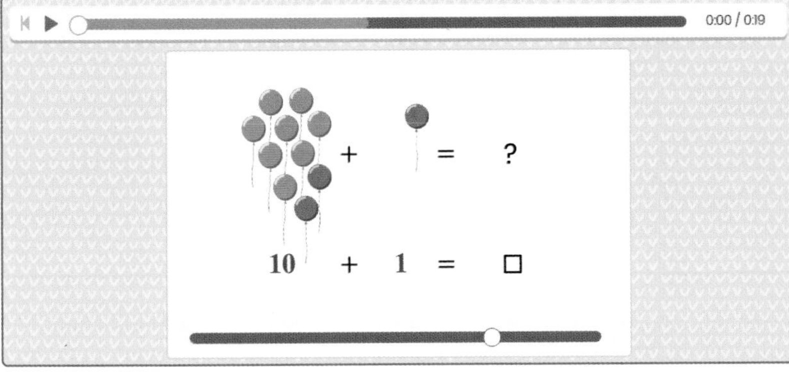

Conceptual Explorations

Procedural Explanations

Making Math Relevant with Real-World, Concrete Examples

Math 2 intentionally progresses from concrete, real-world scenarios and models to visual models and finally to abstracted math to build a depth of knowledge.

0:00 / 0:17

326

100 100 100

10 10

From Concrete

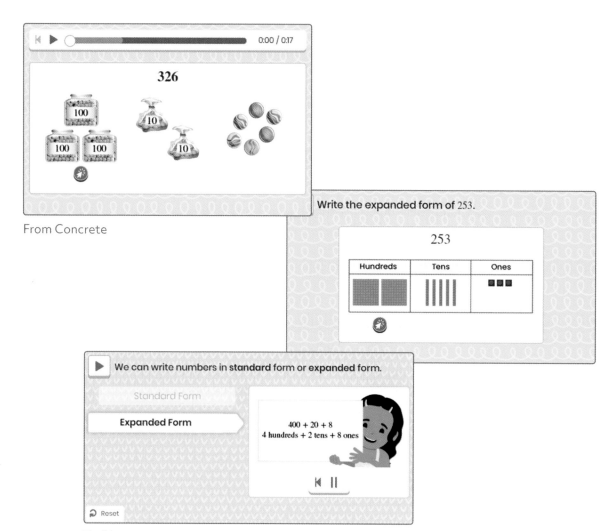

Write the expanded form of 253.

253

Hundreds	Tens	Ones

We can write numbers in **standard** form or **expanded** form.

Standard Form

Expanded Form

400 + 20 + 8
4 hundreds + 2 tens + 8 ones

Reset

To Abstract

Content Focus

- Students expand their understanding of place value to include three-digit numbers. They use a variety of models to count, read, write, represent, compare, and order numbers through 1,000. Students investigate the relationship between tens and hundreds to discover that it is similar to the relationship between tens and ones. They learn that 1 hundred is the same as 10 tens, similar to how 1 ten is the same as 10 ones.
- Students build fluency as they add and subtract within 100 using strategies based on place value, properties of operations, and the relationship between addition and subtraction. They apply these strategies to solve one- and two-step story problems involving amounts that are combined, changed, or compared. Students extend addition and subtraction strategies to add and subtract within 1,000, including adding with three or four addends.
- Students learn about time, money, measurement, and data. They tell and write time from digital and analog clocks to the nearest five minutes and label times as a.m. or p.m. They count the value of coins and bills and solve problems involving coins and bills using the dollar and cent signs appropriately. Students measure, estimate, and compare lengths measured in standard units—inch, centimeter, foot, meter, and yard. They also solve story problems involving lengths. Lastly, students measure and record length data on line plots, and they interpret and represent other types of data in picture and bar graphs.
- Students build a foundation for topics in future math courses. They prepare to multiply and divide as they learn about even and odd numbers, arrays, and skip counting by 2s, 5s, 10s, and 100s. Students prepare to work with fractions as they partition circles and rectangles into two, three, or four equal shares and describe equal shares using the words *half*, *third*, *fourth*, and *quarter*. They also prepare to find area by partitioning rectangles into rows and columns of equal-sized squares and counting those squares.

Individualized Learning

Math 2 is designed to help all students succeed.

Stride Skills Arcade is an engaging teaching tool that motivates students toward mastery and rewards learning with games. Following each concept assessment, students practice related concepts based on their specific needs. Time to use Stride Skills Arcade is integrated right into the course to ensure sufficient independent practice time.

Stride Skills Arcade's adaptive technology guides students to practice where they need it most—and then serves a variety of content that's lively and engaging. The vast database of questions, problems, video lessons, and printable resources deliver grade-level appropriate content aligned to the rigor of the Common Core and individual state standards. Stride Skills Arcade's benchmark and formative assessments identify where students are performing on specific grade-level standards throughout the year and help identify critical foundational gaps missed in prior grade levels. Test prep capabilities pinpoint student strengths and weaknesses for improved student outcomes on end-of-year assessments.

The Help Me button, which is located on the lesson menu, is an additional personalization feature that lets students opt into activities that are dynamically chosen based on the concept they are studying. Recommendations are powered by a sophisticated engine designed to elevate the activities most likely to be effective for individual students.

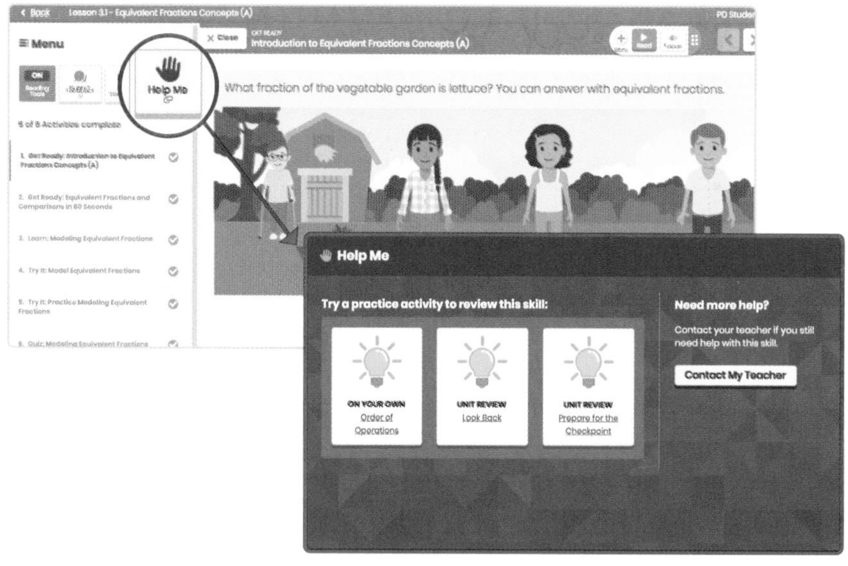

How to Use This Guide

The lesson guide contains information that will be helpful to you as you begin Math 2 and daily as you work through the program. Here is what the lesson guide contains and how to use it.

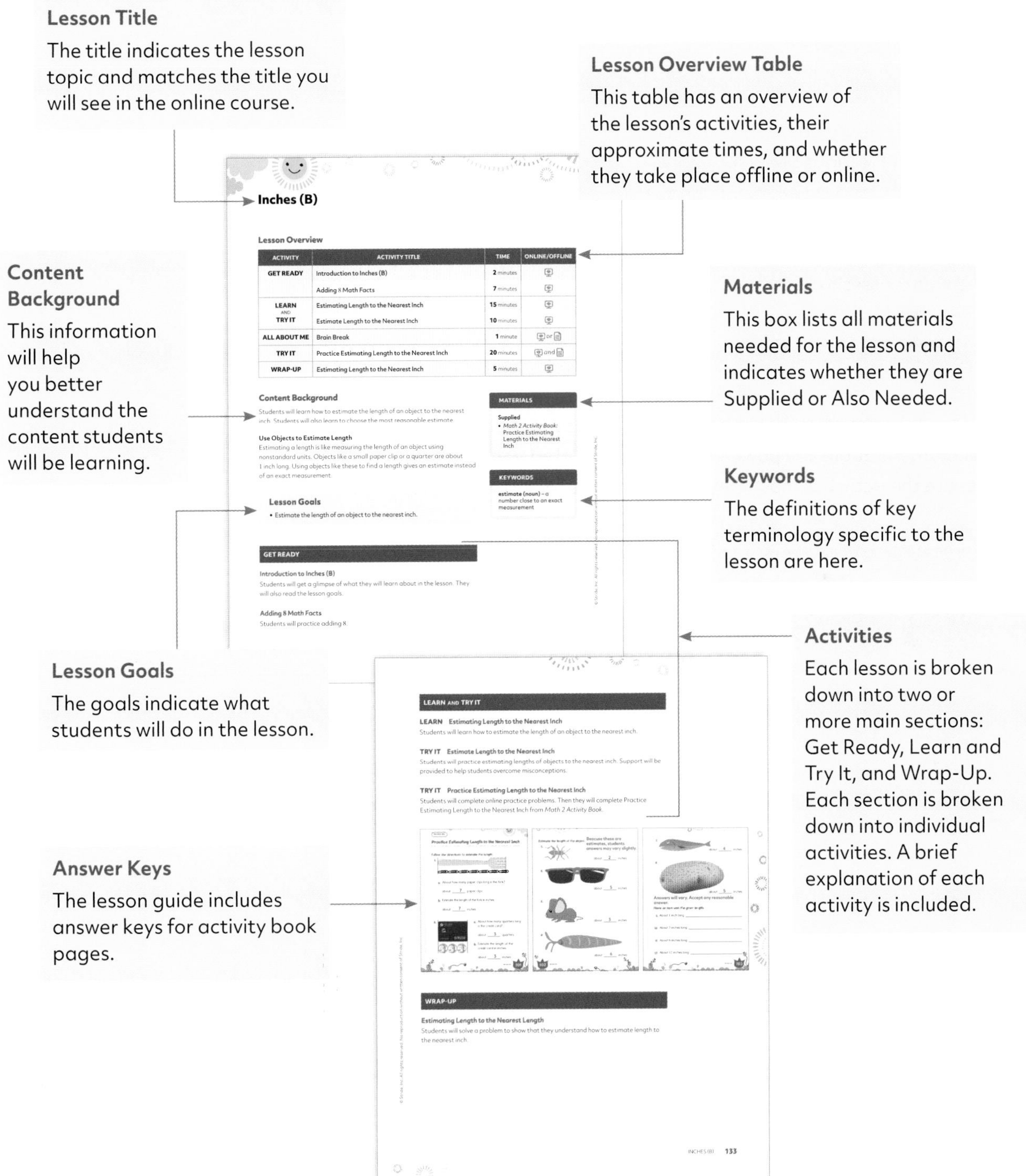

Lesson Title
The title indicates the lesson topic and matches the title you will see in the online course.
Lesson Overview Table
This table has an overview of the lesson's activities, their approximate times, and whether they take place offline or online.
Content Background
This information will help you better understand the content students will be learning.
Materials
This box lists all materials needed for the lesson and indicates whether they are Supplied or Also Needed.
Keywords
The definitions of key terminology specific to the lesson are here.
Activities
Each lesson is broken down into two or more main sections: Get Ready, Learn and Try It, and Wrap-Up. Each section is broken down into individual activities. A brief explanation of each activity is included.
Lesson Goals
The goals indicate what students will do in the lesson.
Answer Keys
The lesson guide includes answer keys for activity book pages.
Inches (B)

Lessons with Graded Assessments

Check in with students when a lesson has a graded assessment.

- The final lesson of every unit has a computer-scored assessment in the Unit Checkpoint.
- Four units also include a teacher-graded assignment as part of the Unit Checkpoint.
- At the end of each semester, students will complete a teacher-graded mini-project.

Check to make sure students have completed and submitted the computer-scored assessments. Learning Coaches may need to help students submit their teacher-graded assignments to their teachers. Discuss the best method of turning in work with your students' teachers.

Remember

Academic support at home is critical to student success. While Math 2 empowers students to work independently, this guide is designed to help you support your students each day.

Keywords

a.m. – label for times after midnight and before noon

addend – one of the two or more numbers that are added to determine a sum
Example: The addends in 35 + 22 are 35 and 22.

analog clock – shows time with an hour hand and a minute hand

angle – the part of a shape formed by two sides and the included vertex

array – a rectangular arrangement of objects in rows and columns

associative property of addition – a rule that says grouping three or more addends in different ways does not change their sum
Example: (2 + 3) + 4 has the same sum as 2 + (3 + 4).

bar graph – a graph that uses bars of different lengths to represent data

bill – unit of paper money
Example: A five-dollar bill has a value of $5.

centimeter – a metric unit used to measure length

coin – unit of money made of metal and shaped like a disc
Example: A nickel is a coin that is worth 5 cents.

commutative property of addition – a rule that says changing the order that three or more addends are added does not change their sum
Example: 3 + 5 + 7 has the same sum as 3 + 7 + 5.

compose a number – put a number together from smaller numbers
Example: 30 + 4 = 34 and 20 + 14 = 34

count on – mental strategy used to add numbers

curve – a shape, or part of a shape, that is not straight

data – pieces of information; the singular is datum

day – unit of time equal to 24 hours

decompose a number – break a number into smaller numbers
Example: 53 = 50 + 3 and 53 = 30 + 23

difference – the answer in a subtraction problem
Example: In the number sentence 5 − 3 = 2, the difference is 2.

digital clock – shows time using numerals with the hour on the left and the minutes on the right

edge – the line where two faces of a solid meet

equal parts – portions of a shape that are equal in area

equals symbol (=) – symbol that means *equals*
Example: "3 = 2 + 1" means "3 equals 2 plus 1."

estimate (noun) – a number close to an exact measurement

expanded form – a way to write a number that shows the place value of each of its digits
Example: 428 = 400 + 20 + 8 or 4 hundreds + 2 tens + 8 ones

face – a flat surface on a solid

fact family – a group of related addition and subtraction number sentences for three numbers

foot – an English unit of length that equals 12 inches

fourth – each part of a shape divided into 4 equal parts

greater-than symbol (>) – symbol that means *greater than*
Example: "3 > 1" means "3 is greater than 1."

half – each part of a shape divided into 2 equal parts

hour – unit of time equal to 60 minutes

inch – the basic English, or customary, unit for measuring length

less-than symbol (<) – symbol that means *less than*
Example: "1 < 3" means "1 is less than 3."

line plot – a graph that shows measurement data as marks above a number line

measure (verb) – to use standard units to find a distance, area, volume, capacity, temperature, or interval of time

meter – a metric unit of length that equals 100 centimeters

meterstick – a tool for measuring length in centimeters or meters

midnight – twelve o'clock at night

minuend – the number from which another number is subtracted
Example: In the number sentence 5 − 3 = 2, the minuend is 5.

minute – unit of time equal to 60 seconds

month – unit of calendar time equal to about 4 weeks
Example: There are 12 months in 1 year.

noon – twelve o'clock during the day

not equal symbol (≠) – symbol that means *not equal*
Example: "3 ≠ 5" means "3 is not equal to 5."

p.m. – label for times after noon and before midnight

picture graph – a graph that uses pictures to represent data

place value – the value of a digit in a number
Example: The place value of the 2 in 23 is 20 or 2 tens.

place-value chart – a chart or arrangement that shows the value of each digit in a number

regroup – use place-value concepts to rename numbers
Example: 1 ten regroups into 10 ones; 1 hundred regroups into 10 tens

regroup (money) – rename a set of coins with a value of 100 cents as 1 dollar
Example: Amelie needs to regroup 4 quarters as 1 dollar to solve the problem.

ruler – a tool for measuring length, usually in inches or centimeters

second – basic unit of time

side – straight part that forms a shape

skip count – to count by a number other than 1

standard form – the conventional way of writing a number using digits
Example: The standard form of 300 + 40 + 8 is 348.

subtrahend – the number that is subtracted from another number
Example: In the number sentence 5 − 3 = 2, the subtrahend is 3.

sum – the solution to an addition problem
Example: The sum of 35 and 22 is 57.

third – each part of a shape divided into 3 equal parts

unit form – a way to write a number by stating the place value of its digits
Example: The unit form of 415 is 4 hundreds, 1 ten, 5 ones.

unit of measure – an amount used to measure
Example: Inches are a unit used to measure length.

vertex of a shape – the place where two sides of a shape meet

vertex of a solid – the place where two or more edges of a solid meet

week – unit of calendar time equal to 7 days

whole – the entire amount
Example: 2 halves or 3 thirds or 4 fourths

yard – an English unit of length that equals 36 inches or 3 feet

yardstick – a tool for measuring length in inches, feet, or yards

year – unit of calendar time equal to 365 or 366 days

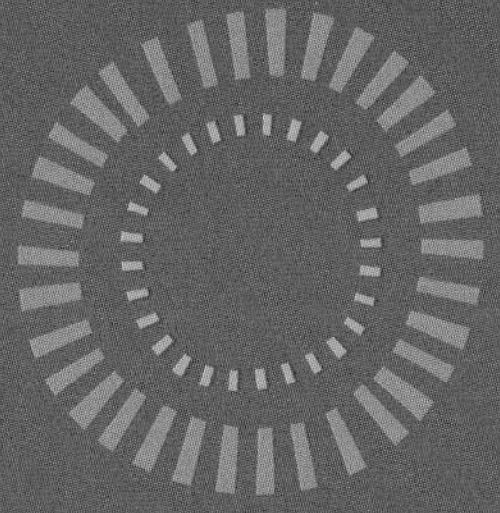

Numbers Through 500

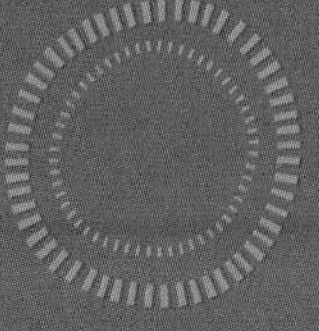

Count and Represent Numbers (A)

Lesson Overview

ACTIVITY	ACTIVITY TITLE	TIME	ONLINE/OFFLINE
GET READY	Introduction to Count and Represent Numbers (A)	**2** minutes	online
	Look Back at Reading and Writing Numbers to 100	**7** minutes	online
LEARN AND TRY IT	Counting by 1s	**7** minutes	online
	Count by 1s	**7** minutes	online
ALL ABOUT ME	Brain Break	**1** minute	online or offline
LEARN AND TRY IT	Reading Numbers	**7** minutes	online
	Read Numbers	**7** minutes	online
	Practice Counting and Reading Numbers	**20** minutes	online and offline
WRAP-UP	Counting and Reading Numbers	**2** minutes	online

Content Background

Students will review counting to 100 and will learn to count through 500. The biggest challenge when counting above 100 is remembering to change to the next hundred after a number ending in 99. Students will also learn to read numbers between 100 and 500 by reading the numbers in the hundreds, tens, and ones places.

MATERIALS

Supplied

- *Math 2 Activity Book:* Practice Counting and Reading Numbers

Lesson Goals

- Count by 1s up to 500.
- Read numbers up to 500.

GET READY

Introduction to Count and Represent Numbers (A)

Students will get a glimpse of what they will learn about in the lesson. They will also read the lesson goals.

Look Back at Reading and Writing Numbers to 100

Students will review and practice the prerequisite skill of reading and writing numbers up to 100.

LEARN AND TRY IT

LEARN Counting by 1s

Students will learn to count by 1s from 100 to 500.

OPTIONAL Encourage students to count aloud, making sure they change to the next hundred after a number ending in ninety-nine.

TRY IT Count by 1s

Students will practice counting by 1s from 100 to 500. Support will be provided to help students overcome misconceptions.

LEARN Reading Numbers

Students will use place value to read numbers from 100 to 500.

TIP Remind students not to say the word *and* when reading a number between 100 and 500. For example, 482 is read *four hundred eighty-two* instead of *four hundred and eighty-two*.

TRY IT Read Numbers

Students will practice reading numbers from 100 to 500. Support will be provided to help students overcome misconceptions.

TRY IT **Practice Counting and Reading Numbers**

Students will complete online practice problems. Then they will complete Practice Counting and Reading Numbers from *Math 2 Activity Book*.

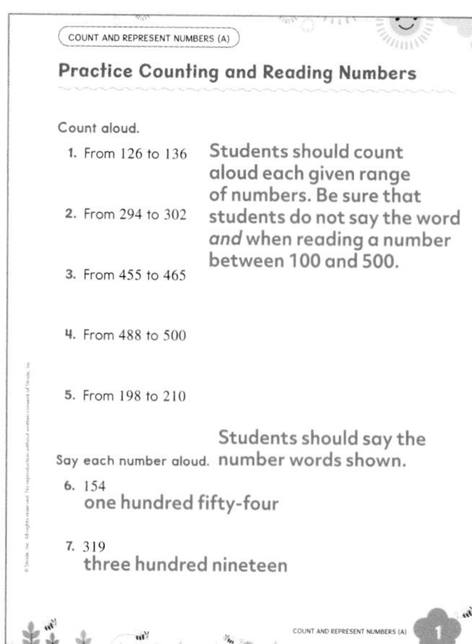
COUNT AND REPRESENT NUMBERS (A)

Practice Counting and Reading Numbers

Count aloud.

1. From 126 to 136
2. From 294 to 302
3. From 455 to 465
4. From 488 to 500
5. From 198 to 210

Students should count aloud each given range of numbers. Be sure that students do not say the word *and* when reading a number between 100 and 500.

Say each number aloud. Students should say the number words shown.

6. 154
   one hundred fifty-four
7. 319
   three hundred nineteen

COUNT AND REPRESENT NUMBERS (A) 1

8. 104
   one hundred four
9. 260
   two hundred sixty
10. 410
   four hundred ten
11. 500
   five hundred
12. The number after 109
   one hundred ten
13. The number after 200
   two hundred one
14. The number after 299
   three hundred
15. The number after 329
   three hundred thirty
16. The number after 410
   four hundred eleven

2 COUNT AND REPRESENT NUMBERS (A)

WRAP-UP

Counting and Reading Numbers

Students will solve problems to show that they understand counting and reading numbers.

Count and Represent Numbers (B)

Lesson Overview

ACTIVITY	ACTIVITY TITLE	TIME	ONLINE/OFFLINE
GET READY	Introduction to Count and Represent Numbers (B)	**2** minutes	online
	Adding 0 and 1 Math Facts	**8** minutes	online
LEARN AND **TRY IT**	Writing Numbers as Number Words	**15** minutes	online
	Write Numbers as Number Words	**10** minutes	online
	Practice Writing Numbers as Number Words	**20** minutes	online and offline
WRAP-UP	Writing Numbers as Number Words	**5** minutes	online

Content Background

Students will learn how to write number words to represent numbers through 500.

Numbers through 99

Students will learn to read and spell the number words for the numbers 1 through 19 and each ten from 20 to 90. Numbers from 21 to 99 that do not end in 0 are written with a hyphen between the word for the tens and the word for the ones. For example, 24 has 2 tens and 4 ones, so it is written *twenty-four*.

Numbers from 100 to 500

Students will learn to read and spell the word *hundred*. Numbers that end in 00 represent a certain number of hundreds. For example, 200 is *two hundred*. Use place value to write number words for numbers between 100 and 500 that do not end in 00. Start with the number of hundreds. Then write the number words for the tens and ones places using the patterns for numbers through 99. For example, 478 has 4 hundreds, 7 tens, and 8 ones, so it is written *four hundred seventy-eight*.

Lesson Goals

- Write number words for numbers.

MATERIALS

Supplied

- *Math 2 Activity Book:* Practice Writing Numbers as Number Words

GET READY

Introduction to Count and Represent Numbers (B)

Students will get a glimpse of what they will learn about in the lesson. They will also read the lesson goals.

Adding 0 and 1 Math Facts

Students will practice adding 0 and 1.

LEARN AND TRY IT

LEARN Writing Numbers as Number Words

Students will write numbers through 500 as number words.

TIP Saying a number aloud can help students figure out how to write the number words that represent that number.

TRY IT Write Numbers as Number Words

Students will practice writing numbers through 500 as number words. Support will be provided to help students overcome misconceptions.

SUPPORT For students having difficulty recalling or spelling number words, allow them to use the Number Words Chart on the first page of Practice Writing Numbers as Number Words in their activity book.

TRY IT Practice Writing Numbers as Number Words

Students will complete online practice problems. Then they will complete Practice Writing Numbers as Number Words from *Math 2 Activity Book*.

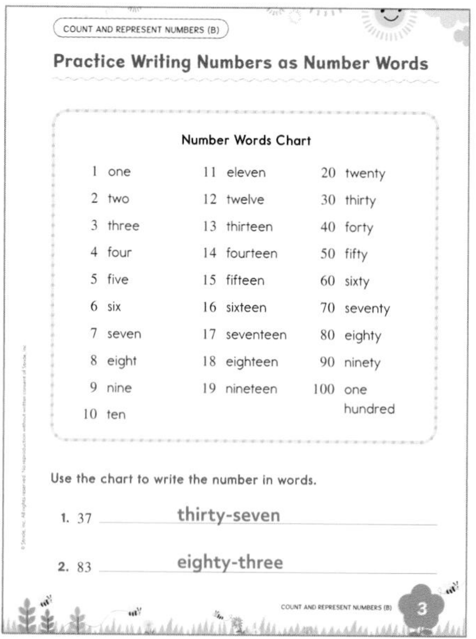
COUNT AND REPRESENT NUMBERS (B)

Practice Writing Numbers as Number Words

Number Words Chart

1	one	11	eleven	20	twenty
2	two	12	twelve	30	thirty
3	three	13	thirteen	40	forty
4	four	14	fourteen	50	fifty
5	five	15	fifteen	60	sixty
6	six	16	sixteen	70	seventy
7	seven	17	seventeen	80	eighty
8	eight	18	eighteen	90	ninety
9	nine	19	nineteen	100	one hundred
10	ten				

Use the chart to write the number in words.

1. 37 thirty-seven
2. 83 eighty-three

COUNT AND REPRESENT NUMBERS (B) 3

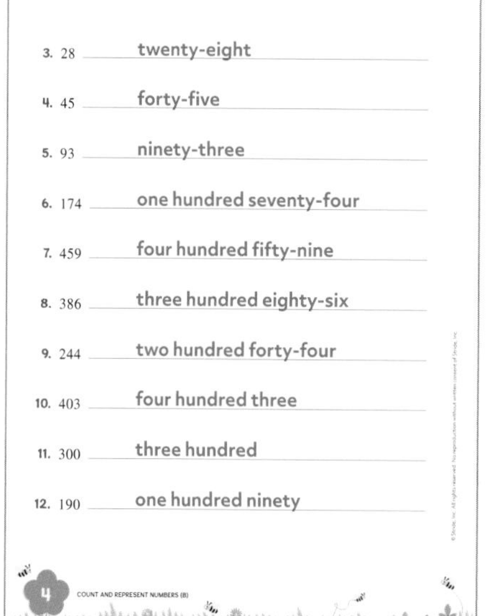
3. 28 twenty-eight
4. 45 forty-five
5. 93 ninety-three
6. 174 one hundred seventy-four
7. 459 four hundred fifty-nine
8. 386 three hundred eighty-six
9. 244 two hundred forty-four
10. 403 four hundred three
11. 300 three hundred
12. 190 one hundred ninety

4 COUNT AND REPRESENT NUMBERS (B)

WRAP-UP

Writing Numbers as Number Words

Students will solve problems to show that they understand how to write numbers through 500 as number words.

Count and Represent Numbers (C)

Lesson Overview

ACTIVITY	ACTIVITY TITLE	TIME	ONLINE/OFFLINE
GET READY	Introduction to Count and Represent Numbers (C)	**2** minutes	online
	Adding 0 and 1 with Instant Recall	**7** minutes	online
LEARN AND **TRY IT**	Writing Numbers from Number Words	**15** minutes	online
	Write Numbers from Number Words	**10** minutes	online
ALL ABOUT ME	Brain Break	**1** minute	online or offline
TRY IT	Practice Writing Numbers from Number Words	**20** minutes	online and offline
WRAP-UP	Writing Numbers from Number Words	**5** minutes	online

Content Background

Students will learn to write numbers from number words using a place-value chart. For example, four hundred seven has 4 hundreds, 0 tens, and 7 ones, so the number is 407.

Lesson Goals

- Write numbers from number words.

MATERIALS

Supplied

- *Math 2 Activity Book:* Practice Writing Numbers from Number Words

GET READY

Introduction to Count and Represent Numbers (C)

Students will get a glimpse of what they will learn about in the lesson. They will also read the lesson goals.

Adding 0 and 1 with Instant Recall

Students will practice adding 0 and 1.

LEARN AND TRY IT

LEARN Writing Numbers from Number Words

Students will use place value to write numbers from number words.

TIP Encourage students to read the number words aloud to help them understand the numbers of hundreds, tens, and ones.

TRY IT Write Numbers from Number Words

Students will practice writing numbers from number words. Support will be provided to help students overcome misconceptions.

TRY IT Practice Writing Numbers from Number Words

Students will complete online practice problems. Then they will complete Practice Writing Numbers from Number Words from *Math 2 Activity Book*.

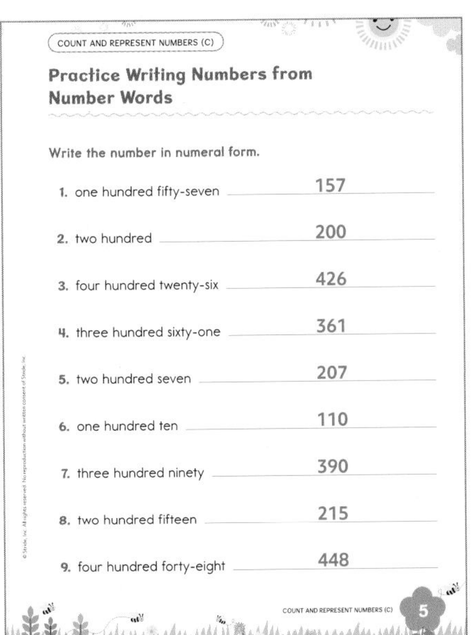

COUNT AND REPRESENT NUMBERS (C)

Practice Writing Numbers from Number Words

Write the number in numeral form.

1. one hundred fifty-seven 157
2. two hundred 200
3. four hundred twenty-six 426
4. three hundred sixty-one 361
5. two hundred seven 207
6. one hundred ten 110
7. three hundred ninety 390
8. two hundred fifteen 215
9. four hundred forty-eight 448

COUNT AND REPRESENT NUMBERS (C) 5

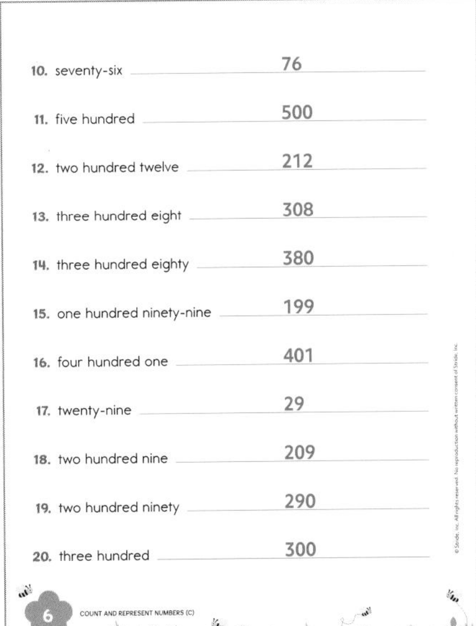

10. seventy-six 76
11. five hundred 500
12. two hundred twelve 212
13. three hundred eight 308
14. three hundred eighty 380
15. one hundred ninety-nine 199
16. four hundred one 401
17. twenty-nine 29
18. two hundred nine 209
19. two hundred ninety 290
20. three hundred 300

6 COUNT AND REPRESENT NUMBERS (C)

WRAP-UP

Writing Numbers from Number Words

Students will solve a problem to show that they understand how to write a number from number words.

Count and Represent Numbers (D)

Lesson Overview

ACTIVITY	ACTIVITY TITLE	TIME	ONLINE/OFFLINE
GET READY	Introduction to Count and Represent Numbers (D)	**2** minutes	
TRY IT	Review Count and Represent Numbers	**18** minutes	
QUIZ	Count and Represent Numbers	**25** minutes	
WRAP-UP	More Math Practice	**15** minutes	

Lesson Goals

- Review counting, reading, and writing numbers.
- Take a quiz.

MATERIALS

There are no materials to gather for this lesson.

GET READY

Introduction to Count and Represent Numbers (D)

Students will read the lesson goals.

TRY IT

Review Count and Represent Numbers

Students will answer questions to review what they have learned about how to count and represent numbers.

QUIZ

Count and Represent Numbers

Students will complete the Count and Represent Numbers quiz.

WRAP-UP

More Math Practice

Students will practice skills according to their individual needs.

Place Value (A)

Lesson Overview

ACTIVITY	ACTIVITY TITLE	TIME	ONLINE/OFFLINE
GET READY	Introduction to Place Value (A)	**2** minutes	
	Look Back at Place Value in Two-Digit Numbers	**8** minutes	
LEARN AND **TRY IT**	Identifying Place Value in Numbers	**15** minutes	
	Identify Place Value in Numbers	**10** minutes	
	Practice Identifying Place Value in Numbers	**20** minutes	and
WRAP-UP	Identifying Place Value in Numbers	**5** minutes	

Content Background

Students will develop a deeper understanding of three-digit numbers using place value. The lesson focuses on numbers through 500. Students will use place value to write a number in unit form.

Base-10 Blocks

Students will use base-10 blocks to find the value of each digit in a three-digit number.

For example, the number 237 has 2 hundreds, 3 tens, and 7 ones, as shown with these base-10 blocks.

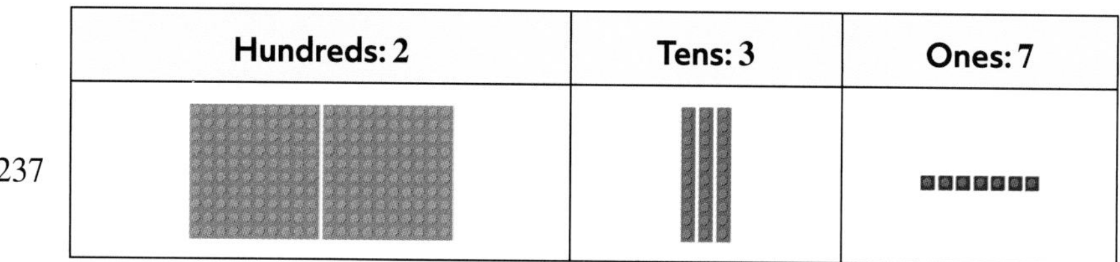

	Hundreds: 2	Tens: 3	Ones: 7
237			

MATERIALS

Supplied

- *Math 2 Activity Book:* Practice Identifying Place Value in Numbers

KEYWORDS

place value – the value of a digit in a number

Example: The place value of the 2 in 23 is 20 or 2 tens.

unit form – a way to write a number by stating the place value of its digits

Example: The unit form of 415 is 4 hundreds, 1 ten, 5 ones.

Lesson Goals

- Find the place value of each digit in a number.
- Write a number in unit form.

GET READY

Introduction to Place Value (A)

Students will get a glimpse of what they will learn about in the lesson. They will also read the lesson goals.

Look Back at Place Value in Two-Digit Numbers

Students will review and practice the prerequisite skill of identifying place value in two-digit numbers.

LEARN AND TRY IT

LEARN Identifying Place Value in Numbers

Students will work with base-10 blocks to identify the place value of each digit in a number. They will also write numbers in unit form.

TRY IT Identify Place Value in Numbers

Students will practice identifying the place value of each digit in a number and writing numbers in unit form. Support will be provided to help students overcome misconceptions.

TRY IT Practice Identifying Place Value in Numbers

Students will complete online practice problems. Then they will complete Practice Identifying Place Value in Numbers from *Math 2 Activity Book*

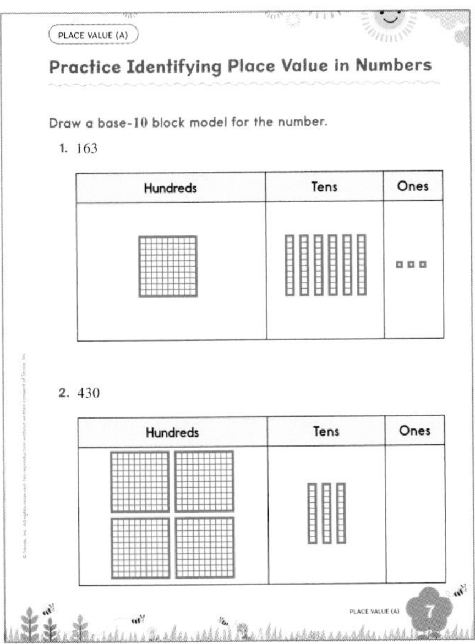

PLACE VALUE (A)

Practice Identifying Place Value in Numbers

Draw a base-10 block model for the number.

1. 163

Hundreds	Tens	Ones

2. 430

Hundreds	Tens	Ones

PLACE VALUE (A) 7

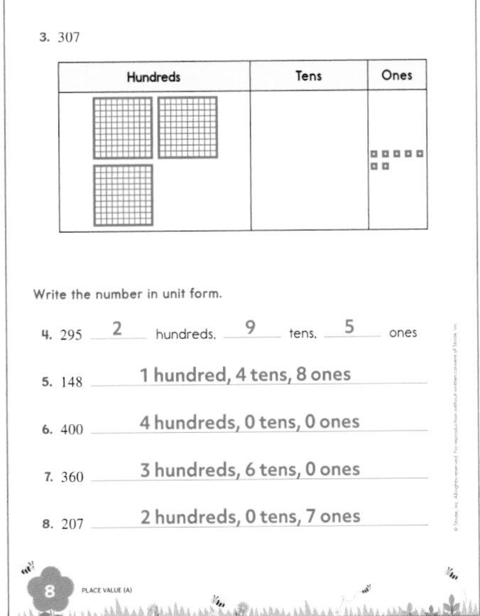

3. 307

Hundreds	Tens	Ones

Write the number in unit form.

4. 295 2 hundreds, 9 tens, 5 ones
5. 148 1 hundred, 4 tens, 8 ones
6. 400 4 hundreds, 0 tens, 0 ones
7. 360 3 hundreds, 6 tens, 0 ones
8. 207 2 hundreds, 0 tens, 7 ones

8 PLACE VALUE (A)

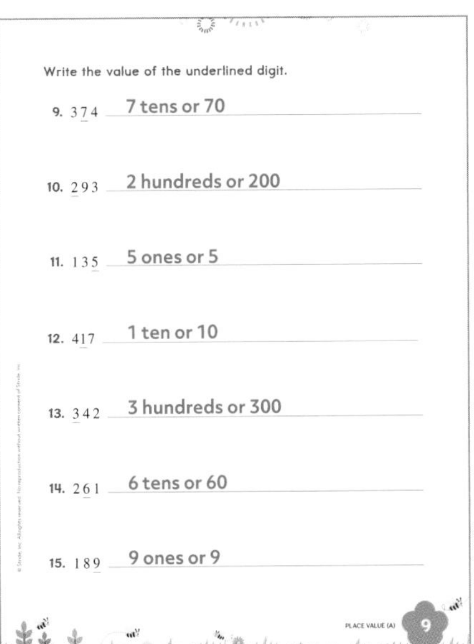

Write the value of the underlined digit.

9. 374 7 tens or 70
10. 293 2 hundreds or 200
11. 135 5 ones or 5
12. 417 1 ten or 10
13. 342 3 hundreds or 300
14. 261 6 tens or 60
15. 189 9 ones or 9

PLACE VALUE (A) 9

WRAP-UP

Identifying Place Value in Numbers

Students will solve problems to show that they understand how to identify place value in numbers.

Place Value (B)

Lesson Overview

ACTIVITY	ACTIVITY TITLE	TIME	ONLINE/OFFLINE
GET READY	Introduction to Place Value (B)	**2** minutes	
	Adding 0 and 1 Math Facts Game	**7** minutes	
LEARN AND **TRY IT**	Writing Numbers in Expanded Form	**7** minutes	
	Write Numbers in Expanded Form	**7** minutes	
ALL ABOUT ME	Brain Break	**1** minute	or
LEARN AND **TRY IT**	Writing Numbers in Standard Form	**7** minutes	
	Write Numbers in Standard Form	**7** minutes	
	Practice Writing Numbers	**20** minutes	and
WRAP-UP	Writing Numbers	**2** minutes	

Content Background

Students will learn how to convert between the standard form and the expanded form of numbers. Students will use models and an understanding of place value to determine the numbers of hundreds, tens, and ones in a three-digit number.

Expanded Form

The expanded form of a number represents the value of each digit in the number. It can be written using words or numbers. For example, these base-10 blocks model the number 321.

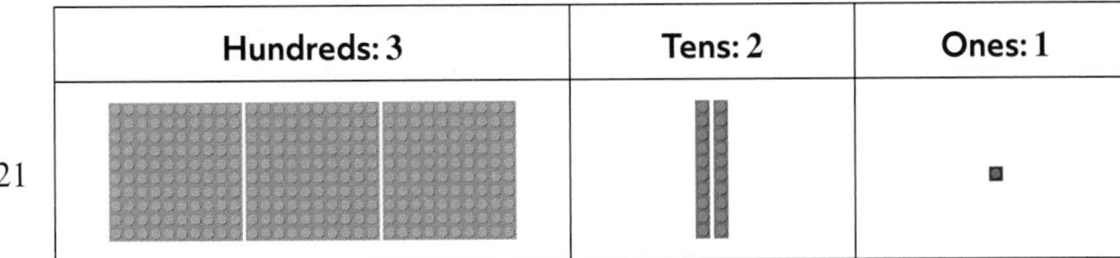

This model shows that 321 contains 3 hundreds, 2 tens, and 1 one. The expanded form of 321 is 3 hundreds + 2 tens + 1 one or 300 + 20 + 1.

MATERIALS

Supplied

- *Math 2 Activity Book:* Practice Writing Numbers

KEYWORDS

expanded form – a way to write a number that shows the place value of each of its digits

Example: 428 = 400 + 20 + 8 or 4 hundreds + 2 tens + 8 ones

standard form – the usual way of writing a number using digits

Example: The standard form of 300 + 40 + 8 is 348.

Standard Form

Standard form is the usual way of writing a number using digits. When a number has hundreds, tens, and ones, the standard form of the number is a three-digit number. For example, 5 hundreds + 5 tens + 7 ones = 557, and $700 + 30 + 9 = 739$.

Lesson Goals

- Write numbers in expanded form.
- Write numbers in standard form.

GET READY

Introduction to Place Value (B)

Students will get a glimpse of what they will learn about in the lesson. They will also read the lesson goals.

Adding 0 and 1 Math Facts Game

Students will play a game to practice adding 0 and 1.

LEARN AND TRY IT

LEARN Writing Numbers in Expanded Form

Students will learn how to write numbers in expanded form when given numbers in standard form.

SUPPORT If students have difficulty recognizing the value of each digit, encourage them to model the number using base-10 blocks.

TRY IT Write Numbers in Expanded Form

Students will practice writing numbers in expanded form. Support will be provided to help students overcome misconceptions.

LEARN Writing Numbers in Standard Form

Students will learn how to write numbers in standard form when given numbers in expanded form.

TRY IT Write Numbers in Standard Form

Students will practice writing numbers in standard form. Support will be provided to help students overcome misconceptions.

TRY IT Practice Writing Numbers

Students will complete online practice problems. Then they will complete Practice Writing Numbers from *Math 2 Activity Book*.

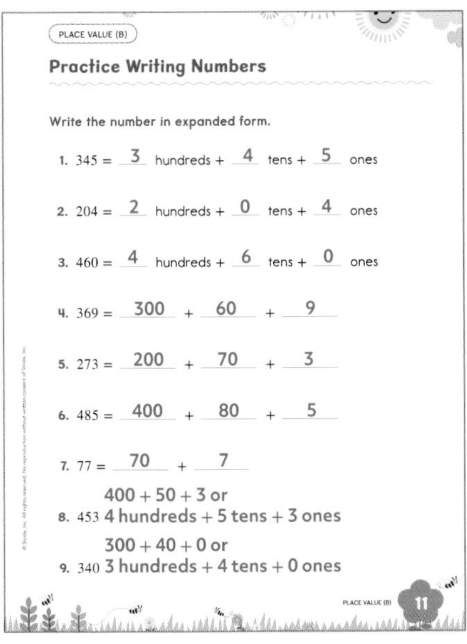

PLACE VALUE (B)

Practice Writing Numbers

Write the number in expanded form.

1. 345 = 3 hundreds + 4 tens + 5 ones
2. 204 = 2 hundreds + 0 tens + 4 ones
3. 460 = 4 hundreds + 6 tens + 0 ones
4. 369 = 300 + 60 + 9
5. 273 = 200 + 70 + 3
6. 485 = 400 + 80 + 5
7. 77 = 70 + 7
8. 453 400 + 50 + 3 or 4 hundreds + 5 tens + 3 ones
9. 340 300 + 40 + 0 or 3 hundreds + 4 tens + 0 ones

PLACE VALUE (B) 11

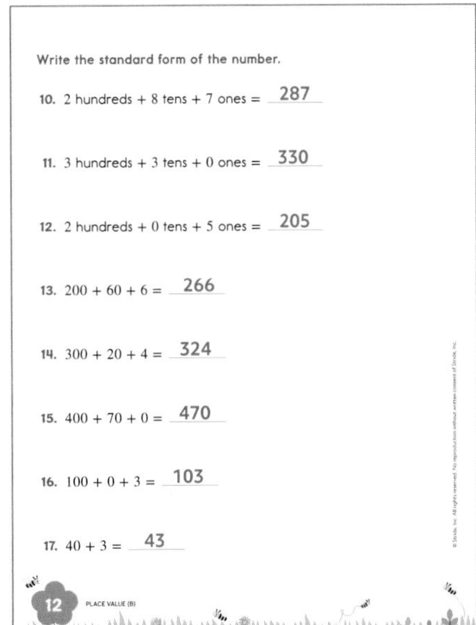

Write the standard form of the number.

10. 2 hundreds + 8 tens + 7 ones = 287
11. 3 hundreds + 3 tens + 0 ones = 330
12. 2 hundreds + 0 tens + 5 ones = 205
13. 200 + 60 + 6 = 266
14. 300 + 20 + 4 = 324
15. 400 + 70 + 0 = 470
16. 100 + 0 + 3 = 103
17. 40 + 3 = 43

12 PLACE VALUE (B)

WRAP-UP

Writing Numbers

Students will solve problems to show that they understand how to write numbers in both standard form and expanded form.

Place Value (C)

Lesson Overview

ACTIVITY	ACTIVITY TITLE	TIME	ONLINE/OFFLINE
GET READY	Introduction to Place Value (C)	**2** minutes	online
	Adding 2 Math Facts	**7** minutes	online
LEARN AND TRY IT	Finding a Hundred in a Group of Tens	**7** minutes	online
	Find a Hundred in a Group of Tens	**7** minutes	online
ALL ABOUT ME	Brain Break	**1** minute	online or offline
LEARN AND TRY IT	Composing and Decomposing Numbers	**7** minutes	online
	Compose and Decompose Numbers	**7** minutes	online
	Practice Composing and Decomposing Numbers	**20** minutes	online and offline
WRAP-UP	Composing and Decomposing Numbers	**2** minutes	online

Content Background

Students will learn how to regroup 1 hundred into 10 tens and how to use regrouping to compose and decompose numbers. Students will use base-10 blocks to investigate different ways to compose and decompose a number.

OPTIONAL Students can use physical base-10 blocks as they work through this lesson to help them solve problems. A printable version of base-10 blocks is linked in the lesson.

MATERIALS

Supplied

- *Math 2 Activity Book:* Practice Composing and Decomposing Numbers

Decompose

To decompose a number means to break it into smaller numbers. A number can be decomposed by place value. It can be further decomposed by regrouping 1 hundred into 10 tens or regrouping 1 ten into 10 ones. Here are some ways to decompose 184.

184 = 1 hundred + 8 tens + 4 ones

184 = 1 hundred + 7 tens + 14 ones

184 = 16 tens + 24 ones

Compose

To compose a number means to make a number by putting smaller numbers together. Here are some ways to compose 215.

2 hundreds + 1 ten + 5 ones = 215

1 hundred + 11 tens + 5 ones = 215

21 tens + 5 ones = 215

Lesson Goals

- Explain that 10 tens make a hundred.
- Decompose a number in more than one way.
- Compose a number in more than one way.

KEYWORDS

compose a number – put a number together from smaller numbers

Example: 30 + 4 = 34 and 20 + 14 = 34

decompose a number – break a number into smaller numbers

Example: 53 = 50 + 3 and 53 = 30 + 23

regroup – use place-value concepts to rename numbers

Examples: 1 ten regroups into 10 ones; 1 hundred regroups into 10 tens

GET READY

Introduction to Place Value (C)

Students will get a glimpse of what they will learn about in the lesson. They will also read the lesson goals.

Adding 2 Math Facts

Students will practice adding 2.

LEARN AND TRY IT

LEARN Finding a Hundred in a Group of Tens

Students will use base-10 blocks to determine the number of tens that make up 1 hundred.

TRY IT Find a Hundred in a Group of Tens

Students will practice finding groups of 10 tens to make 1 hundred. Support will be provided to help students overcome misconceptions.

LEARN Composing and Decomposing Numbers

Students will learn to regroup to compose and decompose numbers.

TRY IT Compose and Decompose Numbers

Students will practice regrouping to compose and decompose numbers. Support will be provided to help students overcome misconceptions.

TRY IT Practice Composing and Decomposing Numbers

Students will complete online practice problems. Then they will complete Practice Composing and Decomposing Numbers from *Math 2 Activity Book*.

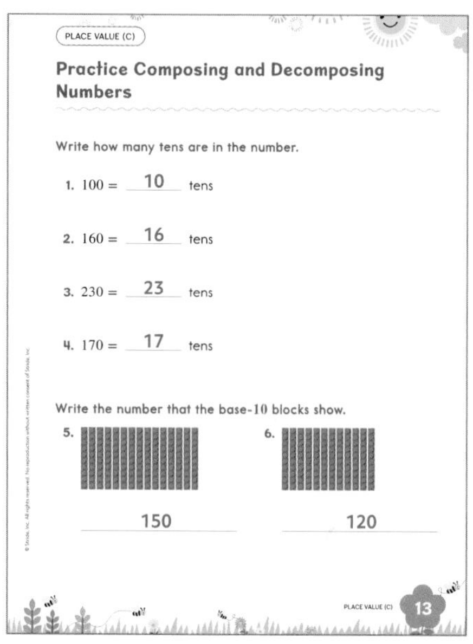

PLACE VALUE (C)

Practice Composing and Decomposing Numbers

Write how many tens are in the number.

1. 100 = 10 tens
2. 160 = 16 tens
3. 230 = 23 tens
4. 170 = 17 tens

Write the number that the base-10 blocks show.

5. 150
6. 120

PLACE VALUE (C) 13

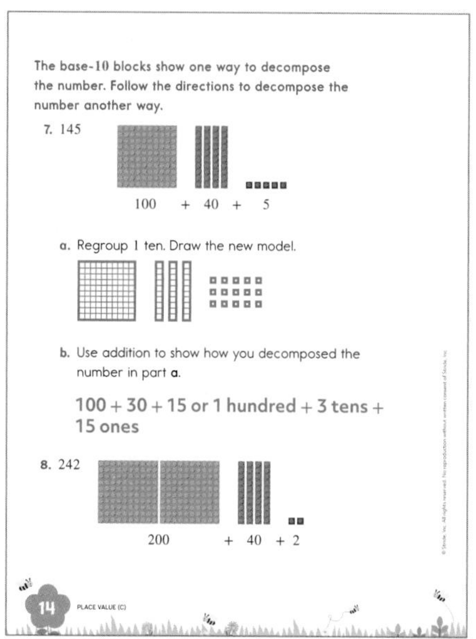

The base-10 blocks show one way to decompose the number. Follow the directions to decompose the number another way.

7. 145

100 + 40 + 5

a. Regroup 1 ten. Draw the new model.

b. Use addition to show how you decomposed the number in part **a**.

100 + 30 + 15 or 1 hundred + 3 tens + 15 ones

8. 242

200 + 40 + 2

14 PLACE VALUE (C)

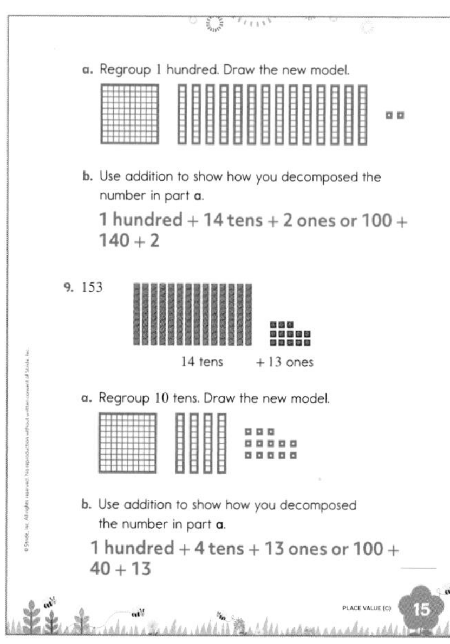

a. Regroup 1 hundred. Draw the new model.

b. Use addition to show how you decomposed the number in part **a**.

1 hundred + 14 tens + 2 ones or 100 + 140 + 2

9. 153

14 tens + 13 ones

a. Regroup 10 tens. Draw the new model.

b. Use addition to show how you decomposed the number in part **a**.

1 hundred + 4 tens + 13 ones or 100 + 40 + 13

PLACE VALUE (C) 15

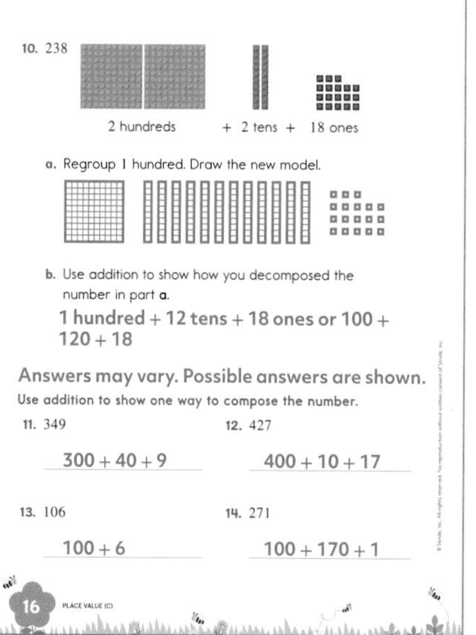

10. 238

2 hundreds + 2 tens + 18 ones

a. Regroup 1 hundred. Draw the new model.

b. Use addition to show how you decomposed the number in part **a**.

1 hundred + 12 tens + 18 ones or 100 + 120 + 18

Answers may vary. Possible answers are shown.

Use addition to show one way to compose the number.

11. 349 — 300 + 40 + 9
12. 427 — 400 + 10 + 17
13. 106 — 100 + 6
14. 271 — 100 + 170 + 1

16 PLACE VALUE (C)

WRAP-UP

Composing and Decomposing Numbers

Students will solve problems to show that they understand composing and decomposing numbers.

Place Value (D)

Lesson Overview

ACTIVITY	ACTIVITY TITLE	TIME	ONLINE/OFFLINE
GET READY	Introduction to Place Value (D)	**2** minutes	
TRY IT	Review Place Value	**18** minutes	
QUIZ	Place Value	**25** minutes	
WRAP-UP	More Math Practice	**15** minutes	

Lesson Goals

- Review place value and expanded form.
- Review composing and decomposing numbers.
- Take a quiz.

MATERIALS

There are no materials to gather for this lesson.

GET READY

Introduction to Place Value (D)

Students will read the lesson goals.

TRY IT

Review Place Value

Students will answer questions to review what they have learned about place value.

OPTIONAL If students have difficulty answering these questions, suggest using base-10 blocks to model the numbers in the questions.

QUIZ

Place Value

Students will complete the Place Value quiz.

WRAP-UP

More Math Practice

Students will practice skills according to their individual needs.

Compare and Order Numbers (A)

Lesson Overview

ACTIVITY	ACTIVITY TITLE	TIME	ONLINE/OFFLINE
GET READY	Introduction to Compare and Order Numbers (A)	**2** minutes	online
	Look Back at Using Symbols to Compare Numbers	**7** minutes	online
LEARN AND TRY IT	Using Models to Compare Numbers	**15** minutes	online
	Use Models to Compare Numbers	**10** minutes	online
ALL ABOUT ME	Brain Break	**1** minute	online or offline
TRY IT	Practice Using Models to Compare Numbers	**20** minutes	online and offline
WRAP-UP	Using Models to Compare Numbers	**5** minutes	online

Content Background

Students learn to compare three-digit numbers with values up to 500. Students will use symbols and words to express the comparisons.

Comparison Symbols

Though students may be familiar with the comparison symbols greater than (>), less than (<), and equals (=), some may need to be refreshed on their use. Remind students that these comparison symbols point to the lesser number and open to the greater number. For example, $6 > 3$ and $4 < 8$.

Base-10 Block Models

To help make comparisons, students are encouraged to build models of the numbers they are comparing using base-10 blocks. To compare the models, students must begin by comparing the numbers of blocks that represent the greatest place value in each number. These base-10 blocks can be used to compare 324 and 342.

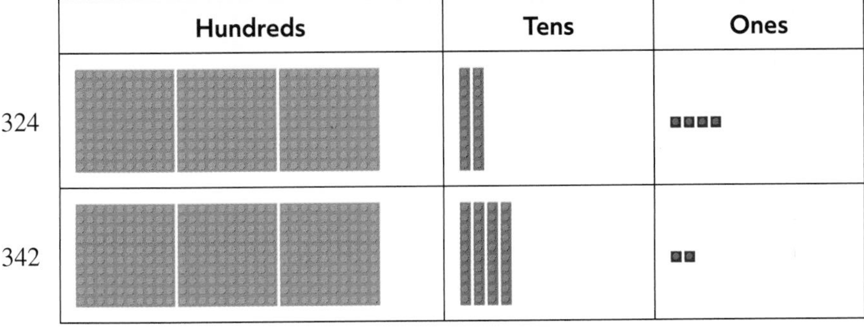

MATERIALS

Supplied

- *Math 2 Activity Book:* Practice Using Models to Compare Numbers

KEYWORDS

equals symbol (=) – symbol that means *equals*

Example: "3 = 2 + 1" means "3 equals 2 plus 1."

greater-than symbol (>) – symbol that means *greater than*

Example: "3 > 1" means "3 is greater than 1."

less-than symbol (<) – symbol that means *less than*

Example: "1 < 3" means "1 is less than 3."

Start with the hundreds. Since the number of hundreds blocks in each model is the same, move to the tens place. Since 324 has 2 tens and 342 has 4 tens, 324 is less than 342. Students will be asked to express their answers using symbols, $324 < 342$, or with words, *324 is less than 342*.

Lesson Goals

- Use models to compare numbers.

GET READY

Introduction to Compare and Order Numbers (A)

Students will get a glimpse of what they will learn about in the lesson. They will also read the lesson goals.

Look Back at Using Symbols to Compare Numbers

Students will review and practice the prerequisite skill of using symbols to compare numbers.

LEARN AND TRY IT

LEARN Using Models to Compare Numbers

Students will learn to use base-10 block models to compare numbers.

OPTIONAL Students may use a physical place-value mat and base-10 blocks as they work through the lesson.

TRY IT Use Models to Compare Numbers

Students will practice using base-10 block models to compare numbers. Support will be provided to help students overcome misconceptions.

TRY IT Practice Using Models to Compare Numbers

Students will complete online practice problems. Then they will complete Practice Using Models to Compare Numbers from *Math 2 Activity Book.*

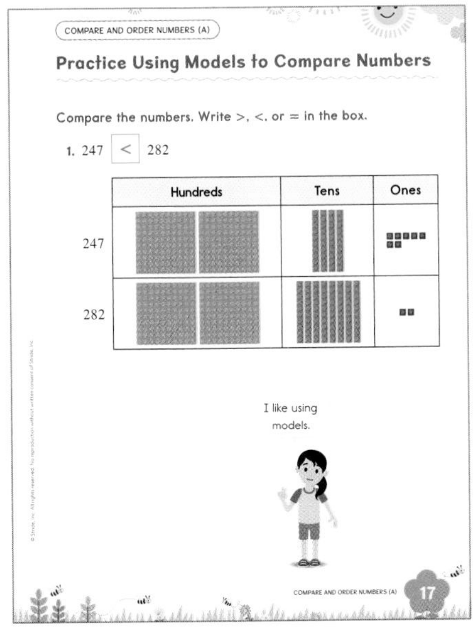
COMPARE AND ORDER NUMBERS (A)

Practice Using Models to Compare Numbers

Compare the numbers. Write >, <, or = in the box.

1. 247 [<] 282

	Hundreds	Tens	Ones
247			
282			

I like using models.

COMPARE AND ORDER NUMBERS (A) 17

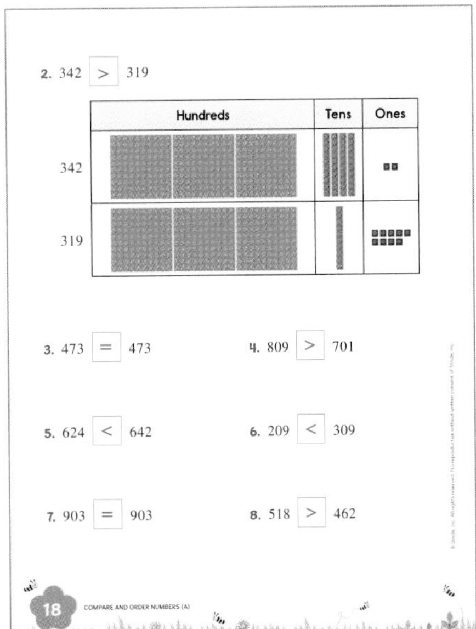
2. 342 [>] 319

	Hundreds	Tens	Ones
342			
319			

3. 473 [=] 473
4. 809 [>] 701
5. 624 [<] 642
6. 209 [<] 309
7. 903 [=] 903
8. 518 [>] 462

18 COMPARE AND ORDER NUMBERS (A)

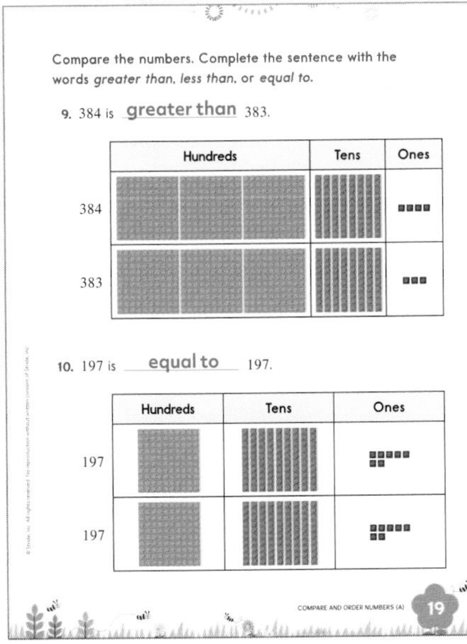
Compare the numbers. Complete the sentence with the words *greater than, less than,* or *equal to.*

9. 384 is greater than 383.

	Hundreds	Tens	Ones
384			
383			

10. 197 is equal to 197.

	Hundreds	Tens	Ones
197			
197			

COMPARE AND ORDER NUMBERS (A) 19

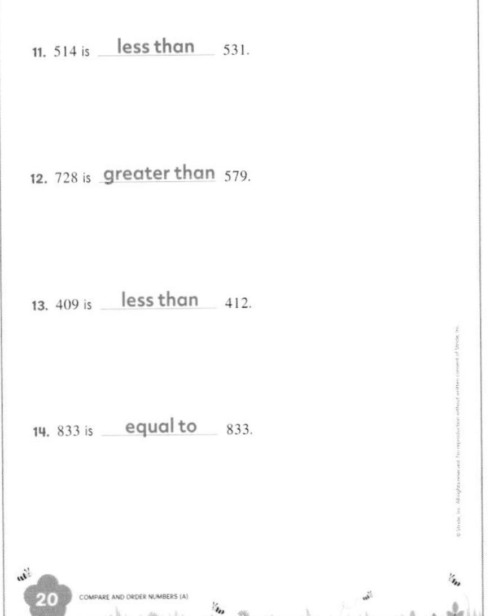
11. 514 is less than 531.

12. 728 is greater than 579.

13. 409 is less than 412.

14. 833 is equal to 833.

20 COMPARE AND ORDER NUMBERS (A)

WRAP-UP

Using Models to Compare Numbers

Students will solve problems to show that they understand how to compare numbers. Students may use base-10 block models to help them solve each problem.

Compare and Order Numbers (B)

Lesson Overview

ACTIVITY	ACTIVITY TITLE	TIME	ONLINE/OFFLINE
GET READY	Introduction to Compare and Order Numbers (B)	2 minutes	online
	Adding 2 with Instant Recall	8 minutes	online
LEARN AND TRY IT	Comparing Numbers Using Place Value	15 minutes	online
	Compare Numbers Using Place Value	10 minutes	online
	Practice Comparing Numbers Using Place Value	20 minutes	online and offline
WRAP-UP	Comparing Numbers Using Place Value	5 minutes	online

Content Background

Students will compare two numbers up to 500 by using a place-value chart to compare their numbers of hundreds, tens, and/or ones. To compare numbers, students must find the greatest place value where the numbers are different.

Hundreds

Hundreds	Tens	Ones
4	6	3
2	6	5

463 has 4 hundreds and 265 has 2 hundreds. Since 4 is greater than 2, 463 is greater than 265 or $463 > 265$.

Tens

Hundreds	Tens	Ones
4	3	2
4	6	5

Both 432 and 465 have 4 hundreds, so students must compare the tens. 432 has 3 tens and 465 has 6 tens. Since 3 is less than 6, 432 is less than 465 or $432 < 465$.

MATERIALS

Supplied

- *Math 2 Activity Book:* Practice Comparing Numbers Using Place Value

Ones

Hundreds	Tens	Ones
1	5	9
1	5	3

Both 159 and 153 have 1 hundred and 5 tens, so students must compare the ones. 159 has 9 ones and 153 has 3 ones. Since 9 is greater than 3, 159 is greater than 153 or 159 > 153.

Lesson Goals

- Use place value to compare two numbers.

GET READY

Introduction to Compare and Order Numbers (B)

Students will get a glimpse of what they will learn about in the lesson. They will also read the lesson goals.

Adding 2 with Instant Recall

Students will practice adding 2.

LEARN AND TRY IT

LEARN Comparing Numbers Using Place Value

Students will use place-value charts to compare two numbers.

TIP Ask students to explain why one number is greater than or less than another number. The explanation should involve comparing the numbers of hundreds, tens, and/or ones.

TRY IT Compare Numbers Using Place Value

Students will practice using place value to compare two numbers. Support will be provided to help students overcome misconceptions.

TRY IT Practice Comparing Numbers Using Place Value

Students will complete online practice problems. Then they will complete Practice Comparing Numbers Using Place Value from *Math 2 Activity Book*.

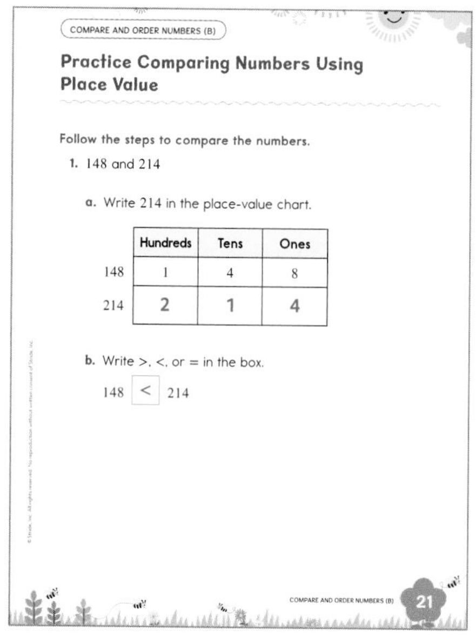

COMPARE AND ORDER NUMBERS (B)

Practice Comparing Numbers Using Place Value

Follow the steps to compare the numbers.

1. 148 and 214

   a. Write 214 in the place-value chart.

	Hundreds	Tens	Ones
148	1	4	8
214	2	1	4

   b. Write >, <, or = in the box.

   148 [<] 214

COMPARE AND ORDER NUMBERS (B) 21

2. 393 and 385

   a. Write 393 and 385 in the place-value chart.

	Hundreds	Tens	Ones
393	3	9	3
385	3	8	5

   b. Write >, <, or = in the box.

   393 [>] 385

Compare the numbers. Write a number sentence using >, <, or =.

3. 403 and 420 ____ 403 < 420
4. 228 and 228 ____ 228 = 228
5. 362 and 366 ____ 362 < 366

22 COMPARE AND ORDER NUMBERS (B)

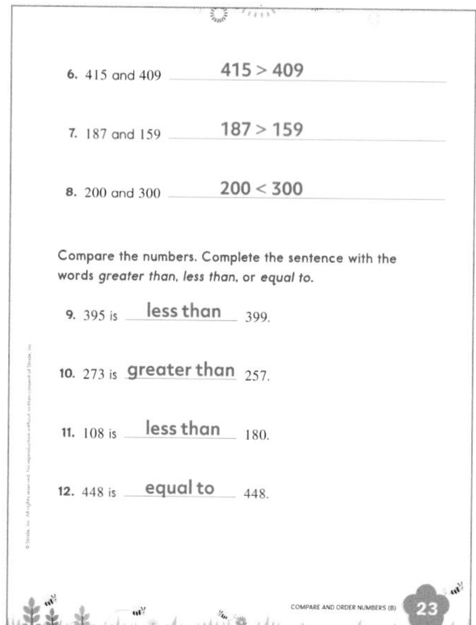

6. 415 and 409 ____ 415 > 409
7. 187 and 159 ____ 187 > 159
8. 200 and 300 ____ 200 < 300

Compare the numbers. Complete the sentence with the words *greater than*, *less than*, or *equal to*.

9. 395 is ____ less than ____ 399.
10. 273 is ____ greater than ____ 257.
11. 108 is ____ less than ____ 180.
12. 448 is ____ equal to ____ 448.

COMPARE AND ORDER NUMBERS (B) 23

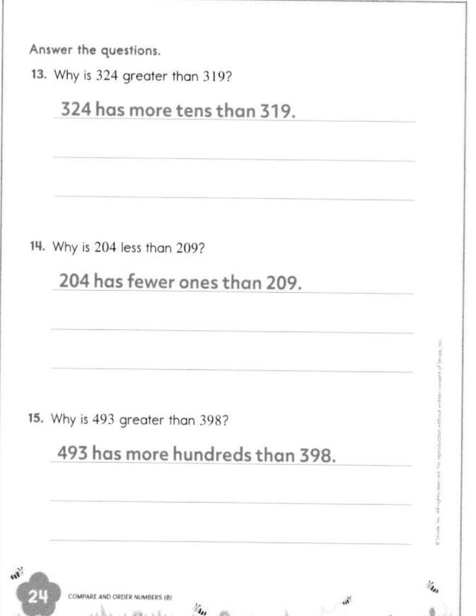

Answer the questions.

13. Why is 324 greater than 319?

    324 has more tens than 319.

14. Why is 204 less than 209?

    204 has fewer ones than 209.

15. Why is 493 greater than 398?

    493 has more hundreds than 398.

24 COMPARE AND ORDER NUMBERS (B)

WRAP-UP

Comparing Numbers Using Place Value

Students will solve problems to show that they understand comparing numbers.

Compare and Order Numbers (C)

Lesson Overview

ACTIVITY	ACTIVITY TITLE	TIME	ONLINE/OFFLINE
GET READY	Introduction to Compare and Order Numbers (C)	**2** minutes	
	Adding 2 Math Facts Game	**7** minutes	
LEARN AND TRY IT	Ordering Numbers from Least to Greatest	**7** minutes	
	Order Numbers from Least to Greatest	**7** minutes	
ALL ABOUT ME	Brain Break	**1** minute	or
LEARN AND TRY IT	Ordering Numbers from Greatest to Least	**7** minutes	
	Order Numbers from Greatest to Least	**7** minutes	
	Practice Ordering Numbers	**20** minutes	and
WRAP-UP	Ordering Numbers	**2** minutes	

Content Background

Students will use their knowledge of comparing numbers to put three numbers up to 500 in order from least to greatest and then from greatest to least. Place-value charts and number lines are useful tools for ordering numbers.

MATERIALS

Supplied

- *Math 2 Activity Book:* Practice Ordering Numbers

Least to Greatest

This place-value chart and number line can be used to order 298, 312, and 303 from least to greatest.

Hundreds	Tens	Ones
2	9	8
3	1	2
3	0	3

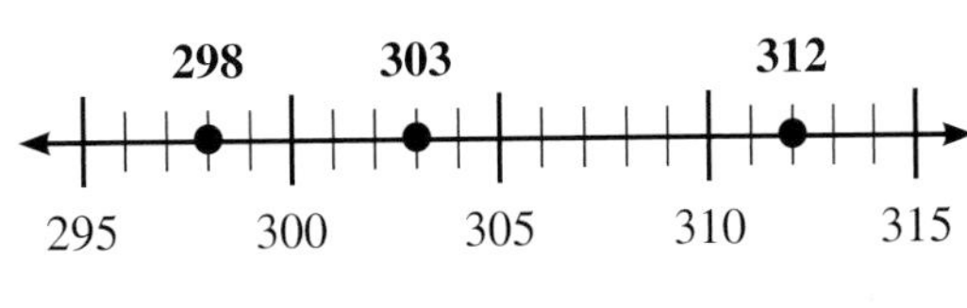

The place-value chart shows that 298 has fewer hundreds than the other numbers, so 298 is the least number. The chart also shows that 303 has fewer tens than 312, so $298 < 303 < 312$. The number line gives the same result because numbers get larger from left to right on a number line.

Greatest to Least

This place-value chart and number line can be used to order 273, 290, and 284 from greatest to least.

Hundreds	Tens	Ones
2	7	3
2	9	0
2	8	4

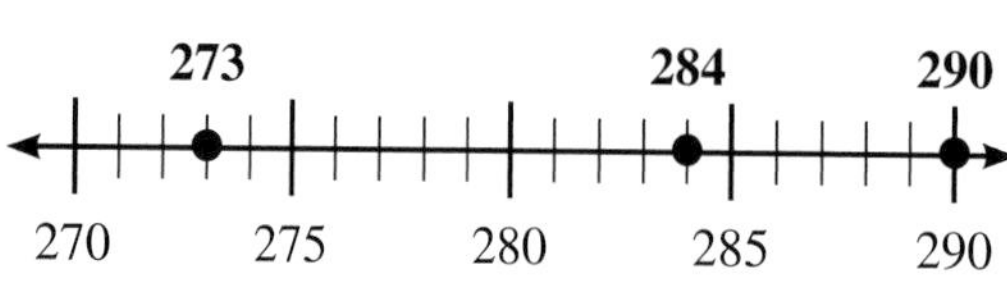

The place-value chart shows that all three numbers have 2 hundreds, so compare the tens. Since 290 has the most tens and 273 has the fewest tens, 290 > 284 > 273. The number line shows the same result because numbers get smaller from right to left on a number line.

Lesson Goals

- Order numbers from least to greatest.
- Order numbers from greatest to least.

GET READY

Introduction to Compare and Order Numbers (C)

Students will get a glimpse of what they will learn about in the lesson. They will also read the lesson goals.

Adding 2 Math Facts Game

Students will play a game to practice adding 2.

LEARN AND TRY IT

LEARN Ordering Numbers from Least to Greatest

Students will use a place-value chart and a number line to order numbers from least to greatest.

SUPPORT Make sure students understand that the smallest number is the *least*, and the largest number is the *greatest*.

TRY IT Order Numbers from Least to Greatest

Students will practice ordering numbers from least to greatest. Support will be provided to help students overcome misconceptions.

LEARN Ordering Numbers from Greatest to Least

Students will use a place-value chart and a number line to order numbers from greatest to least.

TRY IT Order Numbers from Greatest to Least

Students will practice ordering numbers from greatest to least. Support will be provided to help students overcome misconceptions.

TRY IT Practice Ordering Numbers

Students will complete online practice problems. Then they will complete Practice Ordering Numbers from *Math 2 Activity Book*.

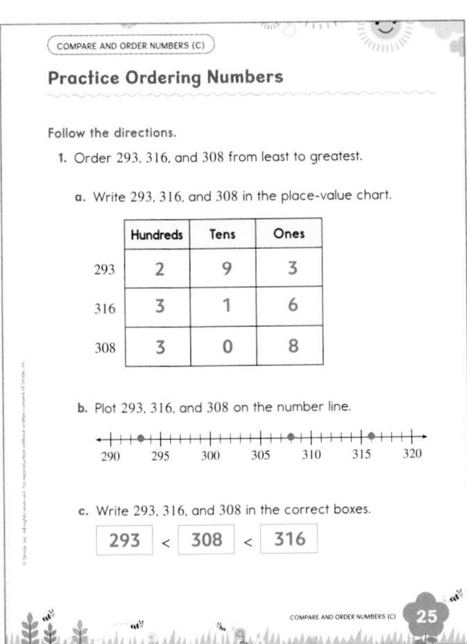

COMPARE AND ORDER NUMBERS (C)

Practice Ordering Numbers

Follow the directions.

1. Order 293, 316, and 308 from least to greatest.

a. Write 293, 316, and 308 in the place-value chart.

	Hundreds	Tens	Ones
293	2	9	3
316	3	1	6
308	3	0	8

b. Plot 293, 316, and 308 on the number line.

290 295 300 305 310 315 320

c. Write 293, 316, and 308 in the correct boxes.

293 < 308 < 316

COMPARE AND ORDER NUMBERS (C) 25

2. Order 344, 336, and 352 from greatest to least.

a. Write 344, 336, and 352 in the place-value chart.

	Hundreds	Tens	Ones
344	3	4	4
336	3	3	6
352	3	5	2

b. Plot 344, 336, and 352 on the number line.

330 335 340 345 350 355 360

c. Write 344, 336, and 352 in the correct boxes.

352 > 344 > 336

26 COMPARE AND ORDER NUMBERS (C)

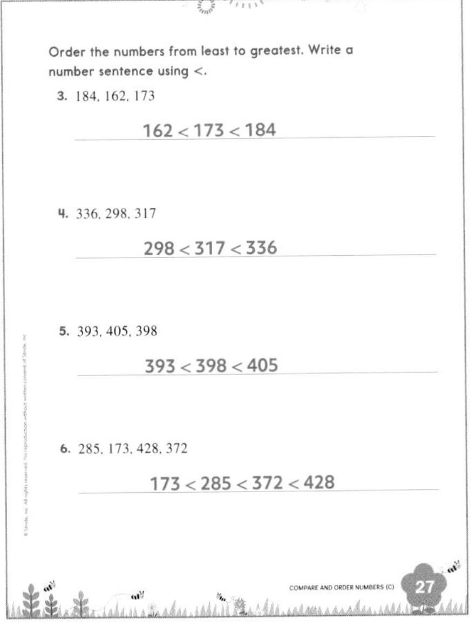

Order the numbers from least to greatest. Write a number sentence using <.

3. 184, 162, 173

162 < 173 < 184

4. 336, 298, 317

298 < 317 < 336

5. 393, 405, 398

393 < 398 < 405

6. 285, 173, 428, 372

173 < 285 < 372 < 428

COMPARE AND ORDER NUMBERS (C) 27

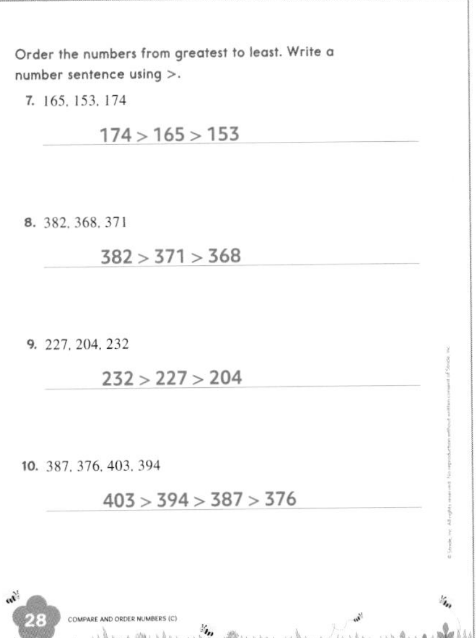

Order the numbers from greatest to least. Write a number sentence using >.

7. 165, 153, 174

174 > 165 > 153

8. 382, 368, 371

382 > 371 > 368

9. 227, 204, 232

232 > 227 > 204

10. 387, 376, 403, 394

403 > 394 > 387 > 376

28 COMPARE AND ORDER NUMBERS (C)

WRAP-UP

Ordering Numbers

Students will solve problems to show that they understand how to order numbers from least to greatest and from greatest to least.

Compare and Order Numbers (D)

Lesson Overview

ACTIVITY	ACTIVITY TITLE	TIME	ONLINE/OFFLINE
GET READY	Introduction to Compare and Order Numbers (D)	**2** minutes	online
TRY IT	Review Compare and Order Numbers	**18** minutes	online
QUIZ	Compare and Order Numbers	**25** minutes	online
WRAP-UP	More Math Practice	**15** minutes	online

Lesson Goals

- Review comparing and ordering numbers.
- Take a quiz.

MATERIALS

There are no materials to gather for this lesson.

GET READY

Introduction to Compare and Order Numbers (D)

Students will read the lesson goals.

TRY IT

Review Compare and Order Numbers

Students will answer questions to review what they have learned about how to compare and order numbers.

QUIZ

Compare and Order Numbers

Students will complete the Compare and Order Numbers quiz.

WRAP-UP

More Math Practice

Students will practice skills according to their individual needs.

Numbers Through 500 Wrap-Up

Lesson Overview

ACTIVITY	ACTIVITY TITLE	TIME	ONLINE/OFFLINE
GET READY	Introduction to Numbers Through 500 Wrap-Up	**2** minutes	
TRY IT	Review Numbers Through 500	**23** minutes	
UNIT CHECKPOINT	Numbers Through 500	**35** minutes	

Lesson Goals

- Review numbers through 500.
- Show what you know about numbers through 500.

MATERIALS

There are no materials to gather for this lesson.

GET READY

Introduction to Numbers Through 500 Wrap-Up

Students will read the lesson goals.

TRY IT

Review Numbers Through 500

Students will answer questions to review what they have learned about numbers through 500.

UNIT CHECKPOINT

Numbers Through 500

Students will complete the Numbers Through 500 Unit Checkpoint.

LEARNING COACH CHECK-IN This is a graded assignment. Make sure students complete the online assessment.

Time and Money

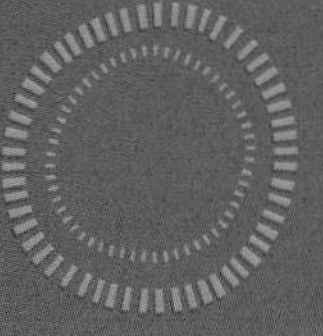

Time (A)

Lesson Overview

ACTIVITY	ACTIVITY TITLE	TIME	ONLINE/OFFLINE
GET READY	Introduction to Time (A)	**2** minutes	online
	Look Back at the Hands on a Clock	**7** minutes	online
LEARN AND **TRY IT**	Understanding How Units of Clock Time Are Related	**7** minutes	online
	Understand How Units of Clock Time Are Related	**7** minutes	online
ALL ABOUT ME	Brain Break	**1** minute	online or offline
LEARN AND **TRY IT**	Understanding How Units of Calendar Time Are Related	**7** minutes	online
	Understand How Units of Calendar Time Are Related	**7** minutes	online
	Practice Understanding Units of Time	**20** minutes	online and offline
WRAP-UP	Understanding Units of Time	**2** minutes	online

Content Background

Students will learn about relationships between units of time, such as minutes in an hour, days in a week, and months in a year.

Clock-Time Relationships

- 60 seconds = 1 minute
- 60 minutes = 1 hour
- 24 hours = 1 day

Calendar-Time Relationships

- 7 days = 1 week
- 52 weeks = 1 year
- 12 months = 1 year

MATERIALS

Supplied

- *Math 2 Activity Book:* Practice Understanding Units of Time

Different months have different numbers of days, and a full year has either 365 or 366 days.

- January, March, May, July, August, October, and December have 31 days every year.
- April, June, September, and November have 30 days every year.
- February has 28 or 29 days every year.

Lesson Goals

- Understand units of time.
- Recall the number of days in each month.

KEYWORDS

day – unit of time equal to 24 hours

hour – unit of time equal to 60 minutes

minute – unit of time equal to 60 seconds

month – unit of calendar time equal to about 4 weeks

Example: There are 12 months in 1 year.

second – basic unit of time

week – unit of calendar time equal to 7 days

year – unit of calendar time equal to 365 or 366 days

GET READY

Introduction to Time (A)

Students will get a glimpse of what they will learn about in the lesson. They will also read the lesson goals.

Look Back at the Hands on a Clock

Students will review and practice the prerequisite skill of understanding the hour and minute hand on a clock. Students will review telling time to the nearest hour.

LEARN AND TRY IT

LEARN Understanding How Units of Clock Time Are Related

Students will learn clock-time relationships.

OPTIONAL Show students a real analog clock and allow them to observe the motions of the hands on the clock.

TRY IT Understand How Units of Clock Time Are Related

Students will practice recalling clock-time relationships. Support will be provided to help students overcome misconceptions.

LEARN Understanding How Units of Calendar Time Are Related

Students will learn calendar-time relationships. Students will learn the number of days in each month of the year.

OPTIONAL Explain to students that the years when February has 29 days are called *leap years* and exist so that each season always occurs during the same months of the year.

TRY IT Understand How Units of Calendar Time Are Related

Students will practice recalling calendar-time relationships. Support will be provided to help students overcome misconceptions.

TIP Remind students to use the technique from the Learn of using their hands to recall the number of days in each month of the year.

TRY IT Practice Understanding Units of Time

Students will complete online practice problems. Then they will complete Practice Understanding Units of Time from *Math 2 Activity Book*.

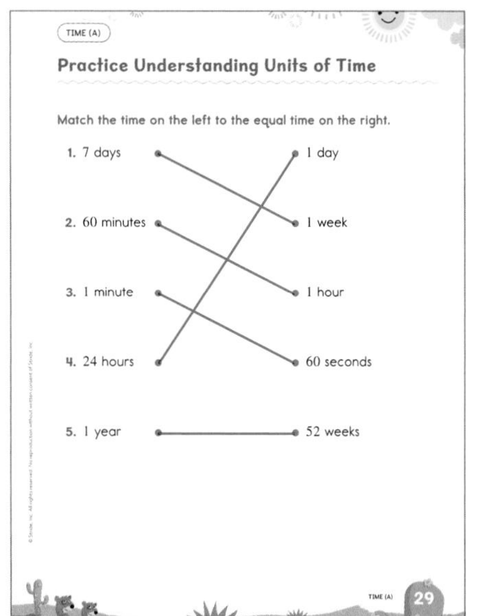

TIME (A)

Practice Understanding Units of Time

Match the time on the left to the equal time on the right.

1. 7 days	1 day
2. 60 minutes	1 week
3. 1 minute	1 hour
4. 24 hours	60 seconds
5. 1 year	52 weeks

TIME (A) 29

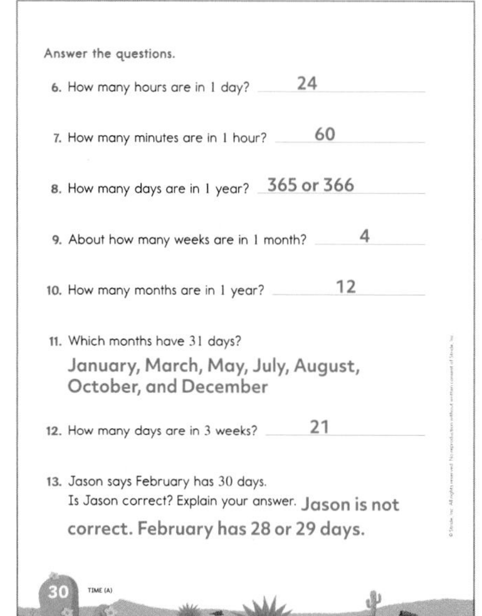

Answer the questions.

6. How many hours are in 1 day? 24
7. How many minutes are in 1 hour? 60
8. How many days are in 1 year? 365 or 366
9. About how many weeks are in 1 month? 4
10. How many months are in 1 year? 12
11. Which months have 31 days? January, March, May, July, August, October, and December
12. How many days are in 3 weeks? 21
13. Jason says February has 30 days. Is Jason correct? Explain your answer. Jason is not correct. February has 28 or 29 days.

30 TIME (A)

WRAP-UP

Understanding Units of Time

Students will solve problems to show that they understand units of time.

Time (B)

Lesson Overview

ACTIVITY	ACTIVITY TITLE	TIME	ONLINE/OFFLINE
GET READY	Introduction to Time (B)	2 minutes	online
	Adding 3 Math Facts	7 minutes	online
LEARN AND TRY IT	Understanding A.M. and P.M.	7 minutes	online
	Understand A.M. and P.M.	7 minutes	online
ALL ABOUT ME	Brain Break	1 minute	online or offline
LEARN AND TRY IT	Telling Time to the Nearest 15 Minutes	7 minutes	online
	Tell Time to the Nearest 15 Minutes	7 minutes	online
	Practice Telling Time to the Nearest 15 Minutes	20 minutes	online and offline
WRAP-UP	Telling Time to the Nearest 15 Minutes	2 minutes	online

Content Background

Students will learn how to tell time to the nearest quarter hour on digital and analog clocks. Students will learn to indicate the time of day using the labels a.m. and p.m.

A.M. and P.M.

Every time on a clock happens twice a day. The labels a.m. and p.m. are used to distinguish between these two times. Twelve o'clock at night is called midnight and 12 o'clock during the day is called noon. Times from midnight to noon use the label a.m. Times from noon to midnight use the label p.m.

Time to the Quarter Hour

Time can be expressed in different formats. Times are often given in the traditional format as seen on a digital clock. However, times are also given using words such as *quarter after, half past*, and *quarter to*.

15 minutes after 7
quarter after 7

30 minutes after 7
half past 7

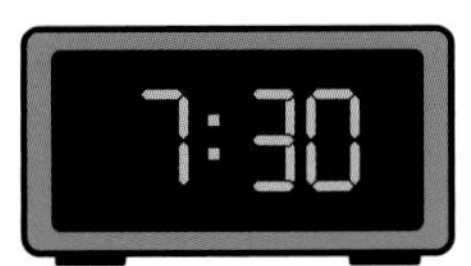

45 minutes after 7
15 minutes before 8
quarter to 8

MATERIALS

Supplied

- *Math 2 Activity Book:* Practice Telling Time to the Nearest 15 Minutes

Lesson Goals

- Understand a.m. and p.m.
- Tell time to the nearest 15 minutes.

KEYWORDS

a.m. – label for times after midnight and before noon

analog clock – shows time with an hour hand and a minute hand

digital clock – shows time using numerals with the hour on the left and the minutes on the right

midnight – twelve o'clock at night

noon – twelve o'clock during the day

p.m. – label for times after noon and before midnight

GET READY

Introduction to Time (B)

Students will get a glimpse of what they will learn about in the lesson. They will also read the lesson goals.

Adding 3 Math Facts

Students will practice adding 3.

LEARN AND TRY IT

LEARN Understanding A.M. and P.M.

Students will learn how to use the labels a.m. and p.m.

OPTIONAL Play a guessing game. State an activity that the student participates in, and the student guesses the correct label.

TRY IT Understand A.M. and P.M.

Students will practice using the labels a.m. and p.m. Support will be provided to help students overcome misconceptions.

LEARN Telling Time to the Nearest 15 Minutes

Students will learn how to tell time to the nearest 15 minutes on both analog and digital clocks. Students will tell time using numbers and using words.

TRY IT Tell Time to the Nearest 15 Minutes

Students will practice telling time to the nearest 15 minutes on both analog and digital clocks. Support will be provided to help students overcome misconceptions.

TRY IT Practice Telling Time to the Nearest 15 Minutes

Students will complete online practice problems. Then they will complete Practice Telling Time to the Nearest 15 Minutes from *Math 2 Activity Book*.

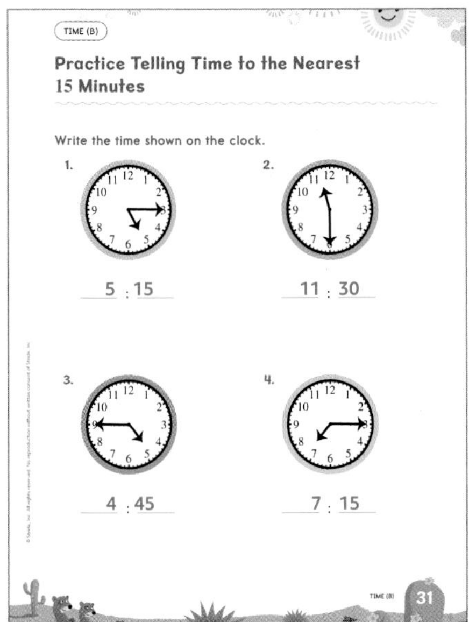
TIME (B)

Practice Telling Time to the Nearest 15 Minutes

Write the time shown on the clock.

1. 5 : 15
2. 11 : 30
3. 4 : 45
4. 7 : 15

TIME (B) 31

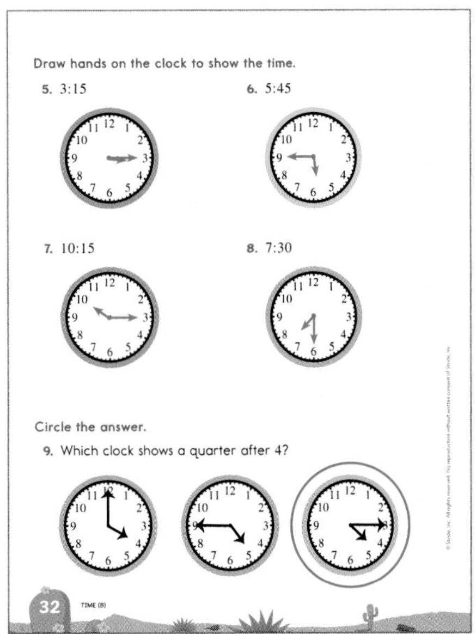
Draw hands on the clock to show the time.

5. 3:15
6. 5:45
7. 10:15
8. 7:30

Circle the answer.

9. Which clock shows a quarter after 4?

32 TIME (B)

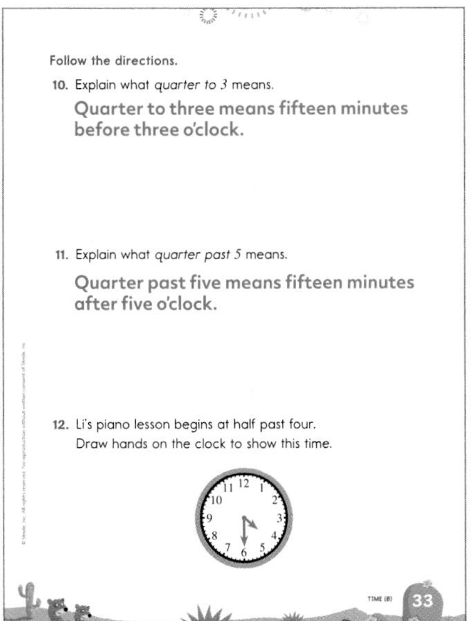
Follow the directions.

10. Explain what *quarter to 3* means.
    Quarter to three means fifteen minutes before three o'clock.

11. Explain what *quarter past 5* means.
    Quarter past five means fifteen minutes after five o'clock.

12. Li's piano lesson begins at half past four.
    Draw hands on the clock to show this time.

TIME (B) 33

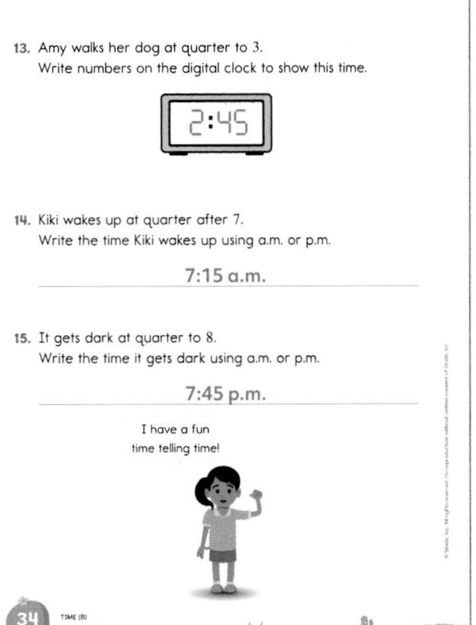
13. Amy walks her dog at quarter to 3.
    Write numbers on the digital clock to show this time.
    2:45

14. Kiki wakes up at quarter after 7.
    Write the time Kiki wakes up using a.m. or p.m.
    7:15 a.m.

15. It gets dark at quarter to 8.
    Write the time it gets dark using a.m. or p.m.
    7:45 p.m.

34 TIME (B)

WRAP-UP

Telling Time to the Nearest 15 Minutes

Students will solve problems to show that they understand how to tell time to the nearest 15 minutes.

Time (C)

Lesson Overview

ACTIVITY	ACTIVITY TITLE	TIME	ONLINE/OFFLINE
GET READY	Introduction to Time (C)	**2** minutes	online
	Adding 3 with Instant Recall	**8** minutes	online
LEARN AND **TRY IT**	Telling Time to the Nearest 5 Minutes	**15** minutes	online
	Tell Time to the Nearest 5 Minutes	**10** minutes	online
	Practice Telling Time to the Nearest 5 Minutes	**20** minutes	online and offline
WRAP-UP	Telling Time to the Nearest 5 Minutes	**5** minutes	online

Content Background

Students have learned to tell time to the nearest quarter hour by recognizing when the minute hand points to the 3, 6, 9, or 12 on an analog clock. In this lesson, students will learn to tell time when the minute hand points to the other numbers. They will learn how to count by 5 to tell time to the nearest 5 minutes on a digital or an analog clock. For example, the minute hand on this clock points to 5. Skip count by 5 five times: 5, 10, 15, 20, 25. The time is 10:25.

SUPPORT For students having difficulty counting by 5, review how to count by 10: 0, 10, 20, and so on. Counting by 5 means saying the number that ends in 5 between each ten: 0, **5**, 10, **15**, 20, and so on. Turn counting practice into a game. One person chooses a starting number that ends in 5 or 0. The other person starts at that number and counts by 5 to 60.

MATERIALS

Supplied

- *Math 2 Activity Book:* Practice Telling Time to the Nearest 5 Minutes

Lesson Goals

- Tell time to the nearest 5 minutes.

GET READY

Introduction to Time (C)

Students will get a glimpse of what they will learn about in the lesson. They will also read the lesson goals.

Adding 3 with Instant Recall

Students will practice adding 3.

LEARN AND TRY IT

LEARN Telling Time to the Nearest 5 Minutes

Students will learn to count by 5 to tell time to the nearest 5 minutes.

TIP Students will learn to tell the number of minutes *after* the hour. They can count by 5 counterclockwise to tell the number of minutes *before* the hour.

TRY IT Tell Time to the Nearest 5 Minutes

Students will practice telling time to the nearest 5 minutes. Support will be provided to help students overcome misconceptions.

TRY IT Practice Telling Time to the Nearest 5 Minutes

Students will complete online practice problems. Then they will complete Practice Telling Time to the Nearest 5 Minutes from *Math 2 Activity Book.*

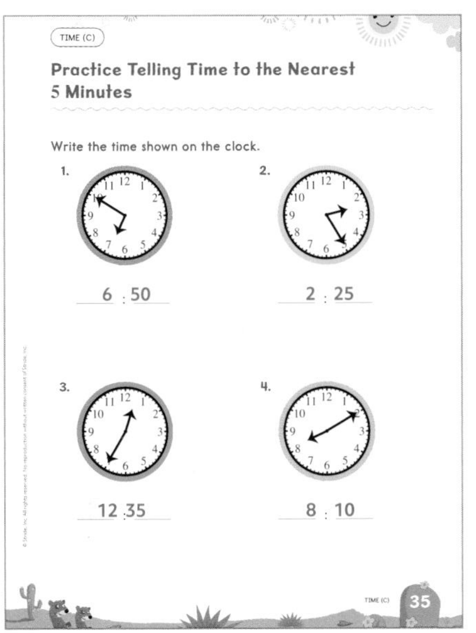

TIME (C)

Practice Telling Time to the Nearest 5 Minutes

Write the time shown on the clock.

1. 6 : 50
2. 2 : 25
3. 12 :35
4. 8 : 10

TIME (C) 35

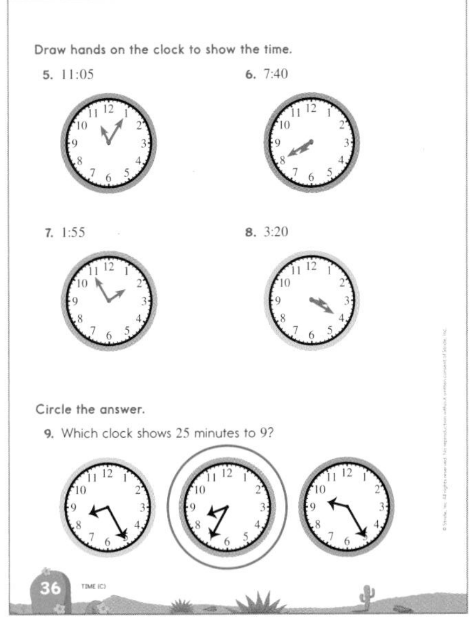

Draw hands on the clock to show the time.

5. 11:05
6. 7:40
7. 1:55
8. 3:20

Circle the answer.

9. Which clock shows 25 minutes to 9?

36 TIME (C)

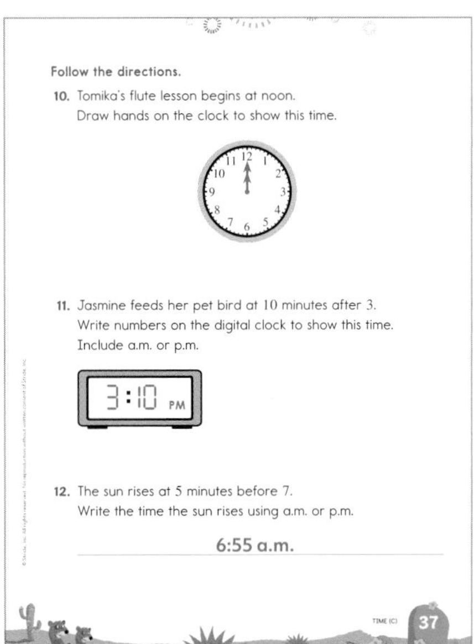

Follow the directions.

10. Tomika's flute lesson begins at noon. Draw hands on the clock to show this time.
11. Jasmine feeds her pet bird at 10 minutes after 3. Write numbers on the digital clock to show this time. Include a.m. or p.m.

3:10 PM

12. The sun rises at 5 minutes before 7. Write the time the sun rises using a.m. or p.m.

6:55 a.m.

TIME (C) 37

WRAP-UP

Telling Time to the Nearest 5 Minutes

Students will solve a problem to show that they understand how to tell time to the nearest 5 minutes.

Time (D)

Lesson Overview

ACTIVITY	ACTIVITY TITLE	TIME	ONLINE/OFFLINE
GET READY	Introduction to Time (D)	**2** minutes	
TRY IT	Review Time	**18** minutes	
QUIZ	Time	**25** minutes	
WRAP-UP	More Math Practice	**15** minutes	

Lesson Goals

- Review understanding units of time and telling time.
- Take a quiz.

MATERIALS

There are no materials to gather for this lesson.

GET READY

Introduction to Time (D)

Students will read the lesson goals.

TRY IT

Review Time

Students will answer questions to review what they have learned about time.

QUIZ

Time

Students will complete the Time quiz.

WRAP-UP

More Math Practice

Students will practice skills according to their individual needs.

Money (A)

Lesson Overview

ACTIVITY	ACTIVITY TITLE	TIME	ONLINE/OFFLINE
GET READY	Introduction to Money (A)	**2** minutes	online
	Look Back at Counting on by 5 and 10	**7** minutes	online
LEARN AND TRY IT	Finding the Value of a Group of Coins	**7** minutes	online
	Find the Value of a Group of Coins	**7** minutes	online
ALL ABOUT ME	Brain Break	**1** minute	online or offline
LEARN AND TRY IT	Solving Story Problems with Coins	**7** minutes	online
	Solve Story Problems with Coins	**7** minutes	online
	Practice Working with Coins	**20** minutes	online and offline
WRAP-UP	Working with Coins	**2** minutes	online

Content Background

Students will count on to find the value of a group of coins. They will also solve story problems involving coins. Students will work with these coins.

- Penny: 1¢
- Nickel: 5¢
- Dime: 10¢
- Quarter: 25¢

Counting On

To find the value of a group of coins, first put the coins in order from greatest value to least value. Then count on by 25, 10, 5, and 1. Students may find it helpful to sketch coins when the coins are given in words.

For example, a group of coins contains a dime, a quarter, a penny, a dime, and a nickel. First, sketch the coins in order from greatest value to least value. Then start with the first coin and count on to find the value of the group of coins.

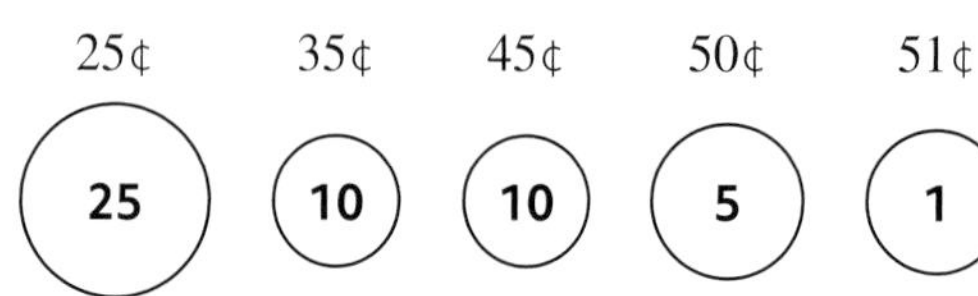

The value of this group of coins is 51¢.

MATERIALS

Supplied

- *Math 2 Activity Book:* Practice Working with Coins

KEYWORDS

coin – unit of money made of metal and shaped like a disc

Example: A nickel is a coin that is worth 5 cents.

count on – mental strategy used to add numbers

Solving Story Problems

Students will learn to solve story problems by working through 3 steps.

- **Understand it.** Carefully read the problem. List or draw a box around facts given in the problem. List or circle what you need to find.
- **Plan it.** Make a plan for how to use the facts to find the solution. A model, such as a drawing or a number sentence, can help organize the facts.
- **Solve it.** Follow the plan and find the solution. Write the solution in a complete sentence to answer the original question.

Story problems involving coins are presented in this lesson. Students will learn how to count on to solve story problems since addition and subtraction with 2-digit numbers is taught in the next unit.

Lesson Goals

- Find the value of a group of coins.
- Solve a problem about coins.

GET READY

Introduction to Money (A)

Students will get a glimpse of what they will learn about in the lesson. They will also read the lesson goals.

Look Back at Counting on by 5 and 10

Students will review and practice the prerequisite skill of counting on by 5 and 10.

LEARN AND TRY IT

LEARN Finding the Value of a Group of Coins

Students will learn to count on to find the value of a group of coins.

SUPPORT For students having difficulty recalling names or values of coins, use real or play coins to model problems.

TRY IT Find the Value of a Group of Coins

Students will practice counting on to find the value of a group of coins. Support will be provided to help students overcome misconceptions.

LEARN Solving Story Problems with Coins

Students will solve story problems involving coins.

TIP Encourage students to sketch a model when the coins are described in words instead of represented as images.

TRY IT Solve Story Problems with Coins

Students will practice solving story problems involving coins. Support will be provided to help students overcome misconceptions.

TRY IT Practice Working with Coins

Students will complete online practice problems. Then they will complete Practice Working with Coins from *Math 2 Activity Book*.

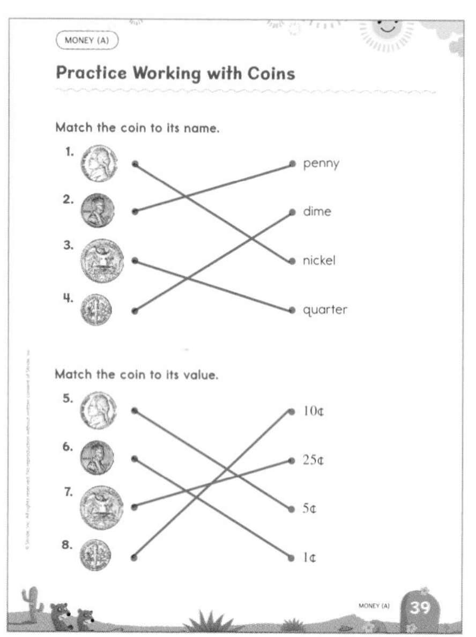
MONEY (A)

Practice Working with Coins

Match the coin to its name.

1. 2. 3. 4.

penny
dime
nickel
quarter

Match the coin to its value.

5. 6. 7. 8.

10¢
25¢
5¢
1¢

MONEY (A) 39

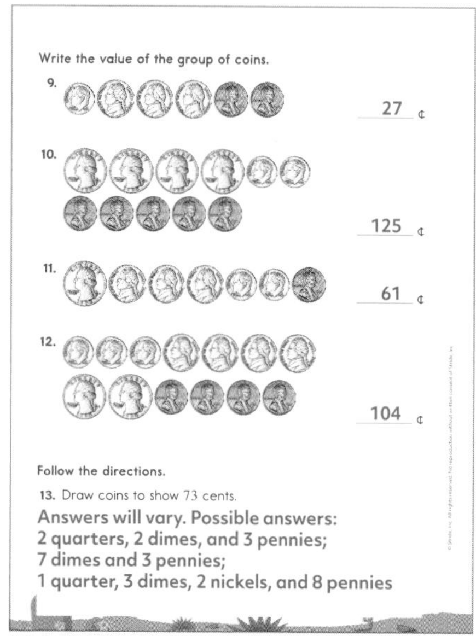
Write the value of the group of coins.

9. 27 ¢

10. 125 ¢

11. 61 ¢

12. 104 ¢

Follow the directions.

13. Draw coins to show 73 cents.

Answers will vary. Possible answers:
2 quarters, 2 dimes, and 3 pennies;
7 dimes and 3 pennies;
1 quarter, 3 dimes, 2 nickels, and 8 pennies

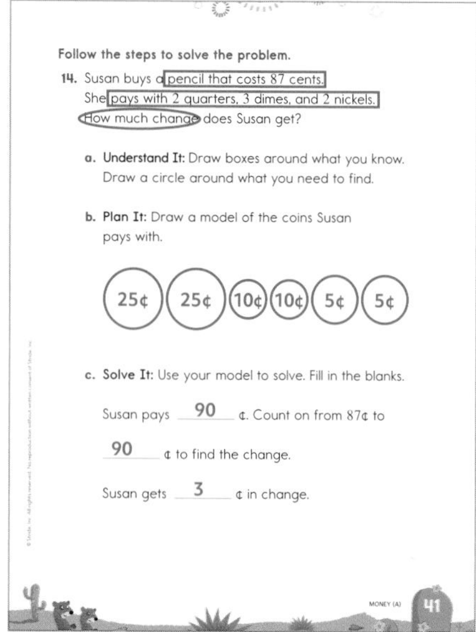
Follow the steps to solve the problem.

14. Susan buys a pencil that costs 87 cents. She pays with 2 quarters, 3 dimes, and 2 nickels. How much change does Susan get?

a. **Understand It:** Draw boxes around what you know. Draw a circle around what you need to find.

b. **Plan It:** Draw a model of the coins Susan pays with.

25¢ 25¢ 10¢ 10¢ 5¢ 5¢

c. **Solve It:** Use your model to solve. Fill in the blanks.

Susan pays 90 ¢. Count on from 87¢ to 90 ¢ to find the change.

Susan gets 3 ¢ in change.

MONEY (A) 41

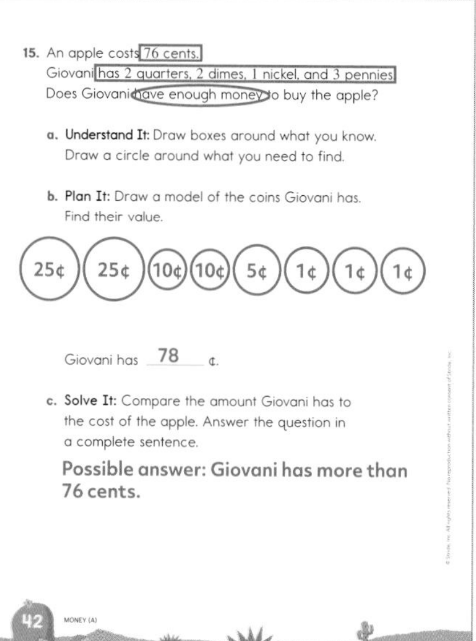
15. An apple costs 76 cents. Giovani has 2 quarters, 2 dimes, 1 nickel, and 3 pennies. Does Giovani have enough money to buy the apple?

a. **Understand It:** Draw boxes around what you know. Draw a circle around what you need to find.

b. **Plan It:** Draw a model of the coins Giovani has. Find their value.

25¢ 25¢ 10¢ 10¢ 5¢ 1¢ 1¢ 1¢

Giovani has 78 ¢.

c. **Solve It:** Compare the amount Giovani has to the cost of the apple. Answer the question in a complete sentence.

Possible answer: Giovani has more than 76 cents.

42 MONEY (A)

WRAP-UP

Working with Coins

Students will solve problems to show that they understand how to work with coins.

Money (B)

Lesson Overview

ACTIVITY	ACTIVITY TITLE	TIME	ONLINE/OFFLINE
GET READY	Introduction to Money (B)	2 minutes	online
	Adding 3 Math Facts Game	7 minutes	online
LEARN AND TRY IT	Finding the Value of a Group of Bills	7 minutes	online
	Find the Value of a Group of Bills	7 minutes	online
ALL ABOUT ME	Brain Break	1 minute	online or offline
LEARN AND TRY IT	Solving Story Problems with Bills	7 minutes	online
	Solve Story Problems with Bills	7 minutes	online
	Practice Working with Bills	20 minutes	online and offline
WRAP-UP	Working with Bills	2 minutes	online

Content Background

Students will count on to find the value of a group of bills. They will also solve story problems involving bills. Students will work with these bills.

- One-dollar bill: $1
- Five-dollar bill: $5
- Ten-dollar bill: $10
- Twenty-dollar bill: $20

Counting On

To find the value of a group of bills, start with the bill with the greatest value and count on to the bill with the least value. For example, a group of bills contains 1 twenty-dollar bill, 2 five-dollar bills, and 2 one-dollar bills. Count on starting with the twenty-dollar bill.

$20 $25 $30 $31 $32

The value of this group of bills is $32.

MATERIALS

Supplied

- *Math 2 Activity Book:* Practice Working with Bills

KEYWORDS

bill – unit of paper money

Example: A five-dollar bill has a value of $5.

Solving Story Problems

Encourage students to read the problem carefully and repeatedly so they can continue to apply the 3 steps for solving story problems: Understand it; Plan it; and Solve it. Some problems in this lesson require multiple calculations to solve.

For example, Marie buys a book that costs $8 and some markers that cost $3. Marie pays with 3 five-dollar bills. How much change does Marie get? Ultimately, students must recognize that they need to count on from the total cost to the total amount Marie pays to find the change. But first they must use the facts in the problem to find the total cost and the total amount paid. Students could find these values during any of the 3 steps for solving story problems depending on how they make sense of the problem.

Lesson Goals

- Find the value of a group of bills.
- Solve a problem about bills.

GET READY

Introduction to Money (B)

Students will get a glimpse of what they will learn about in the lesson. They will also read the lesson goals.

Adding 3 Math Facts Game

Students will play a game to practice adding 3.

LEARN AND TRY IT

LEARN Finding the Value of a Group of Bills

Students will count on to find the value of a group of bills.

SUPPORT For students having difficulty recalling names or values of bills, use real or play bills to model problems.

TRY IT Find the Value of a Group of Bills

Students will practice counting on to find the value of a group of bills. Support will be provided to help students overcome misconceptions.

LEARN Solving Story Problems with Bills

Students will solve story problems involving bills.

TIP Encourage students to plan how to solve a problem before trying to find the solution.

TRY IT Solve Story Problems with Bills

Students will practice solving story problems involving bills. Support will be provided to help students overcome misconceptions.

TRY IT Practice Working with Bills

Students will complete online practice problems. Then they will complete Practice Working with Bills from *Math 2 Activity Book*.

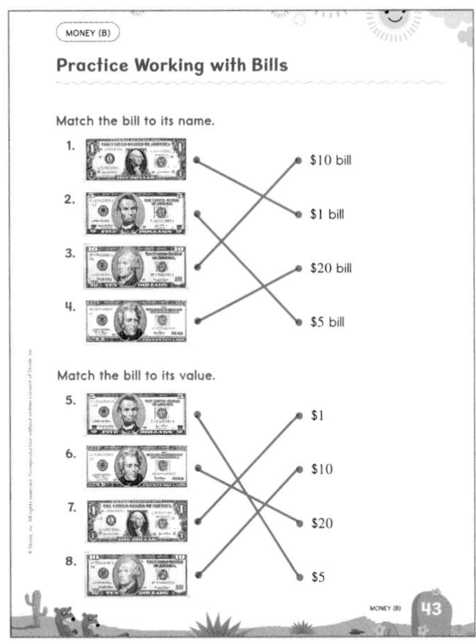

MONEY (B)

Practice Working with Bills

Match the bill to its name.

1.
2.
3.
4.

$10 bill
$1 bill
$20 bill
$5 bill

Match the bill to its value.

5.
6.
7.
8.

$1
$10
$20
$5

MONEY (B) 43

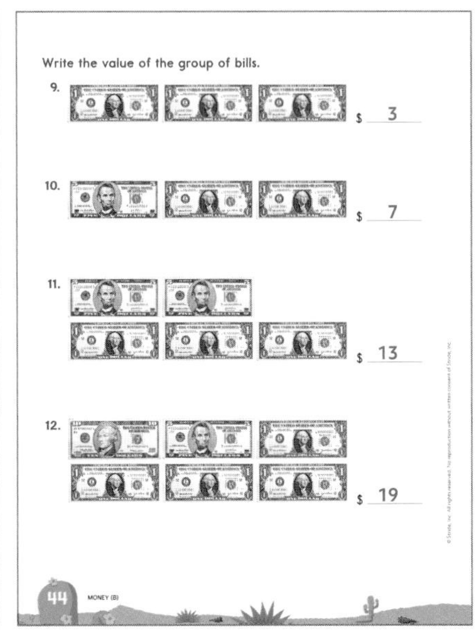

Write the value of the group of bills.

9. $ 3

10. $ 7

11. $ 13

12. $ 19

44 MONEY (B)

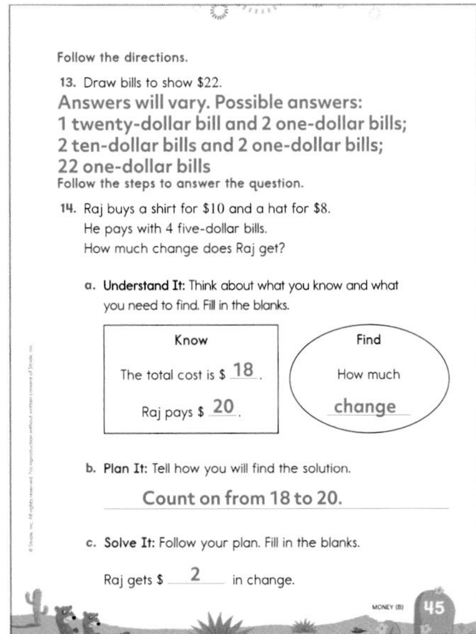

Follow the directions.

13. Draw bills to show $22.

Answers will vary. Possible answers:
1 twenty-dollar bill and 2 one-dollar bills;
2 ten-dollar bills and 2 one-dollar bills;
22 one-dollar bills

Follow the steps to answer the question.

14. Raj buys a shirt for $10 and a hat for $8.
He pays with 4 five-dollar bills.
How much change does Raj get?

a. **Understand It:** Think about what you know and what you need to find. Fill in the blanks.

Know	Find
The total cost is $ 18.	How much
Raj pays $ 20.	change

b. **Plan It:** Tell how you will find the solution.

Count on from 18 to 20.

c. **Solve It:** Follow your plan. Fill in the blanks.

Raj gets $ 2 in change.

MONEY (B) 45

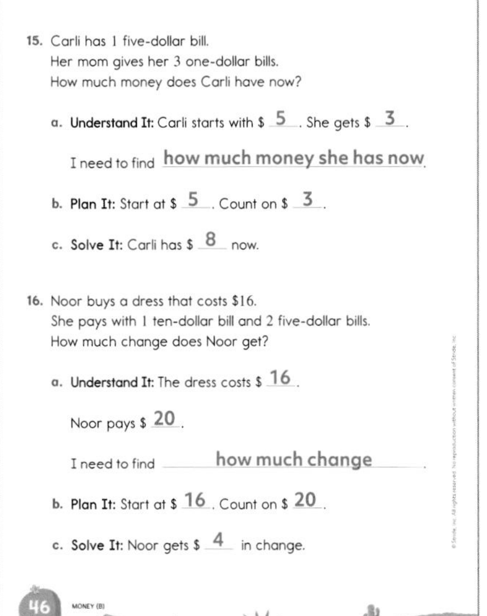

15. Carli has 1 five-dollar bill.
Her mom gives her 3 one-dollar bills.
How much money does Carli have now?

a. **Understand It:** Carli starts with $ 5. She gets $ 3.

I need to find how much money she has now.

b. **Plan It:** Start at $ 5. Count on $ 3.

c. **Solve It:** Carli has $ 8 now.

16. Noor buys a dress that costs $16.
She pays with 1 ten-dollar bill and 2 five-dollar bills.
How much change does Noor get?

a. **Understand It:** The dress costs $ 16.

Noor pays $ 20.

I need to find how much change.

b. **Plan It:** Start at $ 16. Count on $ 20.

c. **Solve It:** Noor gets $ 4 in change.

46 MONEY (B)

WRAP-UP

Working with Bills

Students will solve problems to show that they understand how to work with bills.

Money (C)

Lesson Overview

ACTIVITY	ACTIVITY TITLE	TIME	ONLINE/OFFLINE
GET READY	Introduction to Money (C)	**2** minutes	online
	Adding 4 Math Facts	**7** minutes	online
LEARN AND **TRY IT**	Finding the Value of a Group of Bills and Coins	**7** minutes	online
	Find the Value of a Group of Bills and Coins	**7** minutes	online
ALL ABOUT ME	Brain Break	**1** minute	online or offline
LEARN AND **TRY IT**	Solving Story Problems with Bills and Coins	**7** minutes	online
	Solve Story Problems with Bills and Coins	**7** minutes	online
	Practice Working with Bills and Coins	**20** minutes	online and offline
WRAP-UP	Working with Bills and Coins	**2** minutes	online

Content Background

Students will learn to regroup coins that have a value of 100 cents, find the value of a group of bills and coins, and solve story problems involving bills and coins.

Regrouping Money

Students will regroup coins with a value of 100 cents as 1 dollar. There are many combinations of coins that have a value of 100 cents. Here are some examples.

- 4 quarters = 100 cents = $1
- 2 quarters and 5 dimes = 100 cents = $1
- 20 nickels = 100 cents = $1
- 5 dimes and 3 nickels and 35 pennies = 100 cents = $1

Counting On

To find the value of a group of bills and coins, find the values of the bills and coins separately and then combine them. Regroup the coins if the total value is 100 cents or greater. For example, follow these steps to find the value of a group of bills and coins containing 1 five-dollar bill, 3 one-dollar bills, 3 quarters, and 4 dimes.

MATERIALS

Supplied

- *Math 2 Activity Book:* Practice Working with Bills and Coins

KEYWORDS

regroup (money) – rename a set of coins with a value of 100 cents as one dollar

Example: Amelie needs to regroup 4 quarters as 1 dollar to solve the problem.

Step 1. Count on to find the value of the bills: \$5, \$6, \$7, \$8
Step 2. Count on to find the value of the coins: 25¢, 50¢, 75¢, 85¢, 95¢, 105¢, 115¢
Step 3. Regroup 115¢ as \$1 and 15¢.
Step 4. Combine the values of the bills and coins: \$8 + \$1 and 15¢ = \$9 and 15¢

Lesson Goals

- Find the value of a group of bills and coins.
- Solve a problem about bills and coins.

GET READY

Introduction to Money (C)

Students will get a glimpse of what they will learn about in the lesson. They will also read the lesson goals.

Adding 4 Math Facts

Students will practice adding 4.

LEARN AND TRY IT

LEARN Finding the Value of a Group of Bills and Coins

Students will count on to find the value of a group of bills and coins. Some problems require regrouping 100 cents as 1 dollar.

OPTIONAL Use real or play coins to find combinations of coins that have the same value as 1 dollar.

TRY IT Find the Value of a Group of Bills and Coins

Students will practice finding the value of a group of bills and coins. Support will be provided to help students overcome misconceptions.

LEARN Solving Story Problems with Bills and Coins

Students will solve story problems involving bills and coins.

TRY IT Solve Story Problems with Bills and Coins

Students will practice solving story problems involving bills and coins. Support will be provided to help students overcome misconceptions.

TRY IT Practice Working with Bills and Coins

Students will complete online practice problems. Then they will complete Practice Working with Bills and Coins from *Math 2 Activity Book.*

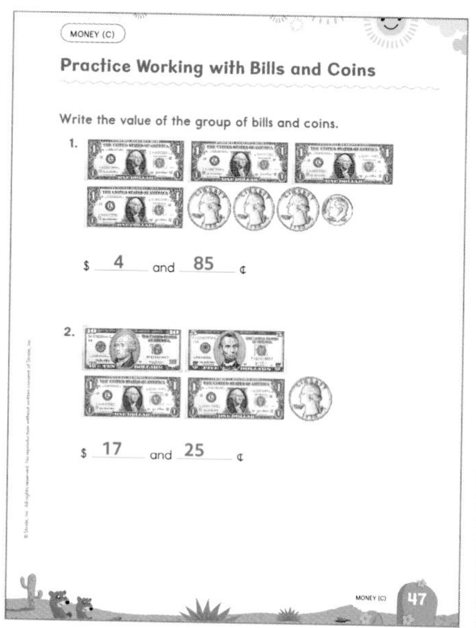

MONEY (C)

Practice Working with Bills and Coins

Write the value of the group of bills and coins.

1\. $ 4 and 85 ¢

2\. $ 17 and 25 ¢

MONEY (C) 47

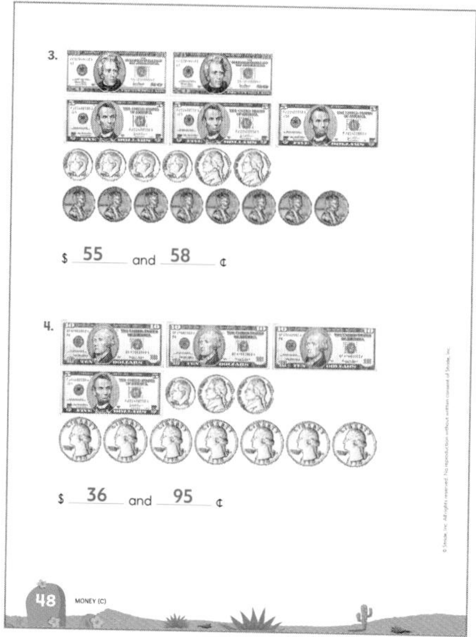

3\. $ 55 and 58 ¢

4\. $ 36 and 95 ¢

48 MONEY (C)

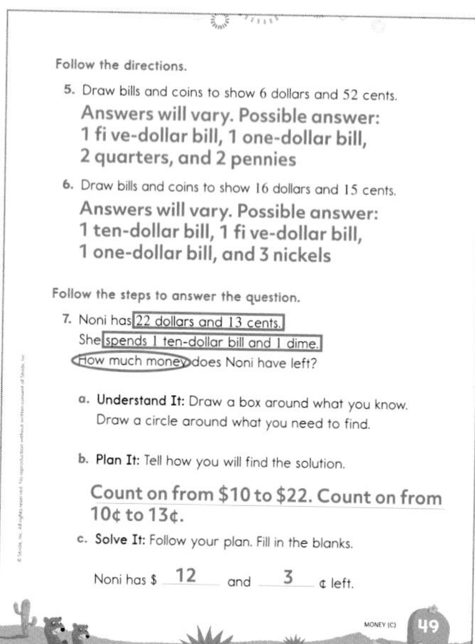

Follow the directions.

5\. Draw bills and coins to show 6 dollars and 52 cents.
Answers will vary. Possible answer: 1 five-dollar bill, 1 one-dollar bill, 2 quarters, and 2 pennies

6\. Draw bills and coins to show 16 dollars and 15 cents.
Answers will vary. Possible answer: 1 ten-dollar bill, 1 five-dollar bill, 1 one-dollar bill, and 3 nickels

Follow the steps to answer the question.

7\. Noni has 22 dollars and 13 cents. She spends 1 ten-dollar bill and 1 dime. How much money does Noni have left?

a. **Understand It:** Draw a box around what you know. Draw a circle around what you need to find.

b. **Plan It:** Tell how you will find the solution.
Count on from $10 to $22. Count on from 10¢ to 13¢.

c. **Solve It:** Follow your plan. Fill in the blanks.

Noni has $ 12 and 3 ¢ left.

MONEY (C) 49

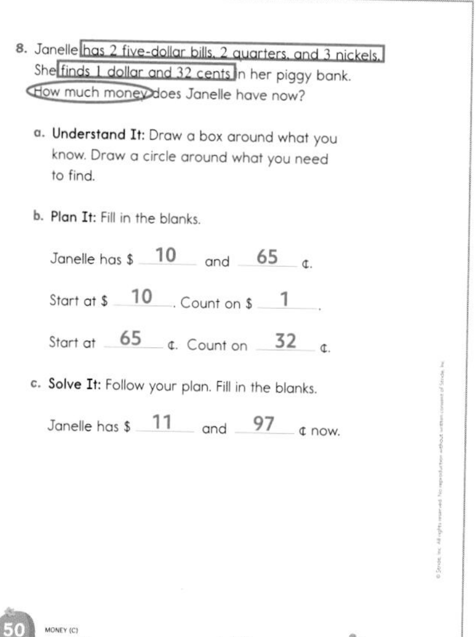

8\. Janelle has 2 five-dollar bills, 2 quarters, and 3 nickels. She finds 1 dollar and 32 cents in her piggy bank. How much money does Janelle have now?

a. **Understand It:** Draw a box around what you know. Draw a circle around what you need to find.

b. **Plan It:** Fill in the blanks.

Janelle has $ 10 and 65 ¢.

Start at $ 10. Count on $ 1.

Start at 65 ¢. Count on 32 ¢.

c. **Solve It:** Follow your plan. Fill in the blanks.

Janelle has $ 11 and 97 ¢ now.

50 MONEY (C)

WRAP-UP

Working with Bills and Coins

Students will solve a problem to show that they understand how to find the value of a group of bills and coins.

Money (D)

Lesson Overview

ACTIVITY	ACTIVITY TITLE	TIME	ONLINE/OFFLINE
GET READY	Introduction to Money (D)	**2** minutes	online
TRY IT	Review Money	**18** minutes	online
QUIZ	Money	**25** minutes	online
WRAP-UP	More Math Practice	**15** minutes	online

Lesson Goals

- Review finding the value of bills and coins.
- Review solving story problems with money.
- Take a quiz.

MATERIALS

There are no materials to gather for this lesson.

GET READY

Introduction to Money (D)

Students will read the lesson goals.

TRY IT

Review Money

Students will answer questions to review what they have learned about money.

QUIZ

Money

Students will complete the Money quiz.

WRAP-UP

More Math Practice

Students will practice skills according to their individual needs.

Time and Money Wrap-Up

Lesson Overview

ACTIVITY	ACTIVITY TITLE	TIME	ONLINE/OFFLINE
GET READY	Introduction to Time and Money Wrap-Up	**2** minutes	
TRY IT	Review Time and Money	**18** minutes	
UNIT CHECKPOINT	Time and Money Online Checkpoint	**18** minutes	
	Time and Money Offline Checkpoint	**20** minutes	
WRAP-UP	Turn in Your Offline Checkpoint	**2** minutes	

Lesson Goals

- Review time and money.
- Show what you know about time and money.

MATERIALS

Supplied

- Time and Money Offline Checkpoint (printout)

GET READY

Introduction to Time and Money Wrap-Up

Students will read the lesson goals.

TRY IT

Review Time and Money

Students will answer questions to review what they have learned about time and money.

UNIT CHECKPOINT

Time and Money Online Checkpoint

Students will complete the Time and Money Unit Checkpoint.

LEARNING COACH CHECK-IN This is a graded assignment. Make sure students complete the online assessment.

Time and Money Offline Checkpoint

Students will complete multistep problems that go beyond the short answer and multiple choice problems in their regular lessons. These problems give students an opportunity to demonstrate problem solving, reasoning, communication, and modeling skills. Students will need to use paper and pencil and/or technology to show their work.

Materials are linked online. The materials are not provided in this lesson guide or the activity book.

LEARNING COACH CHECK-IN This is a graded assignment. Make sure students complete, review, and submit their assignment to the teacher. If you are unsure how to do this, ask students' teacher.

WRAP-UP

Turn in Your Offline Checkpoint

Students will turn in their graded assignment.

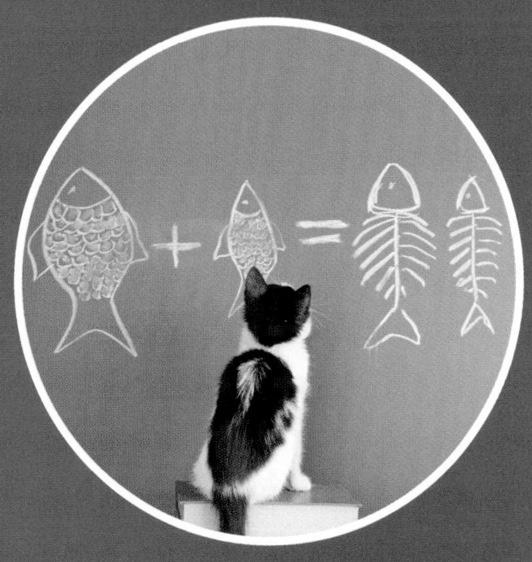

Add and Subtract with Two Digits

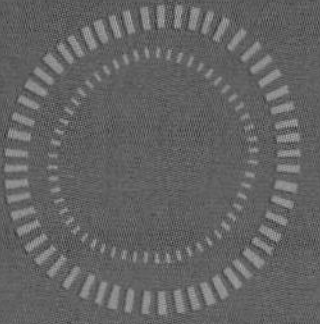

Add Using Place Value (A)

Lesson Overview

ACTIVITY	ACTIVITY TITLE	TIME	ONLINE/OFFLINE
GET READY	Introduction to Add Using Place Value (A)	**2** minutes	
	Look Back at Finding 10 More	**8** minutes	
LEARN AND **TRY IT**	Adding on a Number Line	**15** minutes	
	Add on a Number Line	**10** minutes	
	Practice Adding on a Number Line	**20** minutes	and
WRAP-UP	Adding on a Number Line	**5** minutes	

Content Background

Students will learn how to add two-digit numbers on a number line. Students should have experience adding one-digit numbers on a number line. They jump from 0 to the first number, and then count on by ones for the second number. Where they land is the sum. As numbers get larger, counting on by ones to add is not an efficient strategy. Instead, the key is to break up the second addend by place value and make larger jumps on an open number line.

Open Number Line

An open number line is a number line with no numbers or tick marks. It can be used to record thinking when adding or subtracting. It does not have to start at 0, and the distances between tick marks do not have to be equally spaced. For example, use an open number line to find the sum of 67 and 25. First, mark 67 on the number line. Next, make jumps that total 25, such as $10 + 10 + 3 + 2$. Some students may be ready to make a jump of 20 instead of two jumps of 10. Similarly, students could make a single jump of 5, 5 jumps of 1, or a jump of 3 and a jump of 2. The important point is to break the second addend into groups of tens and ones. This open number line shows that the sum of 67 and 25 is 92.

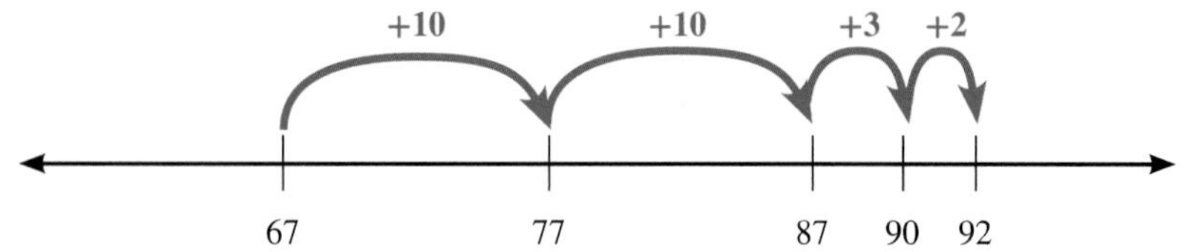

MATERIALS

Supplied

- *Math 2 Activity Book:* Practice Adding on a Number Line

KEYWORDS

addend – one of the two or more numbers that are added to determine a sum

Example: The addends in $35 + 22$ are 35 and 22.

sum – the solution to an addition problem

Example: The sum of 35 and 22 is 57.

Lesson Goals

- Use a number line to add.

GET READY

Introduction to Add Using Place Value (A)

Students will get a glimpse of what they will learn about in the lesson. They will also read the lesson goals.

Look Back at Finding 10 More

Students will review and practice the prerequisite skill of finding 10 more than a given number.

LEARN AND TRY IT

LEARN Adding on a Number Line

Students will learn how to add numbers on a number line.

TIP Some students may find it helpful to write the second addend in expanded form, such as $34 = 30 + 4$. Students can use the expanded form to determine how many tens and ones to count on from the first addend.

TRY IT Add on a Number Line

Students will practice adding on a number line. Support will be provided to help students overcome misconceptions.

TRY IT Practice Adding on a Number Line

Students will complete online practice problems. Then they will complete Practice Adding on a Number Line from *Math 2 Activity Book*.

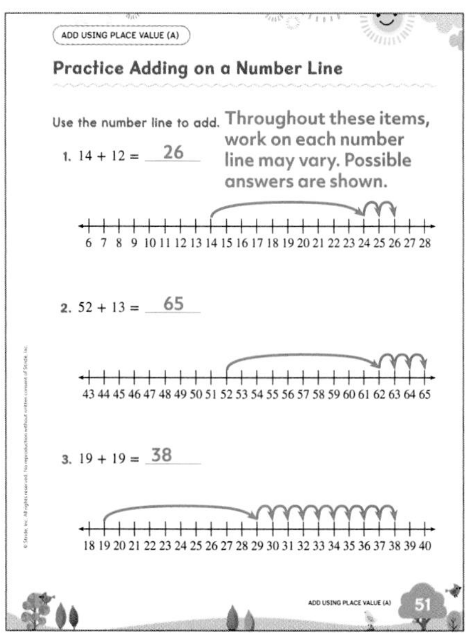

ADD USING PLACE VALUE (A)

Practice Adding on a Number Line

Use the number line to add. **Throughout these items, work on each number line may vary. Possible answers are shown.**

1. 14 + 12 = 26

6 7 8 9 10 11 12 13 14 15 16 17 18 19 20 21 22 23 24 25 26 27 28

2. 52 + 13 = 65

43 44 45 46 47 48 49 50 51 52 53 54 55 56 57 58 59 60 61 62 63 64 65

3. 19 + 19 = 38

18 19 20 21 22 23 24 25 26 27 28 29 30 31 32 33 34 35 36 37 38 39 40

ADD USING PLACE VALUE (A) 51

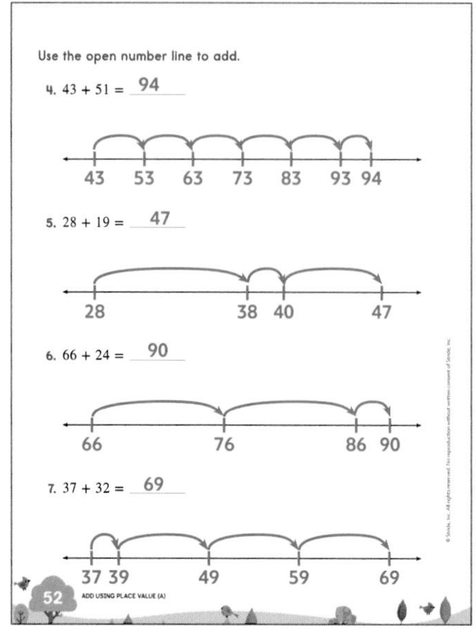

Use the open number line to add.

4. 43 + 51 = 94

43 53 63 73 83 93 94

5. 28 + 19 = 47

28 38 40 47

6. 66 + 24 = 90

66 76 86 90

7. 37 + 32 = 69

37 39 49 59 69

52 ADD USING PLACE VALUE (A)

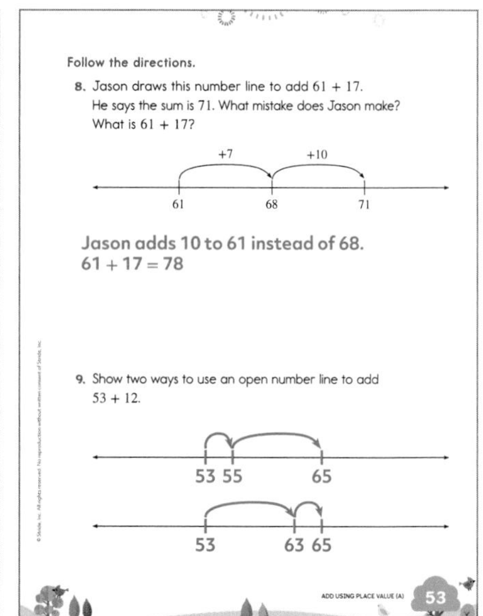

Follow the directions.

8. Jason draws this number line to add 61 + 17. He says the sum is 71. What mistake does Jason make? What is 61 + 17?

+7 +10

61 68 71

Jason adds 10 to 61 instead of 68.
61 + 17 = 78

9. Show two ways to use an open number line to add 53 + 12.

53 55 65

53 63 65

ADD USING PLACE VALUE (A) 53

WRAP-UP

Adding on a Number Line

Students will solve a problem to show that they understand how to add on a number line.

Add Using Place Value (B)

Lesson Overview

ACTIVITY	ACTIVITY TITLE	TIME	ONLINE/OFFLINE
GET READY	Introduction to Add Using Place Value (B)	**2** minutes	online
	Adding 4 with Instant Recall	**7** minutes	online
LEARN AND **TRY IT**	Adding Using Expanded Form without Regrouping	**7** minutes	online
	Add Using Expanded Form without Regrouping	**7** minutes	online
ALL ABOUT ME	Brain Break	**1** minute	online or offline
LEARN AND **TRY IT**	Adding Using Expanded Form with Regrouping	**7** minutes	online
	Add Using Expanded Form with Regrouping	**7** minutes	online
	Practice Adding Using Expanded Form	**20** minutes	online and offline
WRAP-UP	Adding Using Expanded Form	**2** minutes	online

Content Background

Students will learn how to add two-digit numbers by writing each addend in expanded form. Follow these steps to add using expanded form.

1. Write each addend in expanded form.
2. Add the tens.
3. Add the ones. If this sum is more than 10, regroup 1 ten as 10 ones.
4. Add the sum of the tens to the sum of the ones.

Students will apply this strategy to addition problems with and without regrouping. Here are some examples.

Without Regrouping

$$\begin{array}{r} 18 = 10 + 8 \\ +\ 41 = 40 + 1 \\ \hline 50 + 9 = 59 \end{array}$$

With Regrouping

$$37 + 54$$

$$(30 + 7) + (50 + 4)$$

$$80 + 11$$

$$80 + 10 + 1$$

91

MATERIALS

Supplied

- *Math 2 Activity Book:* Practice Adding Using Expanded Form

KEYWORDS

expanded form – a way to write a number that shows the place value of each of its digits

Example: 428 = 400 + 20 + 8 or 4 hundreds + 2 tens + 8 ones

Lesson Goals

- Use expanded form to add.

GET READY

Introduction to Add Using Place Value (B)

Students will get a glimpse of what they will learn about in the lesson. They will also read the lesson goals.

Adding 4 with Instant Recall

Students will practice adding 4.

LEARN AND TRY IT

LEARN Adding Using Expanded Form without Regrouping

Students will learn how to add numbers using expanded form without needing to regroup.

TRY IT Add Using Expanded Form without Regrouping

Students will practice adding numbers using expanded form without regrouping. Support will be provided to help students overcome misconceptions.

LEARN Adding Using Expanded Form with Regrouping

Students will learn how to add using expanded form with regrouping in the ones place.

NOTE Some students may be able to add the sum of the tens and the sum of the ones without needing to write down the regrouping step. It is not essential to write down the regrouping step if students are able to find the sum correctly using mental math.

TRY IT Add Using Expanded Form with Regrouping

Students will practice adding numbers using expanded form with regrouping. Support will be provided to help students overcome misconceptions.

TRY IT Practice Adding Using Expanded Form

Students will complete online practice problems. Then they will complete Practice Adding Using Expanded Form from *Math 2 Activity Book*.

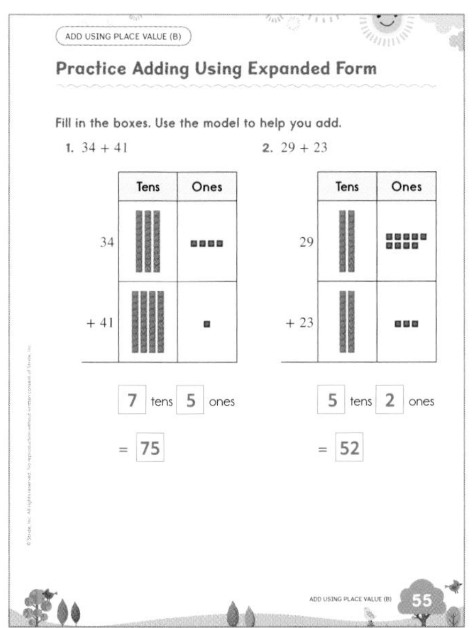
ADD USING PLACE VALUE (B)

Practice Adding Using Expanded Form

Fill in the boxes. Use the model to help you add.

1. 34 + 41

	Tens	Ones
34		
+ 41		

7 tens 5 ones

= 75

2. 29 + 23

	Tens	Ones
29		
+ 23		

5 tens 2 ones

= 52

ADD USING PLACE VALUE (B) 55

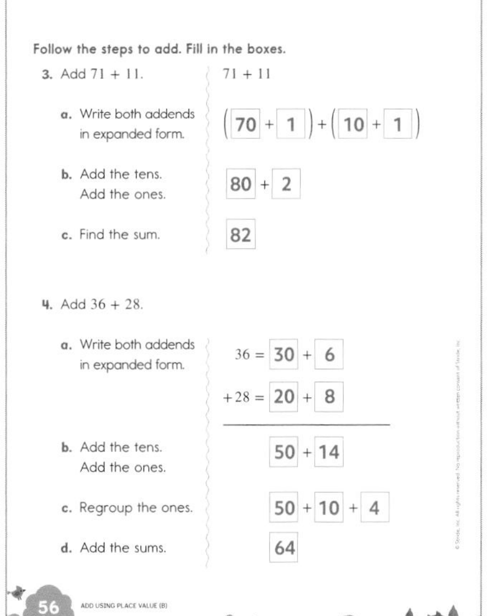
Follow the steps to add. Fill in the boxes.

3. Add 71 + 11.

71 + 11

a. Write both addends in expanded form. (70 + 1) + (10 + 1)

b. Add the tens. Add the ones. 80 + 2

c. Find the sum. 82

4. Add 36 + 28.

a. Write both addends in expanded form.

36 = 30 + 6

+28 = 20 + 8

b. Add the tens. Add the ones. 50 + 14

c. Regroup the ones. 50 + 10 + 4

d. Add the sums. 64

56 ADD USING PLACE VALUE (B)

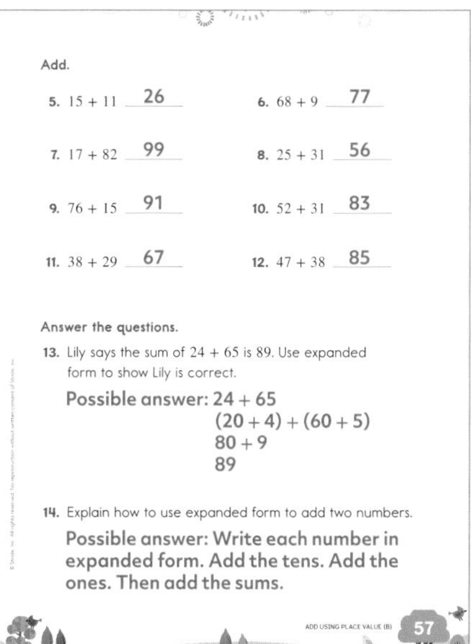
Add.

5. 15 + 11 26

6. 68 + 9 77

7. 17 + 82 99

8. 25 + 31 56

9. 76 + 15 91

10. 52 + 31 83

11. 38 + 29 67

12. 47 + 38 85

Answer the questions.

13. Lily says the sum of 24 + 65 is 89. Use expanded form to show Lily is correct.

Possible answer: 24 + 65
(20 + 4) + (60 + 5)
80 + 9
89

14. Explain how to use expanded form to add two numbers.

Possible answer: Write each number in expanded form. Add the tens. Add the ones. Then add the sums.

ADD USING PLACE VALUE (B) 57

WRAP-UP

Adding Using Expanded Form

Students will solve problems to show that they understand how to add numbers using expanded form.

Add Using Place Value (C)

Lesson Overview

ACTIVITY	ACTIVITY TITLE	TIME	ONLINE/OFFLINE
GET READY	Introduction to Add Using Place Value (C)	**2** minutes	online
	Adding 4 Math Facts Game	**7** minutes	online
LEARN AND TRY IT	Adding Using Place-Value Charts without Regrouping	**7** minutes	online
	Add Using Place-Value Charts without Regrouping	**7** minutes	online
ALL ABOUT ME	Brain Break	**1** minute	online or offline
LEARN AND TRY IT	Adding Using Place-Value Charts with Regrouping	**7** minutes	online
	Add Using Place-Value Charts with Regrouping	**7** minutes	online
	Practice Adding Using Place-Value Charts	**20** minutes	online and offline
WRAP-UP	Adding Using Place-Value Charts	**2** minutes	online

Content Background

Students will learn how to add two-digit numbers using a place-value chart. Students will apply this strategy to addition problems with and without regrouping. In this strategy, it is important for students to add the ones first to determine whether 10 ones can be regrouped into 1 ten.

Without Regrouping

	Tens	Ones
	3	2
+	1	4
	4	6

With Regrouping

	Tens	Ones
	1	
	4	6
+	1	8
	6	4

In the second example, 6 ones + 8 ones is 14 ones. Instead of writing 14 in the ones column, we regroup 14 into 1 ten and 4 ones. Record 4 below the bar in the ones column and add a 1 in the tens column, then add all the tens.

MATERIALS

Supplied

- *Math 2 Activity Book:* Practice Adding Using Place-Value Charts

KEYWORDS

place-value chart – a chart or arrangement that shows the value of each digit in a number

Lesson Goals

- Use place-value charts to add.

GET READY

Introduction to Add Using Place Value (C)

Students will get a glimpse of what they will learn about in the lesson. They will also read the lesson goals.

Adding 4 Math Facts Game

Students will play a game to practice adding 4.

LEARN AND TRY IT

LEARN Adding Using Place-Value Charts without Regrouping

Students will learn how to add numbers using a place-value chart without needing to regroup.

TRY IT Add Using Place-Value Charts without Regrouping

Students will practice adding numbers using a place-value chart without regrouping. Support will be provided to help students overcome misconceptions.

LEARN Adding Using Place-Value Charts with Regrouping

Students will learn how to add numbers using a place-value chart with regrouping in the ones place.

SUPPORT For students having difficulty regrouping in the ones place, encourage them to use base-10 blocks to model the addition problem. Have students physically split the ones into a group of 10 and any additional ones. Then have them exchange 10 ones for 1 ten and place that ten in the tens column on the place-value mat. Finally, have the student record this work in a place-value chart.

TRY IT Add Using Place-Value Charts with Regrouping

Students will practice adding numbers using a place-value chart with regrouping. Support will be provided to help students overcome misconceptions.

TRY IT Practice Adding Using Place-Value Charts

Students will complete online practice problems. Then they will complete Practice Adding Using Place-Value Charts from *Math 2 Activity Book.*

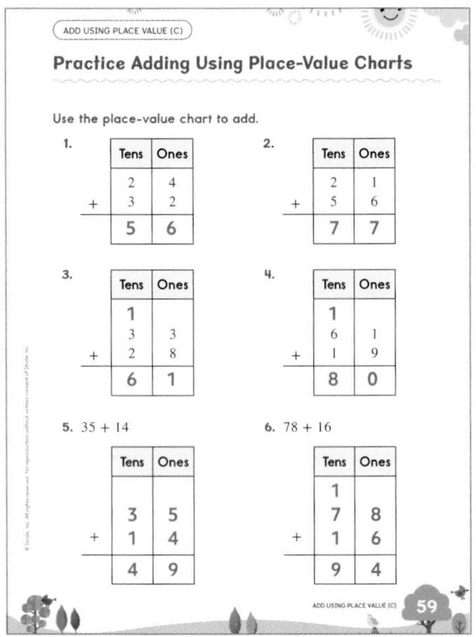

ADD USING PLACE VALUE (C)

Practice Adding Using Place-Value Charts

Use the place-value chart to add.

1.

	Tens	Ones
	2	4
+	3	2
	5	6

2.

	Tens	Ones
	2	1
+	5	6
	7	7

3.

	Tens	Ones
	1	
	3	3
+	2	8
	6	1

4.

	Tens	Ones
	1	
	6	1
+	1	9
	8	0

5. 35 + 14

	Tens	Ones
	3	5
+	1	4
	4	9

6. 78 + 16

	Tens	Ones
	1	
	7	8
+	1	6
	9	4

ADD USING PLACE VALUE (C) 59

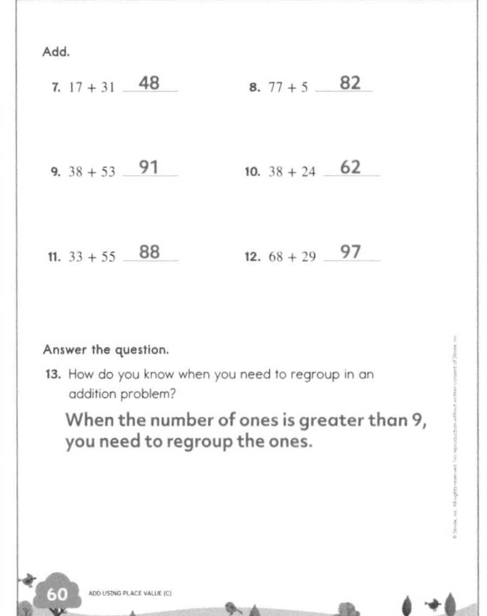

Add.

7. 17 + 31 48
8. 77 + 5 82
9. 38 + 53 91
10. 38 + 24 62
11. 33 + 55 88
12. 68 + 29 97

Answer the question.

13. How do you know when you need to regroup in an addition problem?

When the number of ones is greater than 9, you need to regroup the ones.

60 ADD USING PLACE VALUE (C)

WRAP-UP

Adding Using Place-Value Charts

Students will solve problems to show that they understand how to add two-digit numbers using place-value charts.

Add Using Place Value (D)

Lesson Overview

ACTIVITY	ACTIVITY TITLE	TIME	ONLINE/OFFLINE
GET READY	Introduction to Add Using Place Value (D)	**2** minutes	
TRY IT	Review Add Using Place Value	**18** minutes	
QUIZ	Add Using Place Value	**25** minutes	
WRAP-UP	More Math Practice	**15** minutes	

Lesson Goals

- Review using a number line, expanded form, and place-value charts to add.
- Take a quiz.

MATERIALS

There are no materials to gather for this lesson.

GET READY

Introduction to Add Using Place Value (D)

Students will read the lesson goals.

TRY IT

Review Add Using Place Value

Students will answer questions to review what they have learned about how to add using place value.

QUIZ

Add Using Place Value

Students will complete the Add Using Place Value quiz.

WRAP-UP

More Math Practice

Students will practice skills according to their individual needs.

Subtract Using Place Value (A)

Lesson Overview

ACTIVITY	ACTIVITY TITLE	TIME	ONLINE/OFFLINE
GET READY	Introduction to Subtract Using Place Value (A)	2 minutes	online
	Look Back at Finding 10 Fewer	7 minutes	online
LEARN AND TRY IT	Subtracting on a Number Line	15 minutes	online
	Subtract on a Number Line	10 minutes	online
ALL ABOUT ME	Brain Break	1 minute	online or offline
TRY IT	Practice Subtracting on a Number Line	20 minutes	online and offline
WRAP-UP	Subtracting on a Number Line	5 minutes	online

Content Background

Students will learn how to subtract two-digit numbers on a number line. Students should have experience subtracting one-digit numbers on a number line by counting back by ones. Like addition with larger numbers, counting back by ones to subtract is not an efficient strategy as numbers get larger. Students will learn the first of two strategies for subtracting on an open number line in this lesson.

Counting Back

This strategy works for any numbers, but it is especially useful when the difference between the minuend and subtrahend is large. For example, the difference of 55 and 17 will be large because 17 and 55 are far apart on a number line. To apply this strategy, start at the minuend, 55, on an open number line. Next, make jumps backward that total the subtrahend, 17, such as 10 and 7. The place students land is the difference. Students may find multiple ways to break apart the subtrahend. The important point is to break the subtrahend into groups of tens and ones. This open number line shows that the difference of 55 and 17 is 38.

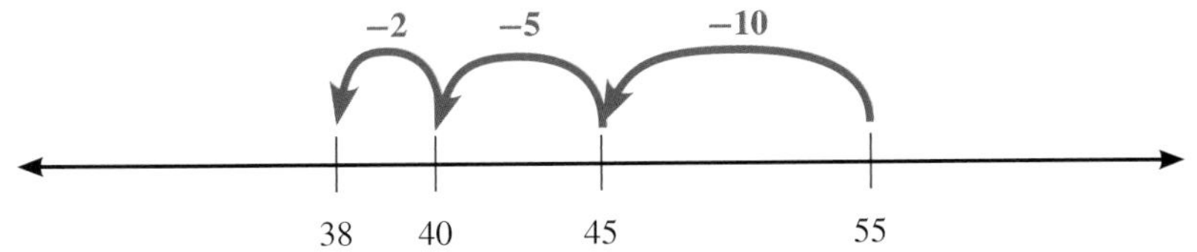

MATERIALS

Supplied

- *Math 2 Activity Book:* Practice Subtracting on a Number Line

KEYWORDS

difference – the answer in a subtraction problem

Example: In the number sentence 5 – 3 = 2, the difference is 2.

minuend – the number from which another number is subtracted

Example: In the number sentence 5 – 3 = 2, the minuend is 5.

subtrahend – the number that is subtracted from another number

Example: In the number sentence 5 – 3 = 2, the subtrahend is 3.

NOTE The second method for subtracting on a number line involves counting between the minuend and the subtrahend. This strategy is based on the relationship between addition and subtraction. It is taught in another lesson in this unit.

Lesson Goals

- Use a number line to subtract.

GET READY

Introduction to Subtract Using Place Value (A)

Students will get a glimpse of what they will learn about in the lesson. They will also read the lesson goals.

Look Back at Finding 10 Fewer

Students will review and practice the prerequisite skill of finding 10 fewer than a given number.

LEARN AND TRY IT

LEARN Subtracting on a Number Line

Students will learn how to subtract numbers on a number line.

TIP Some students may find it helpful to write the subtrahend in expanded form, such as $34 = 30 + 4$. Students can use the expanded form to determine how many tens and ones to count back from the minuend.

TRY IT Subtract on a Number Line

Students will practice subtracting on a number line. Support will be provided to help students overcome misconceptions.

TRY IT **Practice Subtracting on a Number Line**

Students will complete online practice problems. Then they will complete Practice Subtracting on a Number Line from *Math 2 Activity Book.*

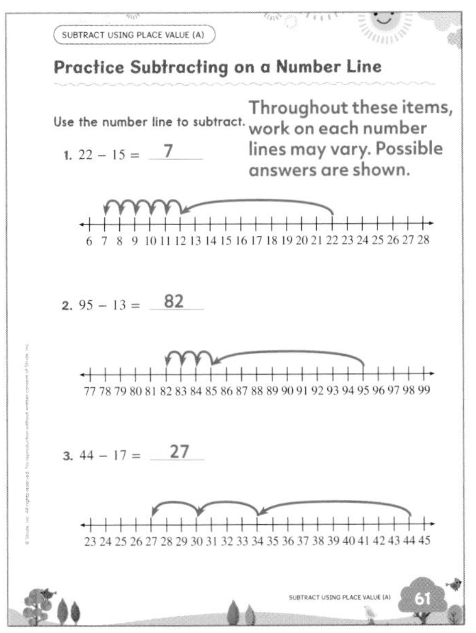
SUBTRACT USING PLACE VALUE (A)

Practice Subtracting on a Number Line

Use the number line to subtract.

Throughout these items, work on each number lines may vary. Possible answers are shown.

1. 22 − 15 = 7

6 7 8 9 10 11 12 13 14 15 16 17 18 19 20 21 22 23 24 25 26 27 28

2. 95 − 13 = 82

77 78 79 80 81 82 83 84 85 86 87 88 89 90 91 92 93 94 95 96 97 98 99

3. 44 − 17 = 27

23 24 25 26 27 28 29 30 31 32 33 34 35 36 37 38 39 40 41 42 43 44 45

SUBTRACT USING PLACE VALUE (A) 61

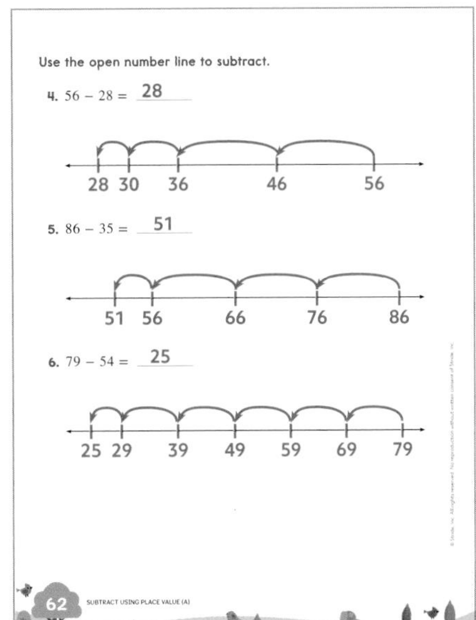
Use the open number line to subtract.

4. 56 − 28 = 28

28 30 36 46 56

5. 86 − 35 = 51

51 56 66 76 86

6. 79 − 54 = 25

25 29 39 49 59 69 79

62 SUBTRACT USING PLACE VALUE (A)

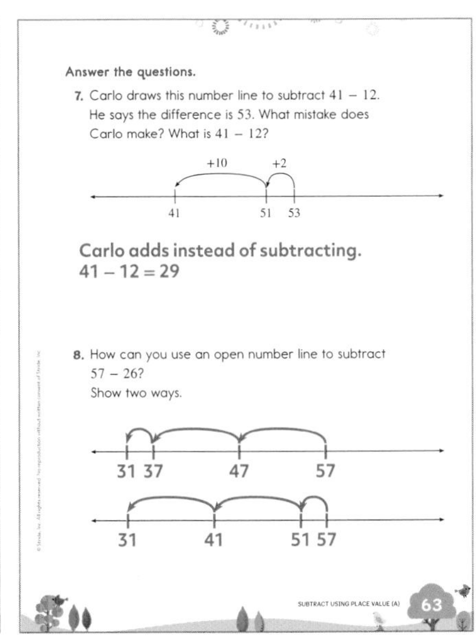
Answer the questions.

7. Carlo draws this number line to subtract 41 − 12. He says the difference is 53. What mistake does Carlo make? What is 41 − 12?

+10 +2

41 51 53

Carlo adds instead of subtracting.
41 − 12 = 29

8. How can you use an open number line to subtract 57 − 26? Show two ways.

31 37 47 57

31 41 51 57

SUBTRACT USING PLACE VALUE (A) 63

WRAP-UP

Subtracting on a Number Line

Students will solve problems to show that they understand how to subtract on a number line.

Subtract Using Place Value (B)

Lesson Overview

ACTIVITY	ACTIVITY TITLE	TIME	ONLINE/OFFLINE
GET READY	Introduction to Subtract Using Place Value (B)	2 minutes	online
	Adding 5 Math Facts	7 minutes	online
LEARN AND TRY IT	Subtracting Using Expanded Form without Regrouping	7 minutes	online
	Subtract Using Expanded Form without Regrouping	7 minutes	online
ALL ABOUT ME	Brain Break	1 minute	online or offline
LEARN AND TRY IT	Subtracting Using Expanded Form with Regrouping	7 minutes	online
	Subtract Using Expanded Form with Regrouping	7 minutes	online
	Practice Subtracting Using Expanded Form	20 minutes	online and offline
WRAP-UP	Subtracting Using Expanded Form	2 minutes	online

Content Background

Students will learn how to subtract two-digit numbers by writing the minuend and the subtrahend in expanded form. Follow these steps to subtract using expanded form.

1. Write the minuend and subtrahend in expanded form.
2. Check the ones. If there are not enough ones to subtract, regroup 1 ten as 10 ones.
3. Subtract the tens.
4. Subtract the ones.
5. Add the difference of the tens to the difference of the ones.

In the last step, it may seem odd to add in order to complete a subtraction problem. However, after Step 4 the answer is still in expanded form. Step 5 converts the answer from expanded form to standard form. Students will apply this strategy to subtraction problems with and without regrouping.

MATERIALS

Supplied

- *Math 2 Activity Book:* Practice Subtracting Using Expanded Form

Without Regrouping

$$\begin{array}{r} 86 = 80 + 6 \\ -\ 33 = 30 + 3 \\ \hline 50 + 3 = 53 \end{array}$$

With Regrouping

$$62 - 49$$

$$(60 + 2) - (40 + 9)$$

$$(50 + 12) - (40 + 9)$$

$$10 + 3$$

$$13$$

In this example, there are not enough ones to subtract 9 from 2. Rewriting 62 as $50 + 12$ lets subtraction continue.

Lesson Goals

- Use expanded form to subtract.

GET READY

Introduction to Subtract Using Place Value (B)

Students will get a glimpse of what they will learn about in the lesson. They will also read the lesson goals.

Adding 5 Math Facts

Students will practice adding 5.

LEARN AND TRY IT

LEARN Subtracting Using Expanded Form without Regrouping

Students will learn how to subtract numbers using expanded form without needing to regroup.

TRY IT Subtract Using Expanded Form without Regrouping

Students will practice subtracting numbers using expanded form without regrouping. Support will be provided to help students overcome misconceptions.

LEARN Subtracting Using Expanded Form with Regrouping

Students will learn how to subtract using expanded form with regrouping in the ones place.

TIP Some students may find it helpful to use base-10 blocks when regrouping.

TRY IT Subtract Using Expanded Form with Regrouping

Students will practice subtracting numbers using expanded form with regrouping. Support will be provided to help students overcome misconceptions.

TRY IT Practice Subtracting Using Expanded Form

Students will complete online practice problems. Then they will complete Practice Subtracting Using Expanded Form from *Math 2 Activity Book*.

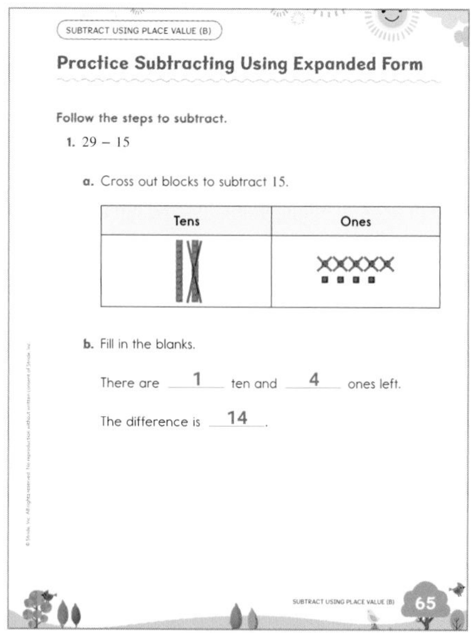

SUBTRACT USING PLACE VALUE (B)

Practice Subtracting Using Expanded Form

Follow the steps to subtract.

1. 29 − 15

a. Cross out blocks to subtract 15.

Tens	Ones

b. Fill in the blanks.

There are 1 ten and 4 ones left.

The difference is 14.

SUBTRACT USING PLACE VALUE (B) 65

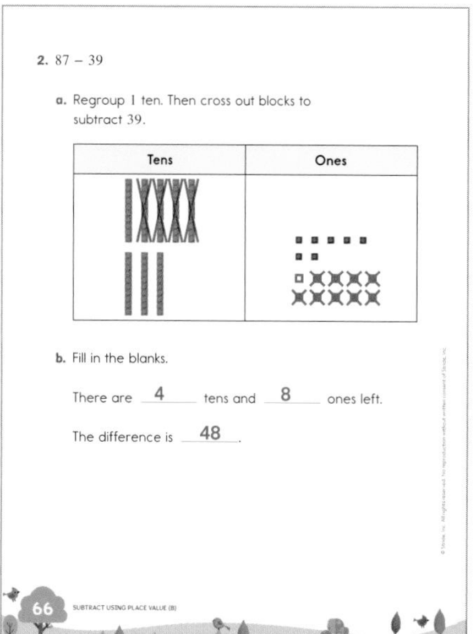

2. 87 − 39

a. Regroup 1 ten. Then cross out blocks to subtract 39.

Tens	Ones

b. Fill in the blanks.

There are 4 tens and 8 ones left.

The difference is 48.

66 SUBTRACT USING PLACE VALUE (B)

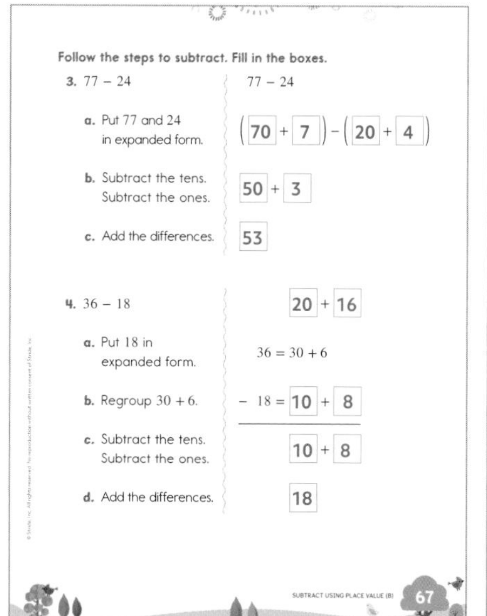

Follow the steps to subtract. Fill in the boxes.

3. 77 − 24 — 77 − 24

a. Put 77 and 24 in expanded form. (70 + 7) − (20 + 4)

b. Subtract the tens. Subtract the ones. 50 + 3

c. Add the differences. 53

4. 36 − 18 — 20 + 16

a. Put 18 in expanded form. 36 = 30 + 6

b. Regroup 30 + 6. − 18 = 10 + 8

c. Subtract the tens. Subtract the ones. 10 + 8

d. Add the differences. 18

SUBTRACT USING PLACE VALUE (B) 67

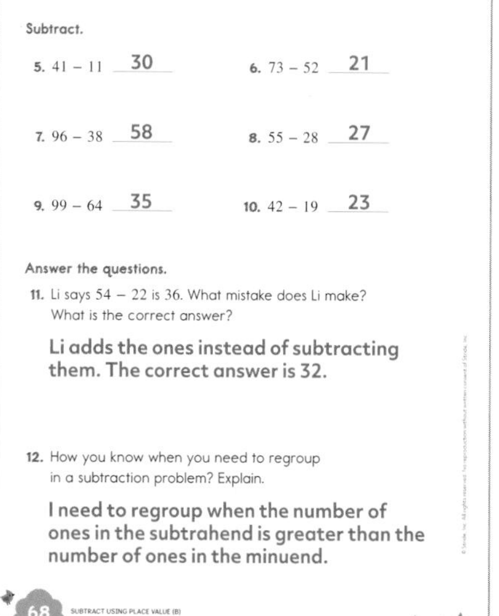

Subtract.

5. 41 − 11 30

6. 73 − 52 21

7. 96 − 38 58

8. 55 − 28 27

9. 99 − 64 35

10. 42 − 19 23

Answer the questions.

11. Li says 54 − 22 is 36. What mistake does Li make? What is the correct answer?

Li adds the ones instead of subtracting them. The correct answer is 32.

12. How you know when you need to regroup in a subtraction problem? Explain.

I need to regroup when the number of ones in the subtrahend is greater than the number of ones in the minuend.

68 SUBTRACT USING PLACE VALUE (B)

WRAP-UP

Subtracting Using Expanded Form

Students will solve problems to show that they understand how to subtract numbers using expanded form.

Subtract Using Place Value (C)

Lesson Overview

ACTIVITY	ACTIVITY TITLE	TIME	ONLINE/OFFLINE
GET READY	Introduction to Subtract Using Place Value (C)	**2** minutes	online
	Adding 5 with Instant Recall	**7** minutes	online
LEARN AND TRY IT	Subtracting Using Place-Value Charts without Regrouping	**7** minutes	online
	Subtract Using Place-Value Charts without Regrouping	**7** minutes	online
ALL ABOUT ME	Brain Break	**1** minute	online or offline
LEARN AND TRY IT	Subtracting Using Place-Value Charts with Regrouping	**7** minutes	online
	Subtract Using Place-Value Charts with Regrouping	**7** minutes	online
	Practice Subtracting Using Place-Value Charts	**20** minutes	online and offline
WRAP-UP	Subtracting Using Place-Value Charts	**2** minutes	online

Content Background

Students will learn how to subtract two-digit numbers using a place-value chart. Students will apply this strategy to subtraction problems with and without regrouping. In this strategy, it is important for students to subtract the ones first to determine whether 1 ten in the minuend must be regrouped into 10 ones.

Without Regrouping

	Tens	Ones
	8	9
–	3	6
	5	3

With Regrouping

	Tens	Ones
	6	17
	~~7~~	~~7~~
–	4	9
	2	8

In the second example, there are not enough ones to subtract 9 ones from 7 ones. Regroup 1 ten in the minuend as 10 ones. Six tens and 17 ones is another way to decompose 77.

MATERIALS

Supplied

- *Math 2 Activity Book:* Practice Subtracting Using Place-Value Charts

Lesson Goals

- Use place-value charts to subtract.

GET READY

Introduction to Subtract Using Place Value (C)

Students will get a glimpse of what they will learn about in the lesson. They will also read the lesson goals.

Adding 5 with Instant Recall

Students will review and practice the prerequisite skill of adding 5.

LEARN AND TRY IT

LEARN Subtracting Using Place-Value Charts without Regrouping

Students will learn how to subtract numbers using a place-value chart without needing to regroup.

TRY IT Subtract Using Place-Value Charts without Regrouping

Students will practice subtracting numbers using a place-value chart without regrouping. Support will be provided to help students overcome misconceptions.

LEARN Subtracting Using Place-Value Charts with Regrouping

Students will learn how to subtract numbers using a place-value chart with regrouping in the ones place.

SUPPORT Some students may have trouble remembering to regroup *before* subtracting the ones because in an addition problem regrouping happens *after* adding in the ones place. To compensate, some students subtract the top number from the bottom number. For students who struggle to remember this step, ask them how they can rewrite the minuend so that there are enough ones to subtract.

TRY IT Subtract Using Place-Value Charts with Regrouping

Students will practice subtracting numbers using a place-value chart with regrouping. Support will be provided to help students overcome misconceptions.

TRY IT Practice Subtracting Using Place-Value Charts

Students will complete online practice problems. Then they will complete Practice Subtracting Using Place-Value Charts from *Math 2 Activity Book*.

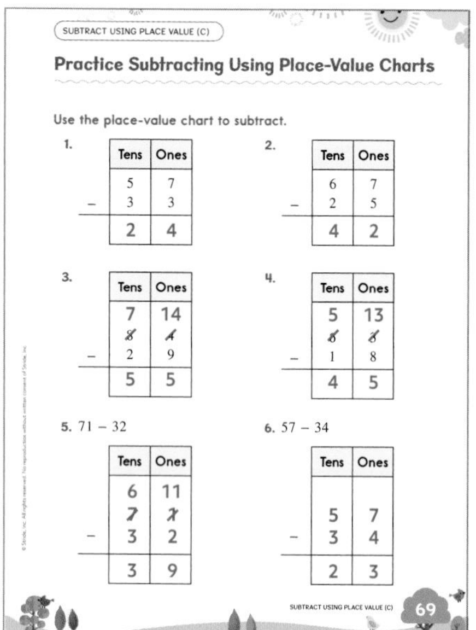

SUBTRACT USING PLACE VALUE (C)

Practice Subtracting Using Place-Value Charts

Use the place-value chart to subtract.

1.

	Tens	Ones
	5	7
−	3	3
	2	4

2.

	Tens	Ones
	6	7
−	2	5
	4	2

3.

	Tens	Ones
	7	14
	8	4
−	2	9
	5	5

4.

	Tens	Ones
	5	13
	6	3
−	1	8
	4	5

5. 71 − 32

	Tens	Ones
	6	11
	7	1
−	3	2
	3	9

6. 57 − 34

	Tens	Ones
	5	7
−	3	4
	2	3

SUBTRACT USING PLACE VALUE (C) 69

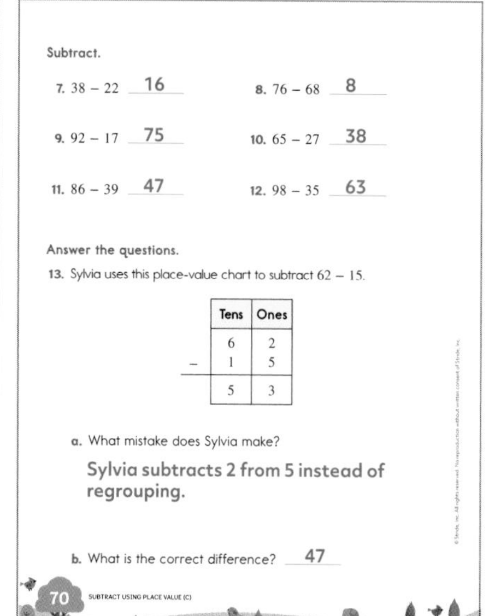

Subtract.

7. 38 − 22 16
8. 76 − 68 8
9. 92 − 17 75
10. 65 − 27 38
11. 86 − 39 47
12. 98 − 35 63

Answer the questions.

13. Sylvia uses this place-value chart to subtract 62 − 15.

	Tens	Ones
	6	2
−	1	5
	5	3

a. What mistake does Sylvia make?
Sylvia subtracts 2 from 5 instead of regrouping.

b. What is the correct difference? 47

70 SUBTRACT USING PLACE VALUE (C)

WRAP-UP

Subtracting Using Place-Value Charts

Students will solve problems to show that they understand how to subtract numbers using place-value charts.

Subtract Using Place Value (D)

Lesson Overview

ACTIVITY	ACTIVITY TITLE	TIME	ONLINE/OFFLINE
GET READY	Introduction to Subtract Using Place Value (D)	**2** minutes	
TRY IT	Review Subtract Using Place Value	**18** minutes	
QUIZ	Subtract Using Place Value	**25** minutes	
WRAP-UP	More Math Practice	**15** minutes	

Lesson Goals

- Review using a number line, expanded form, and place-value charts to subtract.
- Take a quiz.

MATERIALS

There are no materials to gather for this lesson.

GET READY

Introduction to Subtract Using Place Value (D)

Students will read the lesson goals.

TRY IT

Review Subtract Using Place Value

Students will answer questions to review what they have learned about how to subtract using place value.

QUIZ

Subtract Using Place Value

Students will complete the Subtract Using Place Value quiz.

WRAP-UP

More Math Practice

Students will practice skills according to their individual needs.

Add and Subtract Using Properties (A)

Lesson Overview

ACTIVITY	ACTIVITY TITLE	TIME	ONLINE/OFFLINE
GET READY	Introduction to Add and Subtract Using Properties (A)	**2** minutes	online
	Look Back at Making a Ten	**7** minutes	online
LEARN AND **TRY IT**	Adding and Subtracting 0	**15** minutes	online
	Add and Subtract 0	**10** minutes	online
ALL ABOUT ME	Brain Break	**1** minute	online or offline
TRY IT	Practice Adding and Subtracting 0	**20** minutes	online and offline
WRAP-UP	Adding and Subtracting 0	**5** minutes	online

Content Background

Students will learn to fluently add and subtract 0 and any two-digit number. Fluently adding and subtracting 0 is possible knowing these two rules.

- The sum of a number and 0 is the original number.
- The difference of a number and 0 is the original number.

For example, $35 + 0 = 35$ and $87 - 0 = 0$.

NOTE In this concept, students will learn rules and strategies for adding and subtracting fluently that are based on mathematical properties. Although each property does have a name, students are not expected to learn those names now. Students will learn the names of the properties in future units and math courses.

MATERIALS

Supplied

- *Math 2 Activity Book:* Practice Adding and Subtracting 0

Lesson Goals

- Add and subtract 0.

GET READY

Introduction to Add and Subtract Using Properties (A)

Students will get a glimpse of what they will learn about in the lesson. They will also read the lesson goals.

Look Back at Making a Ten

Students will review and practice the prerequisite skill of making a ten in order to add two numbers.

LEARN AND TRY IT

LEARN Adding and Subtracting 0

Students will learn a rule to fluently add or subtract 0 and a two-digit number.

TRY IT Add and Subtract 0

Students will practice adding and subtracting 0. Support will be provided to help students overcome misconceptions.

TRY IT Practice Adding and Subtracting 0

Students will complete online practice problems. Then they will complete Practice Adding and Subtracting 0 from *Math 2 Activity Book*.

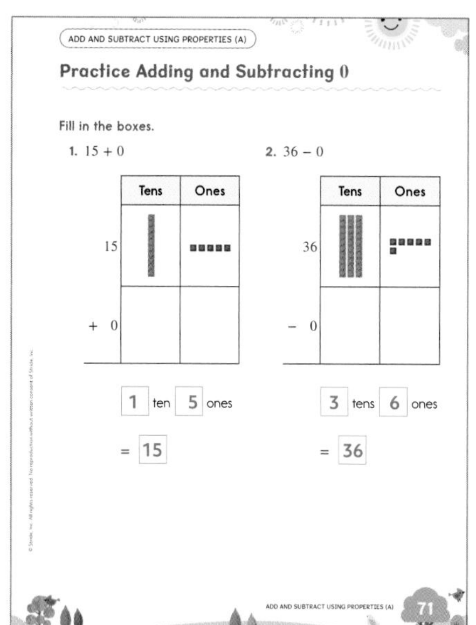
ADD AND SUBTRACT USING PROPERTIES (A)

Practice Adding and Subtracting 0

Fill in the boxes.

1. 15 + 0

	Tens	Ones
15		
+ 0		

1 ten 5 ones

= 15

2. 36 − 0

	Tens	Ones
36		
− 0		

3 tens 6 ones

= 36

ADD AND SUBTRACT USING PROPERTIES (A) 71

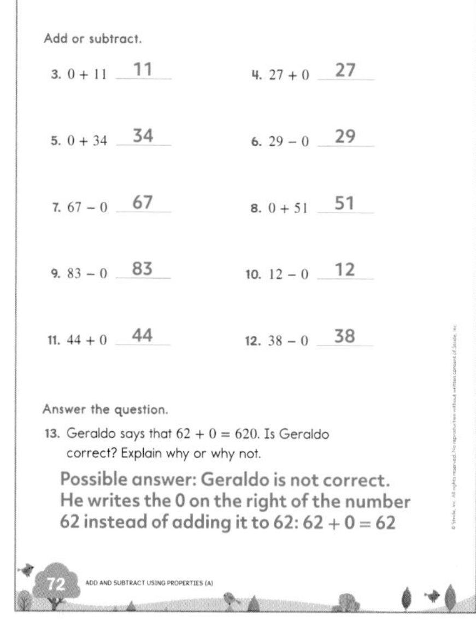
Add or subtract.

3. 0 + 11 11
4. 27 + 0 27
5. 0 + 34 34
6. 29 − 0 29
7. 67 − 0 67
8. 0 + 51 51
9. 83 − 0 83
10. 12 − 0 12
11. 44 + 0 44
12. 38 − 0 38

Answer the question.

13. Geraldo says that 62 + 0 = 620. Is Geraldo correct? Explain why or why not.

Possible answer: Geraldo is not correct. He writes the 0 on the right of the number 62 instead of adding it to 62: 62 + 0 = 62

72 ADD AND SUBTRACT USING PROPERTIES (A)

WRAP-UP

Adding and Subtracting 0

Students will solve problems to show that they understand how to add and subtract 0.

Add and Subtract Using Properties (B)

Lesson Overview

ACTIVITY	ACTIVITY TITLE	TIME	ONLINE/OFFLINE
GET READY	Introduction to Add and Subtract Using Properties (B)	2 minutes	online
	Adding 5 Math Facts Game	7 minutes	online
LEARN AND TRY IT	Grouping Addends to Solve an Addition Problem	15 minutes	online
	Group Addends to Solve an Addition Problem	10 minutes	online
ALL ABOUT ME	Brain Break	1 minute	online or offline
TRY IT	Practice Grouping Addends to Solve an Addition Problem	20 minutes	online and offline
WRAP-UP	Grouping Addends to Solve an Addition Problem	5 minutes	online

Content Background

Students will first review the rule that grouping numbers being added in a different order does not change their sum. Then students will learn how breaking apart one addend and regrouping the addends can make two-digit addition problems easier to solve.

Grouping to Make Ten

The goal of this strategy is to break one addend into two parts so that one part can be grouped with the other addend to make a ten. It doesn't matter which addend students choose to break apart. Here are two ways to solve $37 + 49$.

$37 + 49$		$37 + 49$
$(36 + 1) + 49$		$37 + (3 + 46)$
$36 + (1 + 49)$	or	$(37 + 3) + 46$
$36 + 50$		$40 + 46$
86		86

Notice that in each case some ones were taken from one addend and grouped with the other addend in order to make a ten.

MATERIALS

Supplied

- *Math 2 Activity Book:* Practice Grouping Addends to Solve an Addition Problem

Grouping with Expanded Form

The goal of this strategy is to break one addend into two parts using expanded form so that the tens can be grouped with the other addend. Here this strategy is used to solve $34 + 45$.

$$34 + 45$$

$$34 + (40 + 5)$$

$$(34 + 40) + 5$$

$$74 + 5$$

$$79$$

Lesson Goals

- Add by grouping addends to make ten.
- Add by grouping addends that are tens.

GET READY

Introduction to Add and Subtract Using Properties (B)

Students will get a glimpse of what they will learn about in the lesson. They will also read the lesson goals.

Adding 5 Math Facts Game

Students will play a game to practice adding 5.

LEARN AND TRY IT

LEARN Grouping Addends to Solve an Addition Problem

Students will learn how to break apart an addend and group the parts to solve an addition problem.

OPTIONAL Play a game with students to practice making ten. One person chooses a number from 1 to 9. Then the other person quickly says the number that makes 10 when it is added to the first number.

TRY IT Group Addends to Solve an Addition Problem

Students will practice grouping addends to solve an addition problem. Support will be provided to help students overcome misconceptions.

TRY IT Practice Grouping Addends to Solve an Addition Problem

Students will complete online practice problems. Then they will complete Practice Grouping Addends to Solve an Addition Problem from *Math 2 Activity Book*.

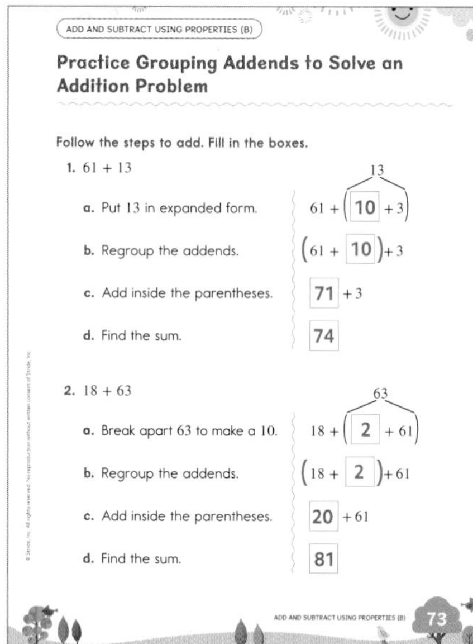
ADD AND SUBTRACT USING PROPERTIES (B)

Practice Grouping Addends to Solve an Addition Problem

Follow the steps to add. Fill in the boxes.

1. 61 + 13
   a. Put 13 in expanded form. 61 + (10 + 3)
   b. Regroup the addends. (61 + 10) + 3
   c. Add inside the parentheses. 71 + 3
   d. Find the sum. 74
2. 18 + 63
   a. Break apart 63 to make a 10. 18 + (2 + 61)
   b. Regroup the addends. (18 + 2) + 61
   c. Add inside the parentheses. 20 + 61
   d. Find the sum. 81

ADD AND SUBTRACT USING PROPERTIES (B) 73

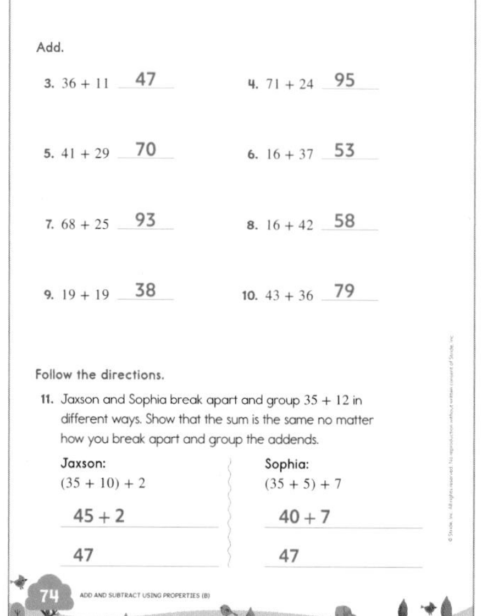
Add.

3. 36 + 11 47
4. 71 + 24 95
5. 41 + 29 70
6. 16 + 37 53
7. 68 + 25 93
8. 16 + 42 58
9. 19 + 19 38
10. 43 + 36 79

Follow the directions.

11. Jaxson and Sophia break apart and group 35 + 12 in different ways. Show that the sum is the same no matter how you break apart and group the addends.

Jaxson: (35 + 10) + 2 — 45 + 2 — 47

Sophia: (35 + 5) + 7 — 40 + 7 — 47

74 ADD AND SUBTRACT USING PROPERTIES (B)

WRAP-UP

Grouping Addends to Solve an Addition Problem

Students will solve a problem to show that they understand how to group addends to solve an addition problem.

Add and Subtract Using Properties (C)

Lesson Overview

ACTIVITY	ACTIVITY TITLE	TIME	ONLINE/OFFLINE
GET READY	Introduction to Add and Subtract Using Properties (C)	**2** minutes	online
	Adding 6 Math Facts	**7** minutes	online
LEARN AND TRY IT	Moving Addends to Solve an Addition Problem	**15** minutes	online
	Move Addends to Solve an Addition Problem	**10** minutes	online
ALL ABOUT ME	Brain Break	**1** minute	online or offline
TRY IT	Practice Moving Addends to Solve an Addition Problem	**20** minutes	online and offline
WRAP-UP	Moving Addends to Solve an Addition Problem	**5** minutes	online

Content Background

Students will first review the rule that putting numbers being added in a different order does not change their sum. Then students will learn how breaking apart the addends and moving the parts can make two-digit addition problems easier to solve.

Moving Addends in Expanded Form

The goal of this strategy is to break both addends into two parts using expanded form and move the parts to make adding easier. This example uses this strategy to solve $19 + 63$.

$$19 + 63$$

$$10 + 9 + 60 + 3$$

$$10 + 60 + 9 + 3$$

$$70 + 12$$

$$82$$

Lesson Goals

- Add by moving addends to change their order.

MATERIALS

Supplied

- *Math 2 Activity Book:* Practice Moving Addends to Solve an Addition Problem

GET READY

Introduction to Add and Subtract Using Properties (C)

Students will get a glimpse of what they will learn about in the lesson. They will also read the lesson goals.

Adding 6 Math Facts

Students will practice adding 6.

LEARN AND TRY IT

LEARN Moving Addends to Solve an Addition Problem

Students will learn how to break apart addends and move the parts to solve an addition problem.

TRY IT Move Addends to Solve an Addition Problem

Students will practice moving addends to solve an addition problem. Support will be provided to help students overcome misconceptions.

TRY IT Practice Moving Addends to Solve an Addition Problem

Students will complete online practice problems. Then they will complete Practice Moving Addends to Solve an Addition Problem from *Math 2 Activity Book*.

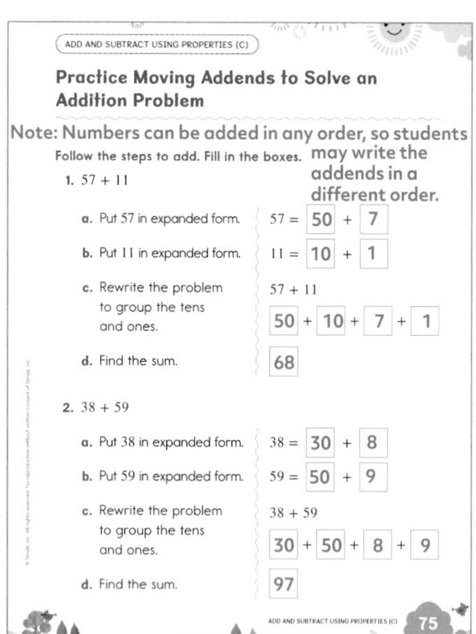

ADD AND SUBTRACT USING PROPERTIES (C)

Practice Moving Addends to Solve an Addition Problem

Note: Numbers can be added in any order, so students may write the addends in a different order.

Follow the steps to add. Fill in the boxes.

1. 57 + 11
   a. Put 57 in expanded form. 57 = 50 + 7
   b. Put 11 in expanded form. 11 = 10 + 1
   c. Rewrite the problem to group the tens and ones. 57 + 11 = 50 + 10 + 7 + 1
   d. Find the sum. 68

2. 38 + 59
   a. Put 38 in expanded form. 38 = 30 + 8
   b. Put 59 in expanded form. 59 = 50 + 9
   c. Rewrite the problem to group the tens and ones. 38 + 59 = 30 + 50 + 8 + 9
   d. Find the sum. 97

ADD AND SUBTRACT USING PROPERTIES (C) 75

Add.

3. 17 + 41 58
4. 63 + 32 95
5. 49 + 16 65
6. 20 + 43 63
7. 24 + 48 72
8. 33 + 17 50
9. 55 + 26 81
10. 84 + 12 96

Follow the directions.

11. Pilar and Nova add 33 + 24 in different ways. Show that the sum is the same no matter how you break apart and order the addends.

Pilar:	Nova:
30 + 20 + 3 + 4	30 + 3 + 20 + 4
50 + 3 + 4	33 + 20 + 4
53 + 4	53 + 4
57	57

76 ADD AND SUBTRACT USING PROPERTIES (C)

WRAP-UP

Moving Addends to Solve an Addition Problem

Students will solve a problem to show that they understand how to move addends to solve an addition problem.

Add and Subtract Using Properties (D)

Lesson Overview

ACTIVITY	ACTIVITY TITLE	TIME	ONLINE/OFFLINE
GET READY	Introduction to Add and Subtract Using Properties (D)	**2** minutes	online
	Adding 6 with Instant Recall	**7** minutes	online
LEARN AND TRY IT	Breaking Apart Numbers to Subtract	**15** minutes	online
	Break Apart Numbers to Subtract	**10** minutes	online
ALL ABOUT ME	Brain Break	**1** minute	online or offline
TRY IT	Practice Breaking Apart Numbers to Subtract	**20** minutes	online and offline
WRAP-UP	Breaking Apart Numbers to Subtract	**5** minutes	online

Content Background

Students will learn how breaking apart one number can make two-digit subtraction problems easier to solve. Students will learn to break apart the subtrahend or the minuend.

Break Apart the Subtrahend

The subtrahend is the number that is being subtracted in a subtraction problem. The goal of this strategy is to break the second number into two parts to make subtracting easier. When you break apart the subtrahend, remember to subtract *both parts*. Here are two examples.

98 – 37	53 – 34
98 – 30 – 7	53 – 33 – 1
68 – 7	20 – 1
61	19

Break Apart the Minuend

The minuend is the number that is being subtracted from in a subtraction problem. The goal of this strategy is to break the first number into two parts and subtract the minuend from *one* part. Since the minuend is broken apart using addition, you end up subtracting and then adding in this strategy. Here are the same examples solved using this strategy.

MATERIALS

Supplied

- *Math 2 Activity Book:* Practice Breaking Apart Numbers to Subtract

98 − 37	53 − 34
(60 + 38) − 37	(13 + 40) − 34
60 + (38 − 37)	13 + (40 − 34)
60 + 1	13 + 6
61	19

Lesson Goals

- Break apart numbers to subtract.

GET READY

Introduction to Add and Subtract Using Properties (D)

Students will get a glimpse of what they will learn about in the lesson. They will also read the lesson goals.

Adding 6 with Instant Recall

Students will practice adding 6.

LEARN AND TRY IT

LEARN Breaking Apart Numbers to Subtract

Students will learn how to break apart one number in a subtraction problem to make it easier to subtract.

TRY IT Break Apart Numbers to Subtract

Students will practice breaking apart numbers to subtract. Support will be provided to help students overcome misconceptions.

TIP There is often more than one way to break apart a number, and it isn't always clear whether breaking the subtrahend or the minuend will make the subtraction problem easier to solve. Encourage students to describe what they notice about each number in a subtraction problem before deciding which number to break apart and how to break it.

TRY IT Practice Breaking Apart Numbers to Subtract

Students will complete online practice problems. Then they will complete Practice Breaking Apart Numbers to Subtract from *Math 2 Activity Book*.

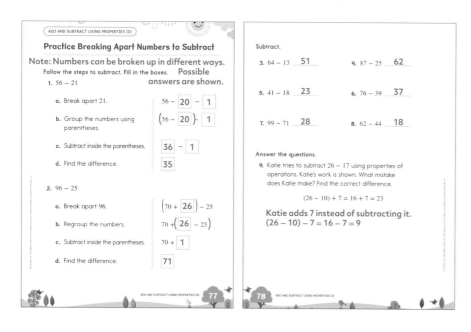

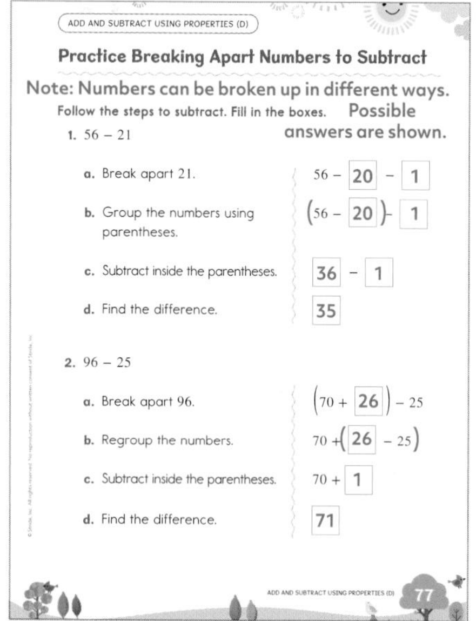

ADD AND SUBTRACT USING PROPERTIES (D)

Practice Breaking Apart Numbers to Subtract

Note: Numbers can be broken up in different ways.

Follow the steps to subtract. Fill in the boxes. Possible answers are shown.

1. 56 − 21
   a. Break apart 21. 56 − 20 − 1
   b. Group the numbers using parentheses. (56 − 20) − 1
   c. Subtract inside the parentheses. 36 − 1
   d. Find the difference. 35
2. 96 − 25
   a. Break apart 96. (70 + 26) − 25
   b. Regroup the numbers. 70 + (26 − 25)
   c. Subtract inside the parentheses. 70 + 1
   d. Find the difference. 71

ADD AND SUBTRACT USING PROPERTIES (D) 77

Subtract.

3. 64 − 13 51
4. 87 − 25 62
5. 41 − 18 23
6. 76 − 39 37
7. 99 − 71 28
8. 62 − 44 18

Answer the questions.

9. Katie tries to subtract 26 − 17 using properties of operations. Katie's work is shown. What mistake does Katie make? Find the correct difference.

   (26 − 10) + 7 = 16 + 7 = 23

   Katie adds 7 instead of subtracting it.
   (26 − 10) − 7 = 16 − 7 = 9

78 ADD AND SUBTRACT USING PROPERTIES (D)

WRAP-UP

Breaking Apart Numbers to Subtract

Students will solve a problem to show that they understand how to break apart numbers to subtract.

Add and Subtract Using Properties (E)

Lesson Overview

ACTIVITY	ACTIVITY TITLE	TIME	ONLINE/OFFLINE
GET READY	Introduction to Add and Subtract Using Properties (E)	2 minutes	online
TRY IT	Review Add and Subtract Using Properties	18 minutes	online
QUIZ	Add and Subtract Using Properties	25 minutes	online
WRAP-UP	More Math Practice	15 minutes	online

Lesson Goals

- Review adding and subtracting using properties.
- Take a quiz.

MATERIALS

There are no materials to gather for this lesson.

GET READY

Introduction to Add and Subtract Using Properties (E)

Students will read the lesson goals.

TRY IT

Review Add and Subtract Using Properties

Students will answer questions to review what they have learned about adding and subtracting using properties.

QUIZ

Add and Subtract Using Properties

Students will complete the Add and Subtract Using Properties quiz.

WRAP-UP

More Math Practice

Students will practice skills according to their individual needs.

Addition and Subtraction Are Related (A)

Lesson Overview

ACTIVITY	ACTIVITY TITLE	TIME	ONLINE/OFFLINE
GET READY	Introduction to Addition and Subtraction Are Related (A)	**2** minutes	online
	Look Back at Finding Missing Numbers	**7** minutes	online
LEARN AND TRY IT	Relating Addition and Subtraction	**7** minutes	online
	Relate Addition and Subtraction	**7** minutes	online
ALL ABOUT ME	Brain Break	**1** minute	online or offline
LEARN AND TRY IT	Relating Addition and Subtraction Using Models	**7** minutes	online
	Relate Addition and Subtraction Using Models	**7** minutes	online
	Practice Relating Addition and Subtraction	**20** minutes	online and offline
WRAP-UP	Relating Addition and Subtraction	**2** minutes	online

Content Background

Students will learn how addition and subtraction facts from the same fact family are related. They will use modeling, part-part-whole charts, and fact-family triangles to identify fact families and to understand how to use addition to write a related subtraction fact and vice versa.

Fact Families

A fact family is a set of number sentences that use the same three numbers. The relationships among the three numbers create the different facts in the fact family. The numbers 5, 9, and 14 are related by addition and subtraction. This is the fact family for the numbers 5, 9, and 14.

$9 + 5 = 14$ $\qquad$ $14 - 5 = 9$

$5 + 9 = 14$ $\qquad$ $14 - 9 = 5$

Opposite Operations

Though the primary purpose of this lesson is to show how addition and subtraction are related in a fact family, students are also introduced to opposites and inverses. Inverse operations are opposite; they undo each other. Addition and subtraction are inverse operations. Students will get a more in-depth study of inverse operations in Math 3.

MATERIALS

Supplied

- *Math 2 Activity Book:* Practice Relating Addition and Subtraction

KEYWORDS

fact family – a group of related addition and subtraction number sentences for three numbers

Lesson Goals

- Understand how addition and subtraction are related.
- Write the number sentences in a fact family.

GET READY

Introduction to Addition and Subtraction Are Related (A)

Students will get a glimpse of what they will learn about in the lesson. They will also read the lesson goals.

Look Back at Finding Missing Numbers

Students will practice the prerequisite skill of finding missing numbers.

LEARN AND TRY IT

LEARN Relating Addition and Subtraction

Students will learn how addition and subtraction are related. They will learn to use objects (modeling) to help them relate three numbers using addition and subtraction. They will learn that a fact family is the number sentences they create using the three numbers.

TIP Ask students to think of opposites in their daily life. Some examples are tying and untying shoes, opening and closing a window or door, and turning a device on and off. Briefly discuss why these examples are inverses of each other.

TRY IT Relate Addition and Subtraction

Students will practice using models to write fact families.

LEARN Relating Addition and Subtraction Using Models

Students will learn to use part-part-whole charts and fact-family triangles to find the facts in a fact family. They will use addition facts to find differences and subtraction facts to find sums.

TRY IT Relate Addition and Subtraction Using Models

Students will practice using addition facts to find differences and using subtraction facts to find sums. Support will be provided to help students overcome misconceptions.

TRY IT Practice Relating Addition and Subtraction

Students will complete online practice problems. Then they will complete Practice Relating Addition and Subtraction from *Math 2 Activity Book*.

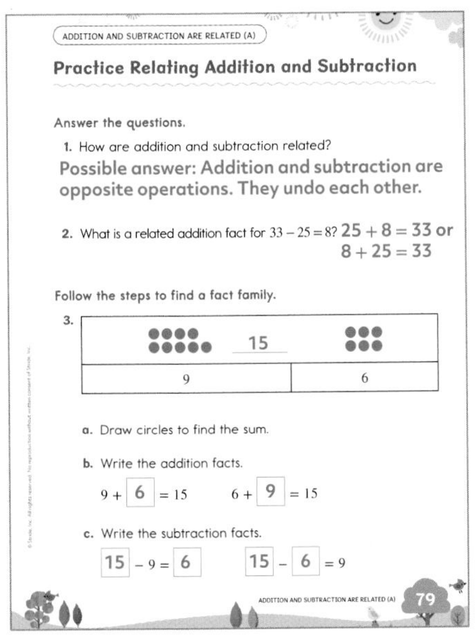

ADDITION AND SUBTRACTION ARE RELATED (A)

Practice Relating Addition and Subtraction

Answer the questions.

1. How are addition and subtraction related?
   Possible answer: Addition and subtraction are opposite operations. They undo each other.
2. What is a related addition fact for $33 - 25 = 8$? $25 + 8 = 33$ or $8 + 25 = 33$

Follow the steps to find a fact family.

3.

15	
9	6

a. Draw circles to find the sum.

b. Write the addition facts.
$9 + 6 = 15$ $6 + 9 = 15$

c. Write the subtraction facts.
$15 - 9 = 6$ $15 - 6 = 9$

ADDITION AND SUBTRACTION ARE RELATED (A) 79

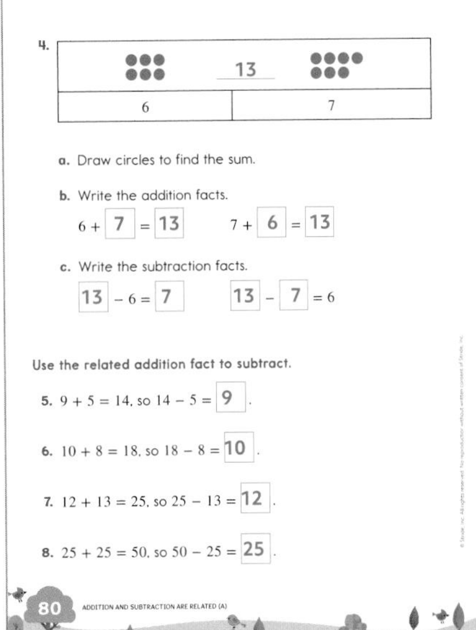

4.

13	
6	7

a. Draw circles to find the sum.

b. Write the addition facts.
$6 + 7 = 13$ $7 + 6 = 13$

c. Write the subtraction facts.
$13 - 6 = 7$ $13 - 7 = 6$

Use the related addition fact to subtract.

5. $9 + 5 = 14$, so $14 - 5 = 9$.
6. $10 + 8 = 18$, so $18 - 8 = 10$.
7. $12 + 13 = 25$, so $25 - 13 = 12$.
8. $25 + 25 = 50$, so $50 - 25 = 25$.

80 ADDITION AND SUBTRACTION ARE RELATED (A)

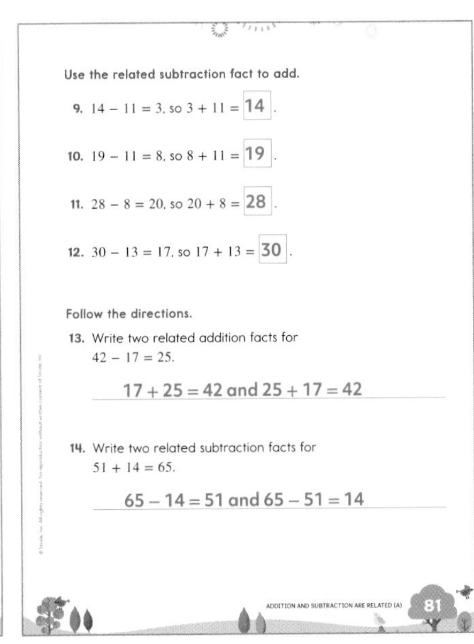

Use the related subtraction fact to add.

9. $14 - 11 = 3$, so $3 + 11 = 14$.
10. $19 - 11 = 8$, so $8 + 11 = 19$.
11. $28 - 8 = 20$, so $20 + 8 = 28$.
12. $30 - 13 = 17$, so $17 + 13 = 30$.

Follow the directions.

13. Write two related addition facts for $42 - 17 = 25$.
    $17 + 25 = 42$ and $25 + 17 = 42$
14. Write two related subtraction facts for $51 + 14 = 65$.
    $65 - 14 = 51$ and $65 - 51 = 14$

ADDITION AND SUBTRACTION ARE RELATED (A) 81

WRAP-UP

Relating Addition and Subtraction

Students will solve problems to show that they understand how to use an addition fact to find differences and a subtraction fact to find sums.

Addition and Subtraction Are Related (B)

Lesson Overview

ACTIVITY	ACTIVITY TITLE	TIME	ONLINE/OFFLINE
GET READY	Introduction to Addition and Subtraction Are Related (B)	**2** minutes	online
	Adding 6 Math Facts Game	**8** minutes	online
LEARN AND TRY IT	Adding with Friendly Numbers	**15** minutes	online
	Add with Friendly Numbers	**10** minutes	online
	Practice Adding with Friendly Numbers	**20** minutes	online and offline
WRAP-UP	Adding with Friendly Numbers	**5** minutes	online

Content Background

Students will learn how friendly numbers can make two-digit addition problems easier to solve.

Making Friendly Numbers

Numbers in an addition problem are "friendly" to each other when they are easier to add. For example, 5 and 2 are friendly, 5 and 9 are less friendly, and 9 and 1 are friendly. In general, numbers that require students to regroup are not particularly friendly. Addition problems can be made simpler by moving some ones from one addend to the other to make one of the addends a friendly number ending in zero. Here are two ways students may show their work.

$$\begin{array}{ccc} 14 & + & 77 \\ \underline{-3} & & \underline{+3} \\ 11 & + & 80 = 91 \end{array} \qquad \begin{array}{r} 18 + 2 = 20 \\ \underline{+\ 26 - 2 = 24} \\ 44 \end{array}$$

Notice that in each problem, the same number of ones are subtracted, or taken, from one number as are added to the other number. Since the same amount is moved from one addend to the other, the sum doesn't change.

MATERIALS

Supplied

- *Math 2 Activity Book:* Practice Adding with Friendly Numbers

Lesson Goals

- Add with friendly numbers.

GET READY

Introduction to Addition and Subtraction Are Related (B)

Students will get a glimpse of what they will learn about in the lesson. They will also read the lesson goals.

Adding 6 Math Facts Game

Students will play a game to practice adding 6.

LEARN AND TRY IT

LEARN Adding with Friendly Numbers

Students will learn how to add by making friendly numbers.

NOTE Students have learned several different strategies to help them solve two-digit addition problems in this unit. Students should try to understand and apply each strategy as it is taught. However, students may choose a strategy that they are comfortable with and can continually apply correctly when a strategy is not specified.

TRY IT Add with Friendly Numbers

Students will practice adding by making friendly numbers. Support will be provided to help students overcome misconceptions.

TRY IT Practice Adding with Friendly Numbers

Students will complete online practice problems. Then they will complete Practice Adding with Friendly Numbers from *Math 2 Activity Book.*

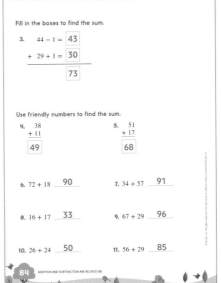

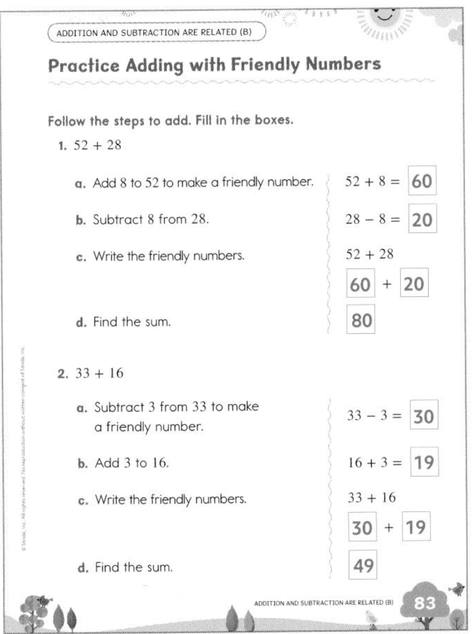

ADDITION AND SUBTRACTION ARE RELATED (B)

Practice Adding with Friendly Numbers

Follow the steps to add. Fill in the boxes.

1. 52 + 28
   a. Add 8 to 52 to make a friendly number. 52 + 8 = 60
   b. Subtract 8 from 28. 28 − 8 = 20
   c. Write the friendly numbers. 52 + 28 → 60 + 20
   d. Find the sum. 80

2. 33 + 16
   a. Subtract 3 from 33 to make a friendly number. 33 − 3 = 30
   b. Add 3 to 16. 16 + 3 = 19
   c. Write the friendly numbers. 33 + 16 → 30 + 19
   d. Find the sum. 49

ADDITION AND SUBTRACTION ARE RELATED (B) 83

Fill in the boxes to find the sum.

3. 44 − 1 = 43
   + 29 + 1 = 30
   73

Use friendly numbers to find the sum.

4. 38 + 11 = 49
5. 51 + 17 = 68
6. 72 + 18 = 90
7. 34 + 57 = 91
8. 16 + 17 = 33
9. 67 + 29 = 96
10. 26 + 24 = 50
11. 56 + 29 = 85

84 ADDITION AND SUBTRACTION ARE RELATED (B)

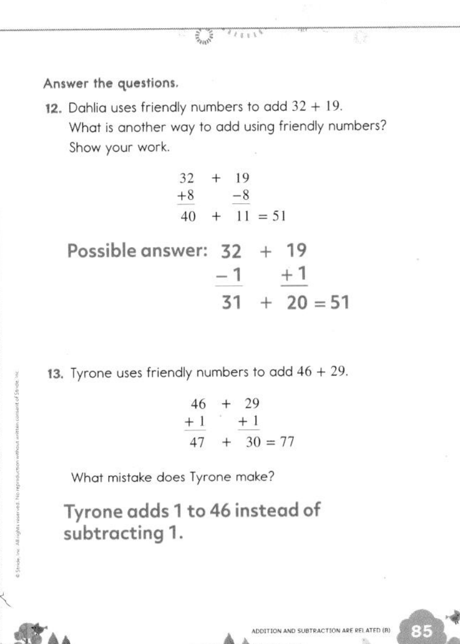

Answer the questions.

12. Dahlia uses friendly numbers to add 32 + 19.
    What is another way to add using friendly numbers?
    Show your work.

    32 + 19
    +8 −8
    40 + 11 = 51

    Possible answer: 32 + 19
    −1 +1
    31 + 20 = 51

13. Tyrone uses friendly numbers to add 46 + 29.

    46 + 29
    +1 +1
    47 + 30 = 77

    What mistake does Tyrone make?

    Tyrone adds 1 to 46 instead of subtracting 1.

ADDITION AND SUBTRACTION ARE RELATED (B) 85

WRAP-UP

Adding with Friendly Numbers

Students will solve a problem to show that they understand how to add by making friendly numbers.

Addition and Subtraction Are Related (C)

Lesson Overview

ACTIVITY	ACTIVITY TITLE	TIME	ONLINE/OFFLINE
GET READY	Introduction to Addition and Subtraction Are Related (C)	**2** minutes	
	Adding 7 Math Facts	**7** minutes	
LEARN AND TRY IT	Using Relationships to Subtract	**15** minutes	
	Use Relationships to Subtract	**10** minutes	
ALL ABOUT ME	Brain Break	**1** minute	or
TRY IT	Practice Using Relationships to Subtract	**20** minutes	and
WRAP-UP	Using Relationships to Subtract	**5** minutes	

Content Background

Students will learn how counting on using a number line and friendly numbers can make two-digit subtraction problems easier to solve.

Counting On

Counting on works for any numbers but it is especially useful when the difference between the minuend and subtrahend is small. For example, the difference of 94 and 86 will be small because 84 and 96 are close on a number line. To apply this strategy, mark both numbers on an open number line. Then start at the subtrahend, 86, and make jumps *forward* until reaching the minuend. The sum of the jumps is the difference. This open number line shows that the difference of 94 and 86 is 8.

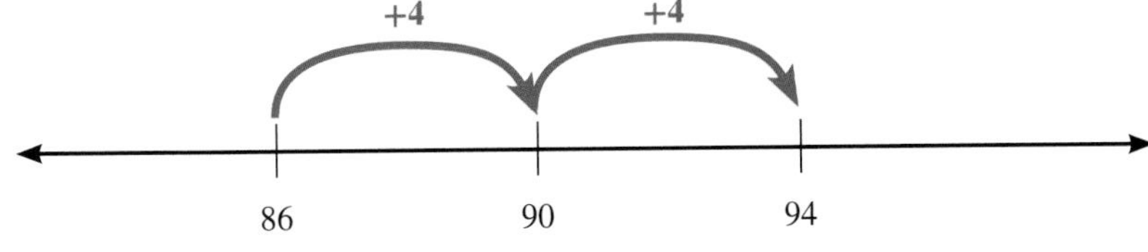

This strategy works because of the relationship between addition and subtraction. In this example, $94 - 86 = 8$ because $86 + 8 = 94$.

Making Friendly Numbers

Students begin by learning an interesting pattern. They can add the same amount to both numbers in a subtraction problem without changing the

MATERIALS

Supplied

- *Math 2 Activity Book:* Practice Using Relationships to Subtract

difference. The same is true for subtracting the same amount from both numbers. This pattern makes it possible to adjust the numbers in a subtraction problem to make them easier to subtract. Specifically, subtrahends that end in 0 are especially friendly, or easy, to subtract. Here are two ways students may show their work.

$$\begin{array}{ccc} 31 & - & 15 \\ +5 & & +5 \\ \hline 36 & - & 20 = 16 \end{array} \qquad \begin{array}{r} 57 - 2 = 55 \\ -\ 32 - 2 = 30 \\ \hline 25 \end{array}$$

Lesson Goals

- Subtract with friendly numbers.
- Subtract by adding.

GET READY

Introduction to Addition and Subtraction Are Related (C)

Students will get a glimpse of what they will learn about in the lesson. They will also read the lesson goals.

Adding 7 Math Facts

Students will practice adding 7.

LEARN AND TRY IT

LEARN Using Relationships to Subtract

Students will learn how to use relationships to subtract. Specific strategies include making friendly numbers and adding on a number line.

NOTE Students have learned several different strategies to help them solve two-digit subtraction problems in this unit. Students should try to understand and apply each strategy as it is taught. However, students may choose a strategy that they are comfortable with and can continually apply correctly when a strategy is not specified.

TRY IT Use Relationships to Subtract

Students will practice using relationships to subtract. Support will be provided to help students overcome misconceptions.

TRY IT Practice Using Relationships to Subtract

Students will complete online practice problems. Then they will complete Practice Using Relationships to Subtract from *Math 2 Activity Book*.

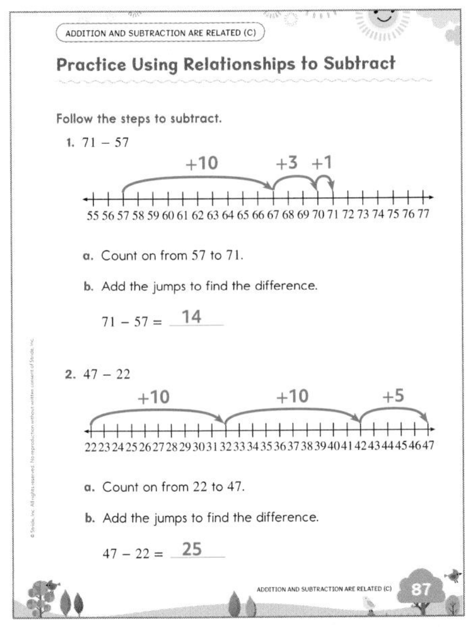

ADDITION AND SUBTRACTION ARE RELATED (C)

Practice Using Relationships to Subtract

Follow the steps to subtract.

1. 71 − 57

a. Count on from 57 to 71.

b. Add the jumps to find the difference.

71 − 57 = 14

2. 47 − 22

a. Count on from 22 to 47.

b. Add the jumps to find the difference.

47 − 22 = 25

ADDITION AND SUBTRACTION ARE RELATED (C) 87

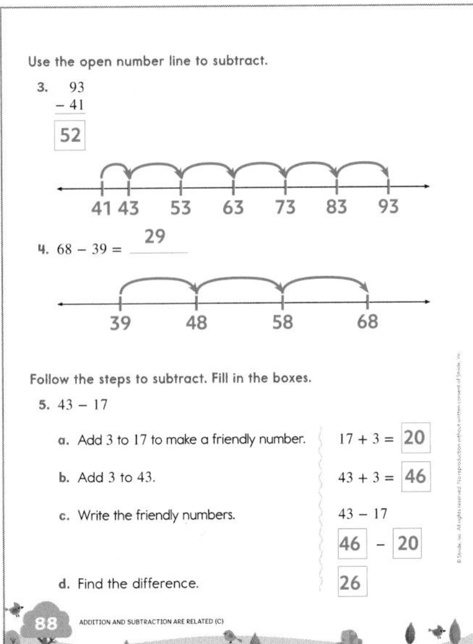

Use the open number line to subtract.

3. 93 − 41 = 52

4. 68 − 39 = 29

Follow the steps to subtract. Fill in the boxes.

5. 43 − 17

a. Add 3 to 17 to make a friendly number. 17 + 3 = 20

b. Add 3 to 43. 43 + 3 = 46

c. Write the friendly numbers. 43 − 17 → 46 − 20

d. Find the difference. 26

88 ADDITION AND SUBTRACTION ARE RELATED (C)

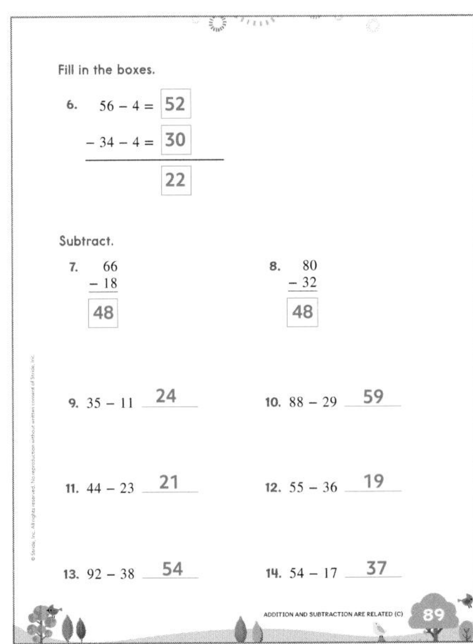

Fill in the boxes.

6. 56 − 4 = 52

− 34 − 4 = 30

22

Subtract.

7. 66 − 18 = 48

8. 80 − 32 = 48

9. 35 − 11 = 24

10. 88 − 29 = 59

11. 44 − 23 = 21

12. 55 − 36 = 19

13. 92 − 38 = 54

14. 54 − 17 = 37

ADDITION AND SUBTRACTION ARE RELATED (C) 89

WRAP-UP

Using Relationships to Subtract

Students will solve problems to show that they understand how to use relationships to subtract.

Addition and Subtraction Are Related (D)

Lesson Overview

ACTIVITY	ACTIVITY TITLE	TIME	ONLINE/OFFLINE
GET READY	Introduction to Addition and Subtraction Are Related (D)	**2** minutes	
TRY IT	Review Addition and Subtraction Are Related	**18** minutes	
QUIZ	Addition and Subtraction Are Related	**25** minutes	
WRAP-UP	More Math Practice	**15** minutes	

Lesson Goals

- Review using relationships to add and subtract.
- Take a quiz.

MATERIALS

There are no materials to gather for this lesson.

GET READY

Introduction to Addition and Subtraction Are Related (D)

Students will read the lesson goals.

TRY IT

Review Addition and Subtraction Are Related

Students will answer questions to review what they have learned about how addition and subtraction are related.

QUIZ

Addition and Subtraction Are Related

Students will complete the Addition and Subtraction Are Related quiz.

WRAP-UP

More Math Practice

Students will practice skills according to their individual needs.

Add and Subtract with Two Digits Wrap-Up

Lesson Overview

ACTIVITY	ACTIVITY TITLE	TIME	ONLINE/OFFLINE
GET READY	Introduction to Add and Subtract with Two Digits Wrap-Up	**2** minutes	online
TRY IT	Review Add and Subtract with Two Digits	**23** minutes	online
UNIT CHECKPOINT	Add and Subtract with Two Digits	**35** minutes	online

Lesson Goals

- Review adding and subtracting with two digits.
- Show what you know about adding and subtracting with two digits.

MATERIALS

There are no materials to gather for this lesson.

GET READY

Introduction to Add and Subtract with Two Digits Wrap-Up

Students will read the lesson goals.

TRY IT

Review Add and Subtract with Two Digits

Students will answer questions to review what they have learned about adding and subtracting with two digits.

UNIT CHECKPOINT

Add and Subtract with Two Digits

Students will complete the Add and Subtract with Two Digits Unit Checkpoint.

LEARNING COACH CHECK-IN This is a graded assignment. Make sure students complete the online assessment.

Add More Than Two Numbers

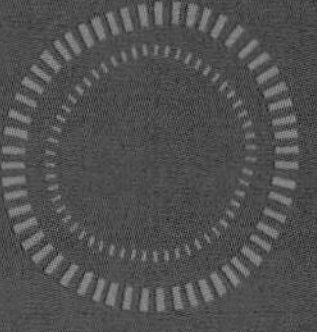

Add Three Numbers (A)

Lesson Overview

ACTIVITY	ACTIVITY TITLE	TIME	ONLINE/OFFLINE
GET READY	Introduction to Add Three Numbers (A)	**2** minutes	online
	Look Back at Solving Addition Story Problems	**7** minutes	online
LEARN AND TRY IT	Understanding the Associative Property	**7** minutes	online
	Understand the Associative Property	**7** minutes	online
ALL ABOUT ME	Brain Break	**1** minute	online or offline
LEARN AND TRY IT	Applying the Associative Property to 3 Addends	**7** minutes	online
	Apply the Associative Property to 3 Addends	**7** minutes	online
	Practice Applying the Associative Property to 3 Addends	**20** minutes	online and offline
WRAP-UP	Applying the Associative Property to 3 Addends	**2** minutes	online

Content Background

Students have learned that three numbers have the same sum regardless of how the numbers are grouped. Students will learn that the name of this fact is the associative property of addition. Then students will apply this property to add three two-digit numbers. They will continue to use the addition strategies they learned for adding two two-digit numbers.

Associative Property of Addition

Although the name of this property is often shortened to just "associative property," it is important to remember that it applies to addition but not subtraction. Students will learn the associative property of *multiplication* in Math 3.

Applying the Associative Property

In some problems with three addends, two of the addends can be grouped to make a ten. Grouping those numbers makes it easier to add using mental math. In the sum $17 + 34 + 26$, the numbers 34 and 26 make a ten. By the end of this lesson, students are expected to choose which numbers to group.

Other problems may not have ones that add to ten. In these problems, students can choose which addends to group to add first. For example, the ones in the addition problem $23 + 41 + 34$ add to 8. Adding 23 to 41 is just as easy as adding 41 to 34 first.

MATERIALS

Supplied

- *Math 2 Activity Book:* Practice Applying the Associative Property to 3 Addends

KEYWORDS

associative property of addition – a rule that says grouping three or more addends in different ways does not change their sum

Example: $(2 + 3) + 4$ has the same sum as $2 + (3 + 4)$.

Lesson Goals

- Understand the associative property.
- Add three numbers by choosing the best way to group them.

GET READY

Introduction to Add Three Numbers (A)

Students will get a glimpse of what they will learn about in the lesson. They will also read the lesson goals.

Look Back at Solving Addition Story Problems

Students will review and practice the prerequisite skill of solving story problems that involve adding three numbers.

LEARN AND TRY IT

LEARN Understanding the Associative Property

Students will review the fact that they can group addends in different ways and get the same sum. They will learn that the name of this rule is the associative property of addition.

TRY IT Understand the Associative Property

Students will practice problems to show they understand the associative property of addition. Support will be provided to help students overcome misconceptions.

LEARN Applying the Associative Property to 3 Addends

Students will apply the associative property to addition problems with three addends.

TRY IT Apply the Associative Property to 3 Addends

Students will practice applying the associative property to addition problems with three addends. Support will be provided to help students overcome misconceptions.

TRY IT Practice Applying the Associative Property to 3 Addends

Students will complete online practice problems. Then they will complete Practice Applying the Associative Property to 3 Addends from *Math 2 Activity Book*.

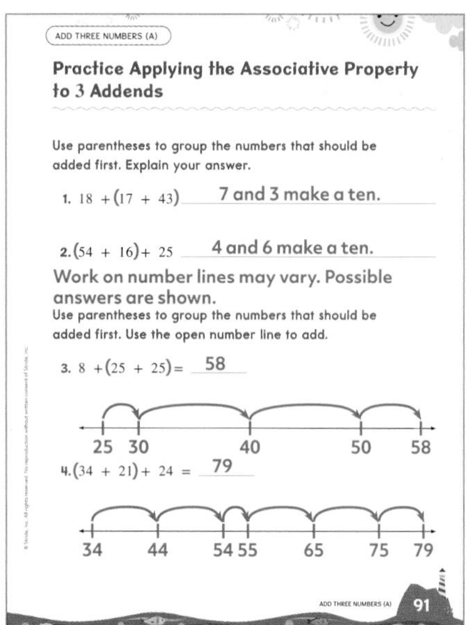

ADD THREE NUMBERS (A)

Practice Applying the Associative Property to 3 Addends

Use parentheses to group the numbers that should be added first. Explain your answer.

1. 18 + (17 + 43) 7 and 3 make a ten.
2. (54 + 16) + 25 4 and 6 make a ten.

Work on number lines may vary. Possible answers are shown.

Use parentheses to group the numbers that should be added first. Use the open number line to add.

3. 8 + (25 + 25) = 58

4. (34 + 21) + 24 = 79

ADD THREE NUMBERS (A) 91

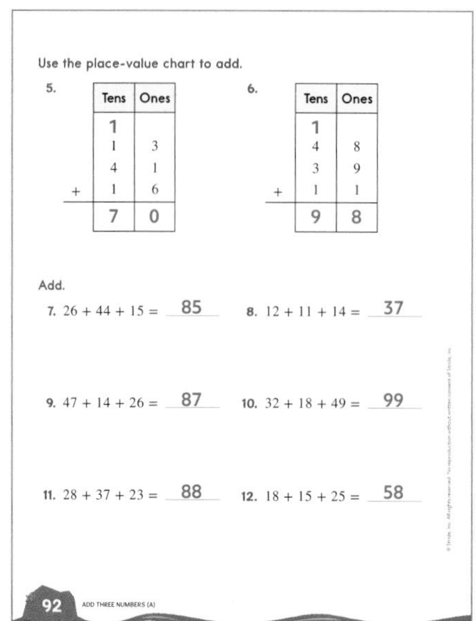

Use the place-value chart to add.

5.

	Tens	Ones
	1	
	1	3
	4	1
+	1	6
	7	0

6.

	Tens	Ones
	1	
	4	8
	3	9
+	1	1
	9	8

Add.

7. 26 + 44 + 15 = 85
8. 12 + 11 + 14 = 37
9. 47 + 14 + 26 = 87
10. 32 + 18 + 49 = 99
11. 28 + 37 + 23 = 88
12. 18 + 15 + 25 = 58

92 ADD THREE NUMBERS (A)

WRAP-UP

Applying the Associative Property to 3 Addends

Students will solve a problem to show that they understand how to apply the associative property of addition to an addition problem with three addends.

Add Three Numbers (B)

Lesson Overview

ACTIVITY	ACTIVITY TITLE	TIME	ONLINE/OFFLINE
GET READY	Introduction to Add Three Numbers (B)	**2** minutes	online
	Adding 7 with Instant Recall	**7** minutes	online
LEARN AND TRY IT	Understanding the Commutative Property	**7** minutes	online
	Understand the Commutative Property	**7** minutes	online
ALL ABOUT ME	Brain Break	**1** minute	online or offline
LEARN AND TRY IT	Applying the Commutative Property to 3 Addends	**7** minutes	online
	Apply the Commutative Property to 3 Addends	**7** minutes	online
	Practice Applying the Commutative Property to 3 Addends	**20** minutes	online and offline
WRAP-UP	Applying the Commutative Property to 3 Addends	**2** minutes	online

Content Background

Students have learned that three numbers have the same sum regardless of the order in which the numbers are added. Students will learn that the name of this fact is the commutative property of addition. Then students will apply this property to add three two-digit numbers. They will continue to use the addition strategies they learned for adding two two-digit numbers.

Commutative Property of Addition

Although the name of this property is often shortened to just "commutative property," it is important to remember that it applies to addition but not subtraction. Students will learn the commutative property of *multiplication* in Math 3.

Applying the Commutative Property

In some problems with three addends, the order of two of the addends can be switched to make a ten. Grouping those numbers makes it easier to add using mental math. In the sum $14 + 42 + 36$, the numbers 14 and 36 make a ten. To add them first, we change the order of the numbers to $14 + 36 + 42$. By the end of this lesson, students are expected to choose which numbers to move.

Students will also encounter problems with ones that add to less than ten. In these problems, students can add the numbers in whichever order makes the most sense to them.

MATERIALS

Supplied

- *Math 2 Activity Book:* Practice Applying the Commutative Property to 3 Addends

KEYWORDS

commutative property of addition – a rule that says changing the order that three or more addends are added does not change their sum

Example: $3 + 5 + 7$ has the same sum as $3 + 7 + 5$.

Lesson Goals

- Understand the commutative property.
- Add three numbers by changing their order.

GET READY

Introduction to Add Three Numbers (B)

Students will get a glimpse of what they will learn about in the lesson. They will also read the lesson goals.

Adding 7 with Instant Recall

Students will practice adding 7.

LEARN AND TRY IT

LEARN Understanding the Commutative Property

Students will review the fact that they can change the order of the addends and get the same sum. They will learn that the name of this rule is the commutative property of addition.

TRY IT Understand the Commutative Property

Students will practice problems to show they understand the commutative property of addition. Support will be provided to help students overcome misconceptions.

LEARN Applying the Commutative Property to 3 Addends

Students will apply the commutative property to addition problems with three addends.

TRY IT Apply the Commutative Property to 3 Addends

Students will practice applying the commutative property to addition problems with three addends. Support will be provided to help students overcome misconceptions.

TRY IT Practice Applying the Commutative Property to 3 Addends

Students will complete online practice problems. Then they will complete Practice Applying the Commutative Property to 3 Addends from *Math 2 Activity Book*.

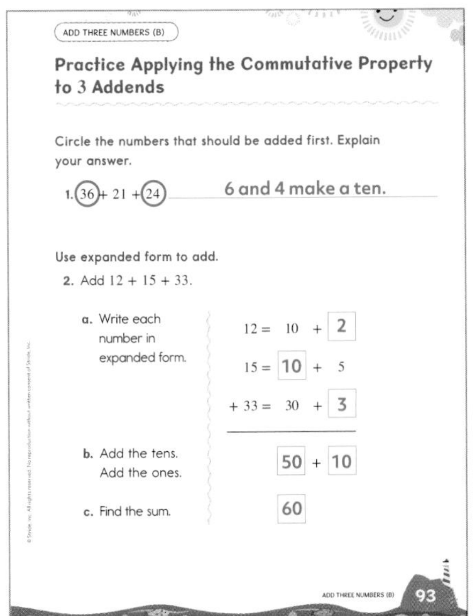

ADD THREE NUMBERS (B)

Practice Applying the Commutative Property to 3 Addends

Circle the numbers that should be added first. Explain your answer.

1. (36) + 21 + (24) 6 and 4 make a ten.

Use expanded form to add.

2. Add 12 + 15 + 33.

a. Write each number in expanded form.

12 = 10 + 2

15 = 10 + 5

+ 33 = 30 + 3

b. Add the tens. Add the ones.

50 + 10

c. Find the sum.

60

ADD THREE NUMBERS (B) 93

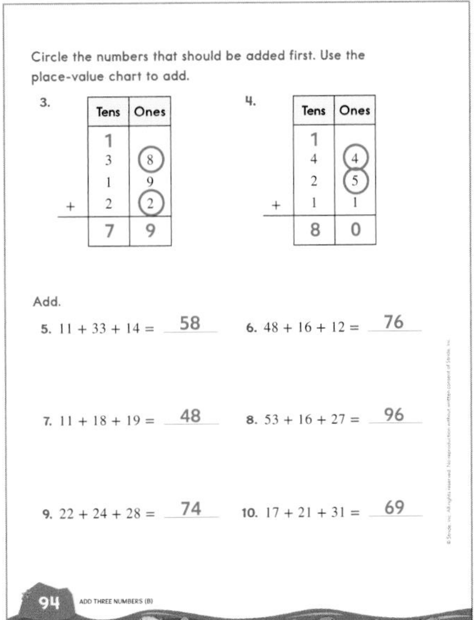

Circle the numbers that should be added first. Use the place-value chart to add.

3.

	Tens	Ones
	1	
	3	(8)
	1	9
+	2	(2)
	7	9

4.

	Tens	Ones
	1	
	4	(4)
	2	(5)
+	1	1
	8	0

Add.

5. 11 + 33 + 14 = 58

6. 48 + 16 + 12 = 76

7. 11 + 18 + 19 = 48

8. 53 + 16 + 27 = 96

9. 22 + 24 + 28 = 74

10. 17 + 21 + 31 = 69

94 ADD THREE NUMBERS (B)

WRAP-UP

Applying the Commutative Property to 3 Addends

Students will solve a problem to show that they understand how to apply the commutative property of addition to an addition problem with three addends.

Add Three Numbers (C)

Lesson Overview

ACTIVITY	ACTIVITY TITLE	TIME	ONLINE/OFFLINE
GET READY	Introduction to Add Three Numbers (C)	**2** minutes	
TRY IT	Review Add Three Numbers	**18** minutes	
QUIZ	Add Three Numbers	**25** minutes	
WRAP-UP	More Math Practice	**15** minutes	

Lesson Goals

- Review adding three numbers.
- Take a quiz.

MATERIALS

There are no materials to gather for this lesson.

GET READY

Introduction to Add Three Numbers (C)

Students will read the lesson goals.

TRY IT

Review Add Three Numbers

Students will answer questions to review what they have learned about adding three numbers.

QUIZ

Add Three Numbers

Students will complete the Add Three Numbers quiz.

WRAP-UP

More Math Practice

Students will practice skills according to their individual needs.

Add Four Numbers (A)

Lesson Overview

ACTIVITY	ACTIVITY TITLE	TIME	ONLINE/OFFLINE
GET READY	Introduction to Add Four Numbers (A)	**2** minutes	online
	Look Back at Ordering and Grouping Addends	**7** minutes	online
LEARN AND TRY IT	Grouping to Add 4 Numbers	**15** minutes	online
	Group to Add 4 Numbers	**10** minutes	online
ALL ABOUT ME	Brain Break	**1** minute	online or offline
TRY IT	Practice Grouping to Add 4 Numbers	**20** minutes	online and offline
WRAP-UP	Grouping to Add 4 Numbers	**5** minutes	online

Content Background

Students will learn how to group four two-digit addends to find their sum. In other words, they will be applying the associative property to an addition problem with four addends. They will continue to use the addition strategies they learned for adding two two-digit numbers.

MATERIALS

Supplied

- *Math 2 Activity Book:* Practice Grouping to Add 4 Numbers

Lesson Goals

- Add four numbers by choosing the best way to group them.

GET READY

Introduction to Add Four Numbers (A)

Students will get a glimpse of what they will learn about in the lesson. They will also read the lesson goals.

Look Back at Ordering and Grouping Addends

Students will review and practice the prerequisite skill of ordering and grouping three addends.

LEARN AND TRY IT

LEARN Grouping to Add 4 Numbers

Students will learn how to group addends to add four numbers.

TRY IT Group to Add 4 Numbers

Students will practice grouping to add four numbers. Support will be provided to help students overcome misconceptions.

TRY IT Practice Grouping to Add 4 Numbers

Students will complete online practice problems. Then they will complete Practice Grouping to Add 4 Numbers from *Math 2 Activity Book*.

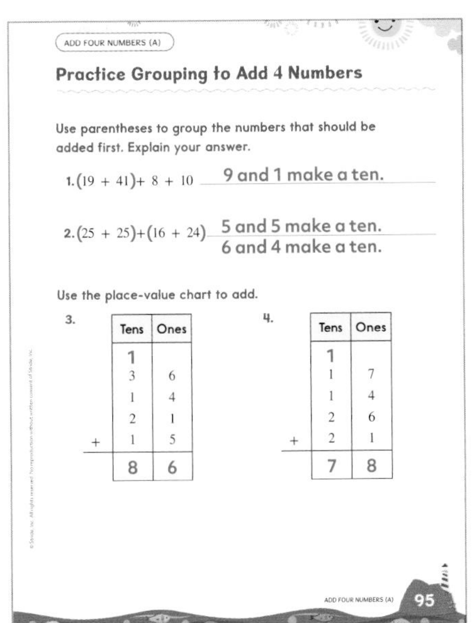

ADD FOUR NUMBERS (A)

Practice Grouping to Add 4 Numbers

Use parentheses to group the numbers that should be added first. Explain your answer.

1. (19 + 41) + 8 + 10 9 and 1 make a ten.
2. (25 + 25) + (16 + 24) 5 and 5 make a ten. 6 and 4 make a ten.

Use the place-value chart to add.

3.

	Tens	Ones
	1	
	3	6
	1	4
	2	1
+	1	5
	8	6

4.

	Tens	Ones
	1	
	1	7
	1	4
	2	6
+	2	1
	7	8

ADD FOUR NUMBERS (A) 95

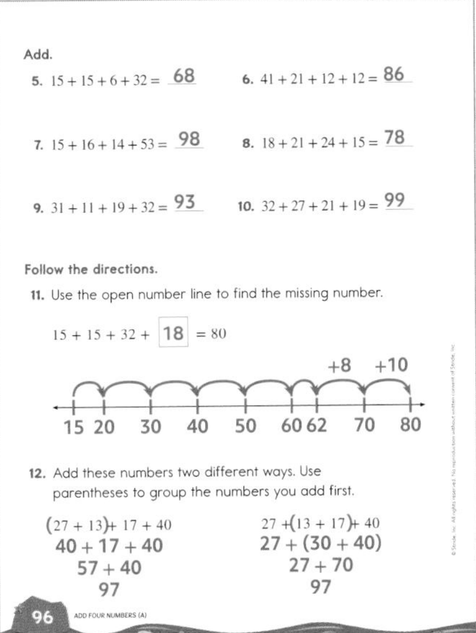

Add.

5. 15 + 15 + 6 + 32 = 68
6. 41 + 21 + 12 + 12 = 86
7. 15 + 16 + 14 + 53 = 98
8. 18 + 21 + 24 + 15 = 78
9. 31 + 11 + 19 + 32 = 93
10. 32 + 27 + 21 + 19 = 99

Follow the directions.

11. Use the open number line to find the missing number.

15 + 15 + 32 + 18 = 80

12. Add these numbers two different ways. Use parentheses to group the numbers you add first.

(27 + 13) + 17 + 40
40 + 17 + 40
57 + 40
97

27 + (13 + 17) + 40
27 + (30 + 40)
27 + 70
97

96 ADD FOUR NUMBERS (A)

WRAP-UP

Grouping to Add 4 Numbers

Students will solve a problem to show that they understand how to group to add four numbers.

Add Four Numbers (B)

Lesson Overview

ACTIVITY	ACTIVITY TITLE	TIME	ONLINE/OFFLINE
GET READY	Introduction to Add Four Numbers (B)	**2** minutes	online
	Adding 7 Math Facts Game	**7** minutes	online
LEARN AND TRY IT	Reordering to Add 4 Numbers	**15** minutes	online
	Reorder to Add 4 Numbers	**10** minutes	online
ALL ABOUT ME	Brain Break	**1** minute	online or offline
TRY IT	Practice Reordering to Add 4 Numbers	**20** minutes	online and offline
WRAP-UP	Reordering to Add 4 Numbers	**5** minutes	online

Content Background

Students will learn how to reorder four two-digit addends to find their sum. In other words, they will be applying the commutative property to an addition problem with four addends. They will continue to use the addition strategies they learned for adding two two-digit numbers.

MATERIALS

Supplied

- *Math 2 Activity Book:* Practice Reordering to Add 4 Numbers

Lesson Goals

- Add four numbers by changing their order.

GET READY

Introduction to Add Four Numbers (B)

Students will get a glimpse of what they will learn about in the lesson. They will also read the lesson goals.

Adding 7 Math Facts Game

Students will play a game to practice adding 7.

LEARN AND TRY IT

LEARN Reordering to Add 4 Numbers

Students will learn how to reorder addends to add four numbers.

TRY IT Reorder to Add 4 Numbers

Students will practice reordering to add four numbers. Support will be provided to help students overcome misconceptions.

TRY IT Practice Reordering to Add 4 Numbers

Students will complete online practice problems. Then they will complete Practice Reordering to Add 4 Numbers from *Math 2 Activity Book*.

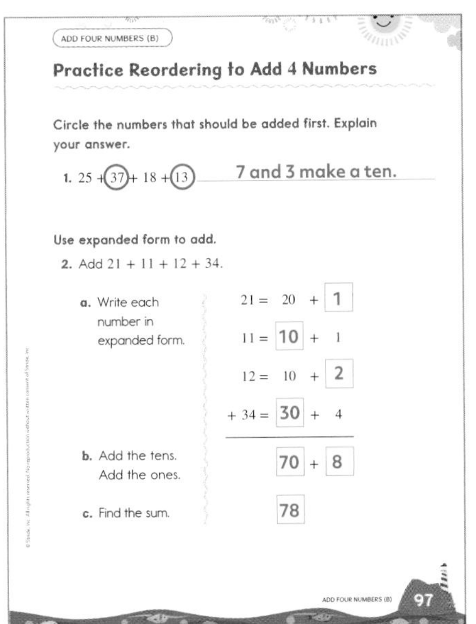

ADD FOUR NUMBERS (B)

Practice Reordering to Add 4 Numbers

Circle the numbers that should be added first. Explain your answer.

1. 25 + (37) + 18 + (13) 7 and 3 make a ten.

Use expanded form to add.

2. Add 21 + 11 + 12 + 34.

a. Write each number in expanded form.

21 = 20 + 1
11 = 10 + 1
12 = 10 + 2
+ 34 = 30 + 4

b. Add the tens. Add the ones. 70 + 8

c. Find the sum. 78

ADD FOUR NUMBERS (B) 97

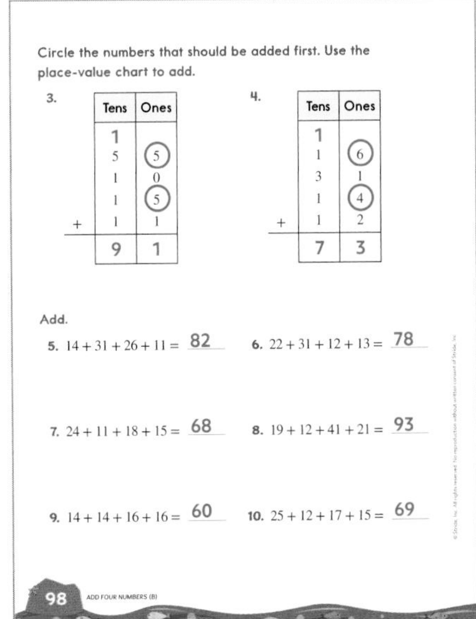

Circle the numbers that should be added first. Use the place-value chart to add.

3.

	Tens	Ones
	1	
	5	(5)
	1	0
	1	(5)
+	1	1
	9	1

4.

	Tens	Ones
	1	
	1	(6)
	3	1
	1	(4)
+	1	2
	7	3

Add.

5. 14 + 31 + 26 + 11 = 82
6. 22 + 31 + 12 + 13 = 78
7. 24 + 11 + 18 + 15 = 68
8. 19 + 12 + 41 + 21 = 93
9. 14 + 14 + 16 + 16 = 60
10. 25 + 12 + 17 + 15 = 69

98 ADD FOUR NUMBERS (B)

WRAP-UP

Reordering to Add 4 Numbers

Students will solve a problem to show that they understand how to reorder to add four numbers.

Add Four Numbers (C)

Lesson Overview

ACTIVITY	ACTIVITY TITLE	TIME	ONLINE/OFFLINE
GET READY	Introduction to Add Four Numbers (C)	2 minutes	
TRY IT	Review Add Four Numbers	18 minutes	
QUIZ	Add Four Numbers	25 minutes	
WRAP-UP	More Math Practice	15 minutes	

Lesson Goals

- Review adding four numbers.
- Take a quiz.

MATERIALS

There are no materials to gather for this lesson.

GET READY

Introduction to Add Four Numbers (C)

Students will read the lesson goals.

TRY IT

Review Add Four Numbers

Students will answer questions to review what they have learned about adding four numbers.

QUIZ

Add Four Numbers

Students will complete the Add Four Numbers quiz.

WRAP-UP

More Math Practice

Students will practice skills according to their individual needs.

Add More Than Two Numbers Wrap-Up

Lesson Overview

ACTIVITY	ACTIVITY TITLE	TIME	ONLINE/OFFLINE
GET READY	Introduction to Add More Than Two Numbers Wrap-Up	**2** minutes	
TRY IT	Review Add More Than Two Numbers	**23** minutes	
UNIT CHECKPOINT	Add More Than Two Numbers	**35** minutes	

Lesson Goals

- Review adding more than two numbers.
- Show what you know about adding more than two numbers.

MATERIALS

There are no materials to gather for this lesson.

GET READY

Introduction to Add More Than Two Numbers Wrap-Up

Students will read the lesson goals.

TRY IT

Review Add More Than Two Numbers

Students will answer questions to review what they have learned about adding more than two numbers.

UNIT CHECKPOINT

Add More Than Two Numbers

Students will complete the Add More Than Two Numbers Unit Checkpoint.

LEARNING COACH CHECK-IN This is a graded assignment. Make sure students complete the online assessment.

Working with Length

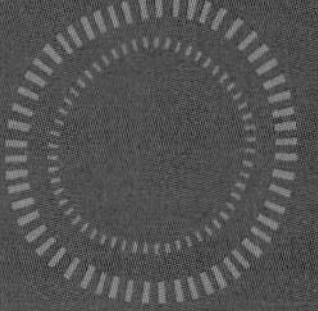

Inches (A)

Lesson Overview

ACTIVITY	ACTIVITY TITLE	TIME	ONLINE/OFFLINE
GET READY	Introduction to Inches (A)	**2** minutes	online
	Look Back at Measuring Length with Smaller Objects	**7** minutes	online
LEARN AND TRY IT	Measuring Length to the Nearest Inch	**15** minutes	online
	Measure Length to the Nearest Inch	**10** minutes	online
ALL ABOUT ME	Brain Break	**1** minute	online or offline
TRY IT	Practice Measuring Length to the Nearest Inch	**20** minutes	online and offline
WRAP-UP	Measuring Length to the Nearest Inch	**5** minutes	online

Content Background

Students have experience measuring with nonstandard units, such as paper clips, cubes, or fingers. In this lesson, students will be introduced to the English, or customary, system of measurement by learning to measure the length of an object to the nearest inch. Students will be introduced to different tools that measure length in inches. They will gain experience measuring with both online and physical rulers.

NOTE Students will not learn the abbreviations for units of length in Math 2. If students encounter the abbreviation for inches, in., explain that it is a shorter way to write inches and it uses a period so that it will not be confused with the word *in*.

MATERIALS

Supplied

- *Math 2 Activity Book:* Practice Measuring Length to the Nearest Inch

Also Needed

- ruler that measures in inches

KEYWORDS

inch – the basic English, or customary, unit for measuring length

measure (verb) – to use standard units to find a distance, area, volume, capacity, temperature, or interval of time

ruler – a tool for measuring length, usually in inches or centimeters

unit of measure – an amount used to measure

Example: Inches are a unit used to measure length.

Lesson Goals

- Find the length of an object to the nearest inch.

GET READY

Introduction to Inches (A)

Students will get a glimpse of what they will learn about in the lesson. They will also read the lesson goals.

Look Back at Measuring Length with Smaller Objects

Students will review and practice the prerequisite skill of measuring length with a smaller object as the unit of measure.

LEARN AND TRY IT

LEARN Measuring Length to the Nearest Inch

Students will learn how to use a ruler to measure the length of an object to the nearest inch.

TRY IT Measure Length to the Nearest Inch

Students will practice measuring lengths of objects to the nearest inch. Support will be provided to help students overcome misconceptions.

TRY IT Practice Measuring Length to the Nearest Inch

Students will complete online practice problems. Then they will complete Practice Measuring Length to the Nearest Inch from *Math 2 Activity Book.*

NOTE A printed ruler is available in the activity book.

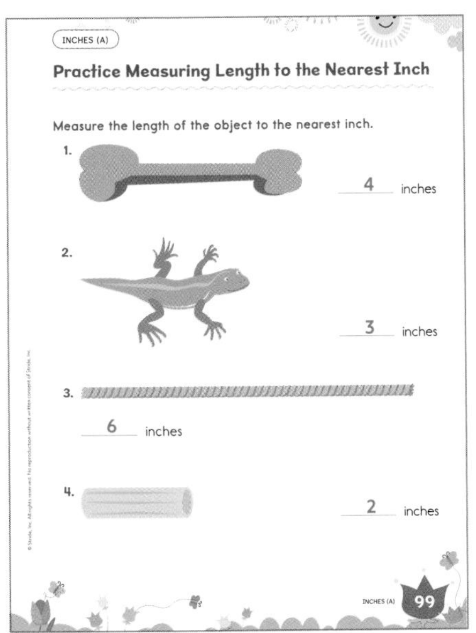
INCHES (A)

Practice Measuring Length to the Nearest Inch

Measure the length of the object to the nearest inch.

1. 4 inches
2. 3 inches
3. 6 inches
4. 2 inches

INCHES (A) 99

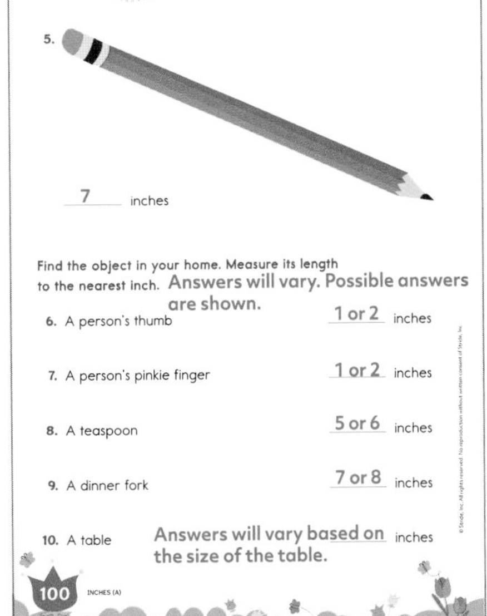
5. 7 inches

Find the object in your home. Measure its length to the nearest inch. Answers will vary. Possible answers are shown.

6. A person's thumb 1 or 2 inches
7. A person's pinkie finger 1 or 2 inches
8. A teaspoon 5 or 6 inches
9. A dinner fork 7 or 8 inches
10. A table Answers will vary based on the size of the table. inches

100 INCHES (A)

WRAP-UP

Measuring Length to the Nearest Inch

Students will solve a problem to show that they understand how to measure the length of an object to the nearest inch.

Inches (B)

Lesson Overview

ACTIVITY	ACTIVITY TITLE	TIME	ONLINE/OFFLINE
GET READY	Introduction to Inches (B)	**2** minutes	online
	Adding 8 Math Facts	**7** minutes	online
LEARN AND TRY IT	Estimating Length to the Nearest Inch	**15** minutes	online
	Estimate Length to the Nearest Inch	**10** minutes	online
ALL ABOUT ME	Brain Break	**1** minute	online or offline
TRY IT	Practice Estimating Length to the Nearest Inch	**20** minutes	online and offline
WRAP-UP	Estimating Length to the Nearest Inch	**5** minutes	online

Content Background

Students will learn how to estimate the length of an object to the nearest inch. Students will also learn to choose the most reasonable estimate.

Use Objects to Estimate Length

Estimating a length is like measuring the length of an object using nonstandard units. Objects like a small paper clip or a quarter are about 1 inch long. Using objects like these to find a length gives an estimate instead of an exact measurement.

MATERIALS

Supplied

- *Math 2 Activity Book:* Practice Estimating Length to the Nearest Inch

KEYWORDS

estimate (noun) – a number close to an exact measurement

Lesson Goals

- Estimate the length of an object to the nearest inch.

GET READY

Introduction to Inches (B)

Students will get a glimpse of what they will learn about in the lesson. They will also read the lesson goals.

Adding 8 Math Facts

Students will practice adding 8.

LEARN AND TRY IT

LEARN Estimating Length to the Nearest Inch

Students will learn how to estimate the length of an object to the nearest inch.

TRY IT Estimate Length to the Nearest Inch

Students will practice estimating lengths of objects to the nearest inch. Support will be provided to help students overcome misconceptions.

TRY IT Practice Estimating Length to the Nearest Inch

Students will complete online practice problems. Then they will complete Practice Estimating Length to the Nearest Inch from *Math 2 Activity Book*.

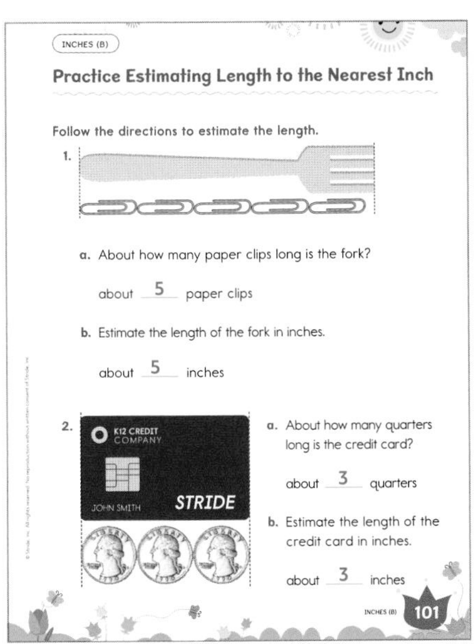
INCHES (B)

Practice Estimating Length to the Nearest Inch

Follow the directions to estimate the length.

1.
a. About how many paper clips long is the fork?

about 5 paper clips

b. Estimate the length of the fork in inches.

about 5 inches

2.

a. About how many quarters long is the credit card?

about 3 quarters

b. Estimate the length of the credit card in inches.

about 3 inches

INCHES (B) 101

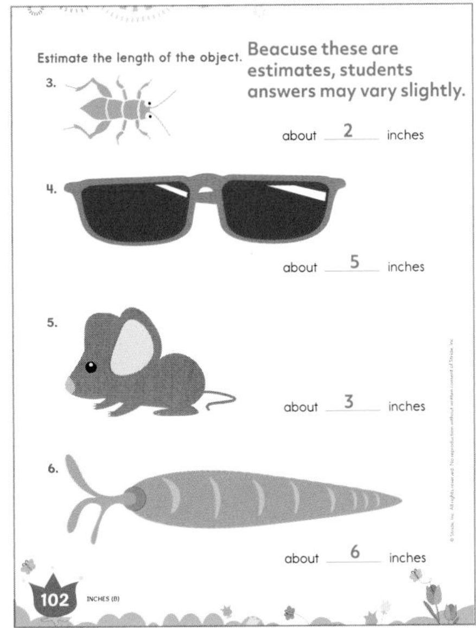
Estimate the length of the object. Beacuse these are estimates, students answers may vary slightly.

3. about 2 inches

4. about 5 inches

5. about 3 inches

6. about 6 inches

102 INCHES (B)

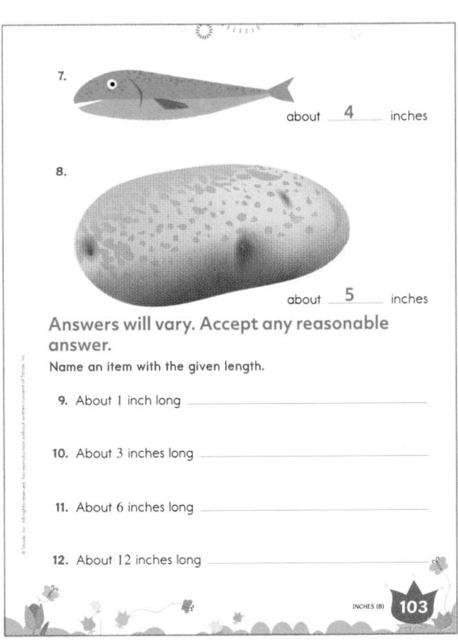
7. about 4 inches

8. about 5 inches

Answers will vary. Accept any reasonable answer.

Name an item with the given length.

9. About 1 inch long ______

10. About 3 inches long ______

11. About 6 inches long ______

12. About 12 inches long ______

INCHES (B) 103

WRAP-UP

Estimating Length to the Nearest Length

Students will solve a problem to show that they understand how to estimate length to the nearest inch.

Inches (C)

Lesson Overview

ACTIVITY	ACTIVITY TITLE	TIME	ONLINE/OFFLINE
GET READY	Introduction to Inches (C)	**2** minutes	
TRY IT	Review Inches	**18** minutes	
QUIZ	Inches	**25** minutes	
WRAP-UP	More Math Practice	**15** minutes	

Lesson Goals

- Review finding and estimating the length of an object to the nearest inch.
- Take a quiz.

MATERIALS

There are no materials to gather for this lesson.

GET READY

Introduction to Inches (C)

Students will read the lesson goals.

TRY IT

Review Inches

Students will answer questions to review what they have learned about inches.

QUIZ

Inches

Students will complete the Inches quiz.

WRAP-UP

More Math Practice

Students will practice skills according to their individual needs.

Centimeters (A)

Lesson Overview

ACTIVITY	ACTIVITY TITLE	TIME	ONLINE/OFFLINE
GET READY	Introduction to Centimeters (A)	**2** minutes	online
	Look Back at Measuring Length with More Than One Object	**8** minutes	online
LEARN AND **TRY IT**	Measuring Length to the Nearest Centimeter	**15** minutes	online
	Measure Length to the Nearest Centimeter	**10** minutes	online
	Practice Measuring Length to the Nearest Centimeter	**20** minutes	online and offline
WRAP-UP	Measuring Length to the Nearest Centimeter	**5** minutes	online

Content Background

Students will learn how to measure the length of an object to the nearest centimeter. Students have used a ruler to measure to the nearest inch. In this lesson, they will learn that they can also measure with a ruler using a different unit of measurement. Students will gain experience measuring with both online and physical rulers.

MATERIALS

Supplied

- *Math 2 Activity Book:* Practice Measuring Length to the Nearest Centimeter

Also Needed

- ruler that measures in centimeters

Lesson Goals

- Find the length of an object to the nearest centimeter.

KEYWORDS

centimeter – a metric unit used to measure length

GET READY

Introduction to Centimeters (A)

Students will get a glimpse of what they will learn about in the lesson. They will also read the lesson goals.

Look Back at Measuring Length with More Than One Object

Students will review and practice the prerequisite skill of measuring the length of an object with more than one nonstandard unit.

LEARN AND TRY IT

LEARN Measuring Length to the Nearest Centimeter

Students will learn how to use a ruler to measure the length of an object to the nearest centimeter.

TIP Measuring tools are often marked with inches on one side and centimeters on the other side. It is important to use the correct side depending on which units are indicated in a problem. Students may need help identifying which side to use when a ruler is marked with both inches and centimeters.

TRY IT Measure Length to the Nearest Centimeter

Students will practice measuring lengths of objects to the nearest centimeter. Support will be provided to help students overcome misconceptions.

TRY IT Practice Measuring Length to the Nearest Centimeter

Students will complete online practice problems. Then they will complete Practice Measuring Length to the Nearest Centimeter from *Math 2 Activity Book.*

NOTE A printed ruler is supplied with the activity book pages in the previous lesson.

CENTIMETERS (A)

Practice Measuring Length to the Nearest Centimeter

Measure the length of the object to the nearest centimeter.

1. 7 centimeters
2. 5 centimeters
3. 6 centimeters
4. 15 centimeters
5. 10 centimeters

CENTIMETERS (A) 105

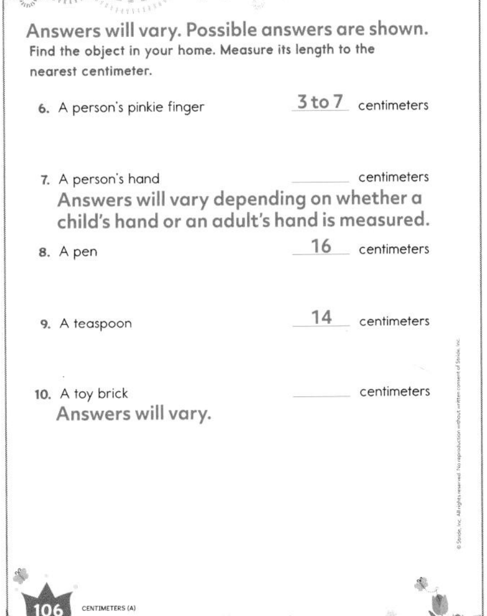

Answers will vary. Possible answers are shown.

Find the object in your home. Measure its length to the nearest centimeter.

6. A person's pinkie finger 3 to 7 centimeters
7. A person's hand ____ centimeters
   Answers will vary depending on whether a child's hand or an adult's hand is measured.
8. A pen 16 centimeters
9. A teaspoon 14 centimeters
10. A toy brick ____ centimeters
    Answers will vary.

106 CENTIMETERS (A)

WRAP-UP

Measuring Length to the Nearest Centimeter

Students will solve a problem to show that they understand how to measure an object to the nearest centimeter.

Centimeters (B)

Lesson Overview

ACTIVITY	ACTIVITY TITLE	TIME	ONLINE/OFFLINE
GET READY	Introduction to Centimeters (B)	**2** minutes	online
	Adding 8 with Instant Recall	**7** minutes	online
LEARN AND **TRY IT**	Estimating Length to the Nearest Centimeter	**15** minutes	online
	Estimate Length to the Nearest Centimeter	**10** minutes	online
ALL ABOUT ME	Brain Break	**1** minute	online or offline
TRY IT	Practice Estimating Length to the Nearest Centimeter	**20** minutes	online and offline
WRAP-UP	Estimating Length to the Nearest Centimeter	**5** minutes	online

Content Background

Students will learn how to estimate the length of an object to the nearest centimeter. Students will also learn to choose the most reasonable estimate.

MATERIALS

Supplied

- *Math 2 Activity Book:* Practice Estimating Length to the Nearest Centimeter

Lesson Goals

- Estimate the length of an object to the nearest centimeter.

GET READY

Introduction to Centimeters (B)

Students will get a glimpse of what they will learn about in the lesson. They will also read the lesson goals.

Adding 8 with Instant Recall

Students will practice adding 8.

LEARN AND TRY IT

LEARN Estimating Length to the Nearest Centimeter

Students will learn how to estimate the length of an object to the nearest centimeter.

TRY IT Estimate Length to the Nearest Centimeter

Students will practice estimating lengths of objects to the nearest centimeter. Support will be provided to help students overcome misconceptions.

TRY IT Practice Estimating Length to the Nearest Centimeter

Students will complete online practice problems. Then they will complete Practice Estimating Length to the Nearest Centimeter from *Math 2 Activity Book*.

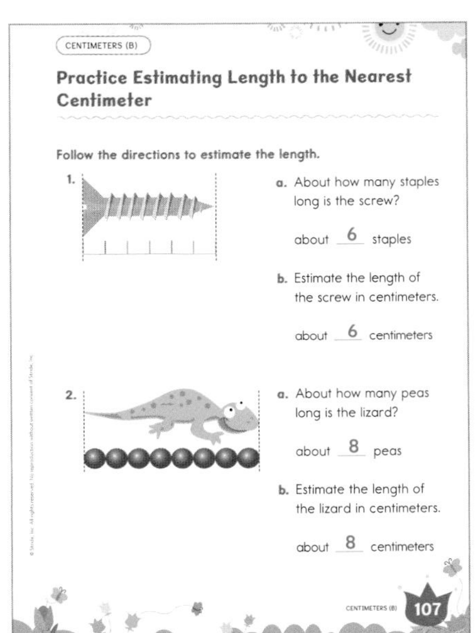
CENTIMETERS (B)

Practice Estimating Length to the Nearest Centimeter

Follow the directions to estimate the length.

1. a. About how many staples long is the screw?
   about 6 staples
   b. Estimate the length of the screw in centimeters.
   about 6 centimeters

2. a. About how many peas long is the lizard?
   about 8 peas
   b. Estimate the length of the lizard in centimeters.
   about 8 centimeters

CENTIMETERS (B) 107

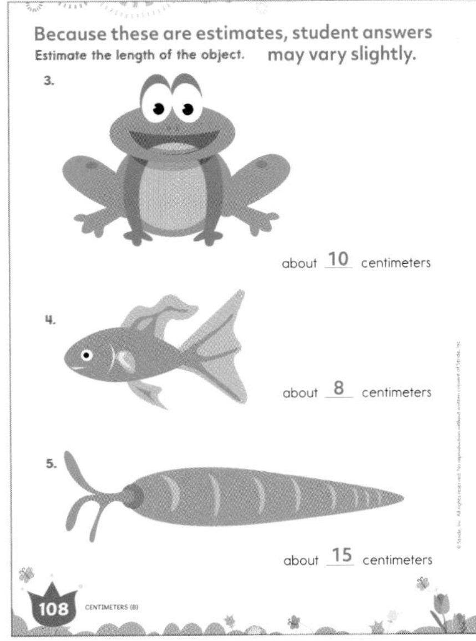
Because these are estimates, student answers may vary slightly.

Estimate the length of the object.

3. about 10 centimeters

4. about 8 centimeters

5. about 15 centimeters

108 CENTIMETERS (B)

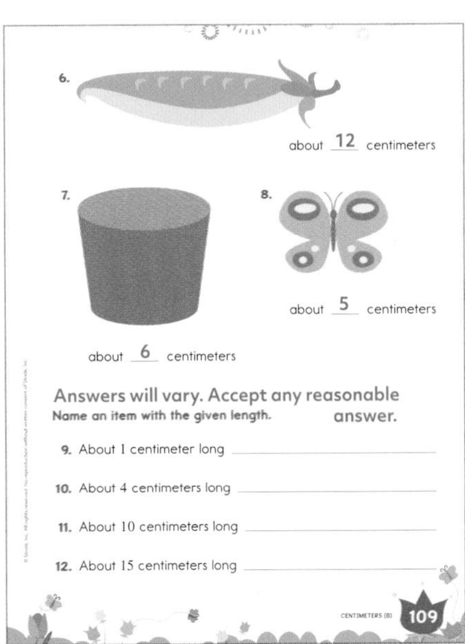
6. about 12 centimeters

7. about 6 centimeters

8. about 5 centimeters

Answers will vary. Accept any reasonable answer.

Name an item with the given length.

9. About 1 centimeter long ______
10. About 4 centimeters long ______
11. About 10 centimeters long ______
12. About 15 centimeters long ______

CENTIMETERS (B) 109

WRAP-UP

Estimating Length to the Nearest Centimeter

Students will solve a problem to show that they understand how to estimate length to the nearest centimeter.

Centimeters (C)

Lesson Overview

ACTIVITY	ACTIVITY TITLE	TIME	ONLINE/OFFLINE
GET READY	Introduction to Centimeters (C)	**2** minutes	
TRY IT	Review Centimeters	**18** minutes	
QUIZ	Centimeters	**25** minutes	
WRAP-UP	More Math Practice	**15** minutes	

Lesson Goals

- Review finding and estimating the length of an object to the nearest centimeter.
- Take a quiz.

MATERIALS

There are no materials to gather for this lesson.

GET READY

Introduction to Centimeters (C)

Students will read the lesson goals.

TRY IT

Review Centimeters

Students will answer questions to review what they have learned about centimeters.

QUIZ

Centimeters

Students will complete the Centimeters quiz.

WRAP-UP

More Math Practice

Students will practice skills according to their individual needs.

Length with Larger Objects (A)

Lesson Overview

ACTIVITY	ACTIVITY TITLE	TIME	ONLINE/OFFLINE
GET READY	Introduction to Length with Larger Objects (A)	**2** minutes	online
	Look Back at Measuring Length with More Than One Unit	**7** minutes	online
LEARN AND TRY IT	Measuring Length to the Nearest Foot or Yard	**7** minutes	online
	Measure Length to the Nearest Foot or Yard	**7** minutes	online
ALL ABOUT ME	Brain Break	**1** minute	online or offline
LEARN AND TRY IT	Measuring Length to the Nearest Meter	**7** minutes	online
	Measure Length to the Nearest Meter	**7** minutes	online
	Practice Measuring Length Using Longer Units	**20** minutes	online and offline
WRAP-UP	Measuring Length Using Longer Units	**2** minutes	online

Content Background

Students have measured objects in inches and centimeters. In this lesson, students will learn how to measure objects in feet, yards, and meters.

NOTE Examples and exercises in the lesson use representations of measuring tools that are scaled down to fit the screen or activity book pages. Students will build a better understanding of the relationships among inches, feet, and yards and between centimeters and meters through opportunities to measure objects in their own environments with real tools.

Systems of Measurement

Inches, feet, and yards belong to the English, or U.S. customary, system of measurement. Centimeters and meters belong to the metric system of measurement. Students will learn the following relationships in this course, but they are not expected to memorize them.

- There are 12 inches in 1 foot.
- There are 36 inches in 1 yard.
- There are 3 feet in 1 yard.
- There are 100 centimeters in 1 meter.

MATERIALS

Supplied

- *Math 2 Activity Book:* Practice Measuring Length Using Longer Units

KEYWORDS

foot – an English unit of length that equals 12 inches

meter – a metric unit of length that equals 100 centimeters

meterstick – a tool for measuring length in centimeters or meters

yard – an English unit of length that equals 36 inches or 3 feet

yardstick – a tool for measuring length in inches, feet, or yards

Measurement Technique

It is important to reposition the ruler, yardstick, or meterstick correctly when measuring objects that are longer than 1 foot, 1 yard, or 1 meter. For example, place the ruler to measure the first foot of a larger object. Touch the object at the 12-inch mark on the ruler, then move the ruler to line up the 0-inch mark to where you are touching the object. Continue until you have measured the entire length of the object.

Mixed Measurements

Some objects cannot be measured accurately to the nearest foot, yard, or meter, so you may need to use a combination of feet and inches, yards and inches, or meters and centimeters. For example, an object that measures 122 centimeters long is also 1 meter 22 centimeters long.

Lesson Goals

- Find the length of an object to the nearest foot.
- Find the length of an object to the nearest yard.
- Find the length of an object to the nearest meter.

GET READY

Introduction to Length with Larger Objects (A)

Students will get a glimpse of what they will learn about in the lesson. They will also read the lesson goals.

Look Back at Measuring Length with More Than One Unit

Students will review and practice the prerequisite skill of measuring length with more than one nonstandard unit.

LEARN AND TRY IT

LEARN Measuring Length to the Nearest Foot or Yard

Students will learn how to use various tools to measure the length of an object to the nearest foot or yard.

TRY IT Measure Length to the Nearest Foot or Yard

Students will practice measuring lengths of objects to the nearest foot or yard. Support will be provided to help students overcome misconceptions.

LEARN Measuring Length to the Nearest Meter

Students will learn how to use various tools to measure the length of an object to the nearest meter.

TRY IT Measure Length to the Nearest Meter

Students will practice measuring lengths of objects to the nearest meter. Support will be provided to help students overcome misconceptions.

TRY IT Practice Measuring Length Using Longer Units

Students will complete online practice problems. Then they will complete Practice Measuring Length Using Longer Units from *Math 2 Activity Book*.

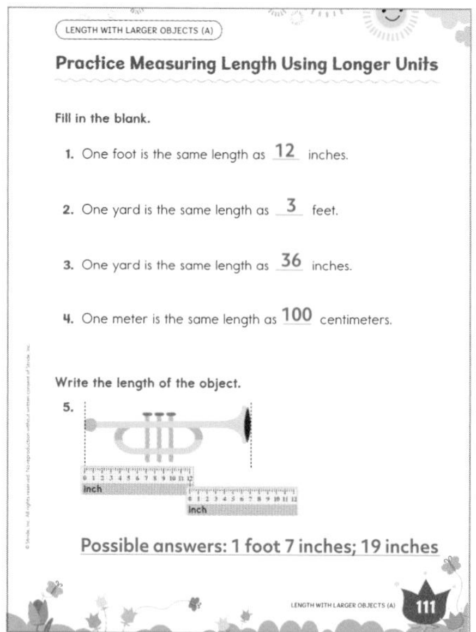

LENGTH WITH LARGER OBJECTS (A)

Practice Measuring Length Using Longer Units

Fill in the blank.

1. One foot is the same length as 12 inches.
2. One yard is the same length as 3 feet.
3. One yard is the same length as 36 inches.
4. One meter is the same length as 100 centimeters.

Write the length of the object.

5. Possible answers: 1 foot 7 inches; 19 inches

LENGTH WITH LARGER OBJECTS (A) 111

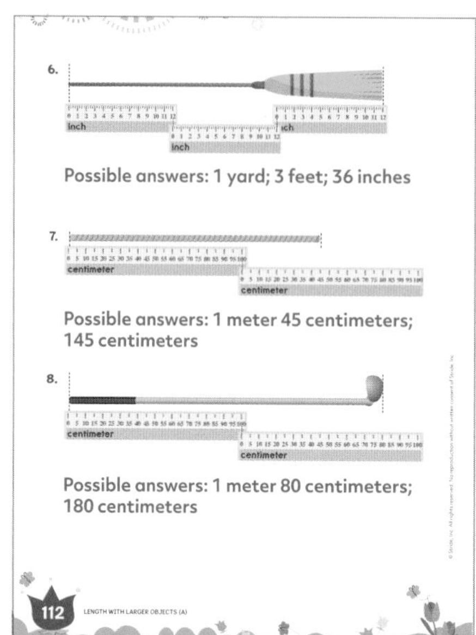

6. Possible answers: 1 yard; 3 feet; 36 inches

7. Possible answers: 1 meter 45 centimeters; 145 centimeters

8. Possible answers: 1 meter 80 centimeters; 180 centimeters

112 LENGTH WITH LARGER OBJECTS (A)

WRAP-UP

Measuring Length Using Longer Units

Students will solve problems to show that they understand how to measure the length of objects using longer units.

Length with Larger Objects (B)

Lesson Overview

ACTIVITY	ACTIVITY TITLE	TIME	ONLINE/OFFLINE
GET READY	Introduction to Length with Larger Objects (B)	**2** minutes	online
	Adding 8 Math Facts Game	**7** minutes	online
LEARN AND TRY IT	Estimating Longer Lengths	**15** minutes	online
	Estimate Longer Lengths	**10** minutes	online
ALL ABOUT ME	Brain Break	**1** minute	online or offline
TRY IT	Practice Estimating Longer Lengths	**20** minutes	online and offline
WRAP-UP	Estimating Longer Lengths	**5** minutes	online

Content Background

Students will learn how to estimate the length of an object to the nearest foot, yard, and meter. Students will also learn to choose the most reasonable estimate.

Use Objects to Estimate Length

Using an object to estimate gives an approximate length instead of an exact measurement. Here are some examples.

- A clipboard is about 1 foot long.
- A baseball bat is about 1 yard long.
- A guitar is about 1 meter long.

Students don't have to measure with an actual object to get an estimate. A common strategy is to imagine how many times an object would be used instead of actually using the object to measure longer lengths.

MATERIALS

Supplied

- *Math 2 Activity Book:* Practice Estimating Longer Lengths

Lesson Goals

- Estimate the length of an object to the nearest foot.
- Estimate the length of an object to the nearest yard.
- Estimate the length of an object to the nearest meter.

GET READY

Introduction to Length with Larger Objects (B)

Students will get a glimpse of what they will learn about in the lesson. They will also read the lesson goals.

Adding 8 Math Facts Game

Students will play a game to practice adding 8.

LEARN AND TRY IT

LEARN Estimating Longer Lengths

Students will learn how to estimate the length of an object to the nearest foot, yard, and meter.

TRY IT Estimate Longer Lengths

Students will practice estimating longer lengths. Support will be provided to help students overcome misconceptions.

TRY IT Practice Estimating Longer Lengths

Students will complete online practice problems. Then they will complete Practice Estimating Longer Lengths from *Math 2 Activity Book*.

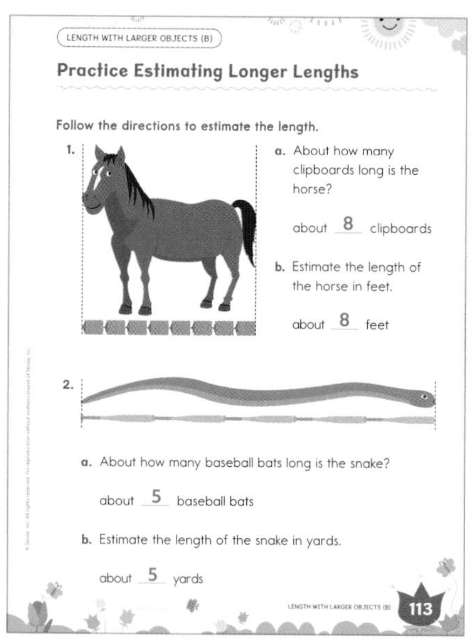

LENGTH WITH LARGER OBJECTS (B)

Practice Estimating Longer Lengths

Follow the directions to estimate the length.

1. a. About how many clipboards long is the horse?
   about 8 clipboards
   b. Estimate the length of the horse in feet.
   about 8 feet
2. a. About how many baseball bats long is the snake?
   about 5 baseball bats
   b. Estimate the length of the snake in yards.
   about 5 yards

LENGTH WITH LARGER OBJECTS (B) 113

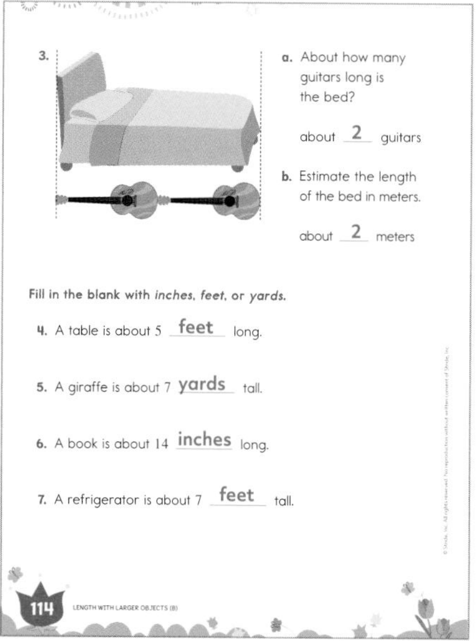

3. a. About how many guitars long is the bed?
   about 2 guitars
   b. Estimate the length of the bed in meters.
   about 2 meters

Fill in the blank with *inches, feet,* or *yards.*

4. A table is about 5 feet long.
5. A giraffe is about 7 yards tall.
6. A book is about 14 inches long.
7. A refrigerator is about 7 feet tall.

114 LENGTH WITH LARGER OBJECTS (B)

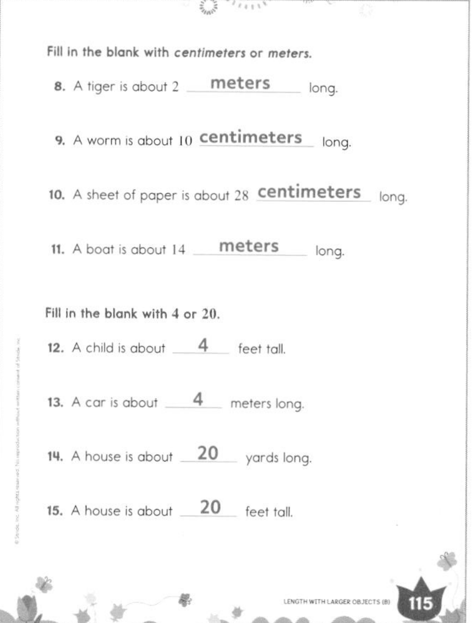

Fill in the blank with *centimeters* or *meters.*

8. A tiger is about 2 meters long.
9. A worm is about 10 centimeters long.
10. A sheet of paper is about 28 centimeters long.
11. A boat is about 14 meters long.

Fill in the blank with 4 or 20.

12. A child is about 4 feet tall.
13. A car is about 4 meters long.
14. A house is about 20 yards long.
15. A house is about 20 feet tall.

LENGTH WITH LARGER OBJECTS (B) 115

WRAP-UP

Estimating Longer Lengths

Students will solve problems to show that they understand how to estimate lengths to the nearest foot, yard, or meter.

Length with Larger Objects (C)

Lesson Overview

ACTIVITY	ACTIVITY TITLE	TIME	ONLINE/OFFLINE
GET READY	Introduction to Length with Larger Objects (C)	**2** minutes	
TRY IT	Review Length with Larger Objects	**18** minutes	
QUIZ	Length with Larger Objects	**25** minutes	
WRAP-UP	More Math Practice	**15** minutes	

Lesson Goals

- Review finding and estimating the length of an object to the nearest, foot, yard, or meter.
- Take a quiz.

MATERIALS

There are no materials to gather for this lesson.

GET READY

Introduction to Length with Larger Objects (C)

Students will read the lesson goals.

TRY IT

Review Length with Larger Objects

Students will answer questions to review what they have learned about length with larger objects.

QUIZ

Length with Larger Objects

Students will complete the Length with Larger Objects quiz.

WRAP-UP

More Math Practice

Students will practice skills according to their individual needs.

Length Story Problems (A)

Lesson Overview

ACTIVITY	ACTIVITY TITLE	TIME	ONLINE/OFFLINE
GET READY	Introduction to Length Story Problems (A)	**2** minutes	online
	Look Back at Solving Story Problems	**8** minutes	online
LEARN AND TRY IT	Adding to Solve Length Problems	**15** minutes	online
	Add to Solve Length Problems	**10** minutes	online
	Practice Adding to Solve Length Problems	**20** minutes	online and offline
WRAP-UP	Adding to Solve Length Problems	**5** minutes	online

Content Background

Students will learn how to solve story problems involving lengths that increase in inches or centimeters. Each problem in this lesson can be solved by adding two lengths.

MATERIALS

Supplied

- *Math 2 Activity Book:* Practice Adding to Solve Length Problems

Solving Length Story Problems

Students will follow these three steps for solving story problems in each lesson in this concept.

Understand it. Students can put a box around facts given in the problem and circle what they need to find. However, a drawing is often more useful than a list for recording details given in length problems. Students label the drawing with the lengths they know and a question mark for the length they need to find.

Plan it. Students use their drawing to write a number sentence that represents a plan to add or subtract in the next step.

Solve it. Students add or subtract to find the unknown value. Students may use any of the strategies they have learned for adding or subtracting two-digit numbers. Remind students to write a complete sentence to answer the original question in the story problem.

Lesson Goals

- Add to solve a length story problem.

GET READY

Introduction to Length Story Problems (A)

Students will get a glimpse of what they will learn about in the lesson. They will also read the lesson goals.

Look Back at Solving Story Problems

Students will review and practice the prerequisite skill of recognizing whether to add or subtract to solve a story problem.

LEARN AND TRY IT

LEARN Adding to Solve Length Problems

Students will learn how to add to solve length problems involving inches or centimeters.

TRY IT Add to Solve Length Problems

Students will practice adding to solve length problems involving inches or centimeters. Support will be provided to help students overcome misconceptions.

TRY IT Practice Adding to Solve Length Problems

Students will complete online practice problems. Then they will complete Practice Adding to Solve Length Problems from *Math 2 Activity Book*.

SUPPORT Remind students that drawing a model can help them understand the problem.

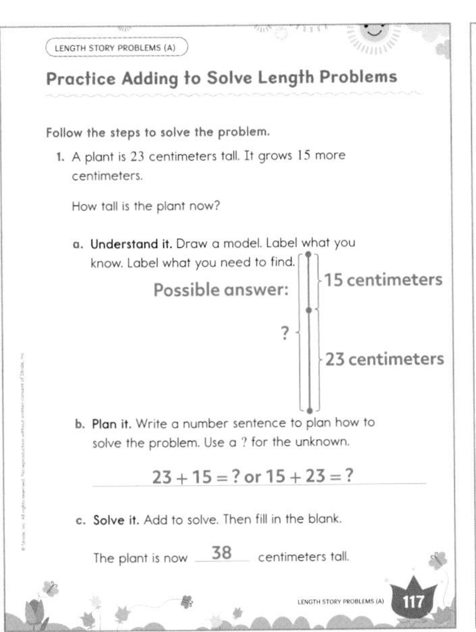

LENGTH STORY PROBLEMS (A)

Practice Adding to Solve Length Problems

Follow the steps to solve the problem.

1. A plant is 23 centimeters tall. It grows 15 more centimeters.

   How tall is the plant now?

   a. **Understand it.** Draw a model. Label what you know. Label what you need to find.

   Possible answer:

   15 centimeters

   ?

   23 centimeters

   b. **Plan it.** Write a number sentence to plan how to solve the problem. Use a ? for the unknown.

   23 + 15 = ? or 15 + 23 = ?

   c. **Solve it.** Add to solve. Then fill in the blank.

   The plant is now 38 centimeters tall.

LENGTH STORY PROBLEMS (A) 117

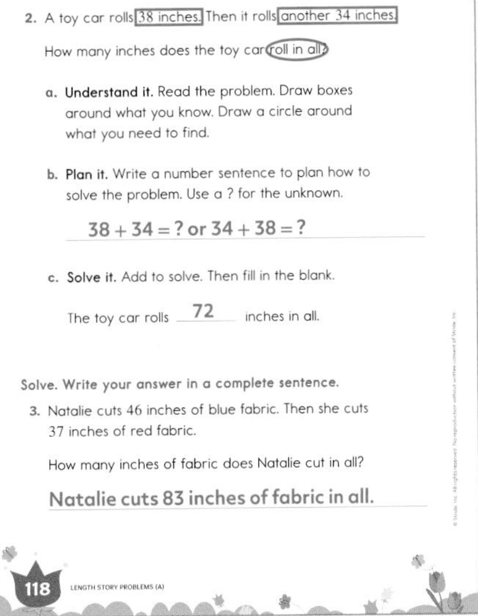

2. A toy car rolls 38 inches. Then it rolls another 34 inches.

   How many inches does the toy car roll in all?

   a. **Understand it.** Read the problem. Draw boxes around what you know. Draw a circle around what you need to find.

   b. **Plan it.** Write a number sentence to plan how to solve the problem. Use a ? for the unknown.

   38 + 34 = ? or 34 + 38 = ?

   c. **Solve it.** Add to solve. Then fill in the blank.

   The toy car rolls 72 inches in all.

Solve. Write your answer in a complete sentence.

3. Natalie cuts 46 inches of blue fabric. Then she cuts 37 inches of red fabric.

   How many inches of fabric does Natalie cut in all?

   Natalie cuts 83 inches of fabric in all.

118 LENGTH STORY PROBLEMS (A)

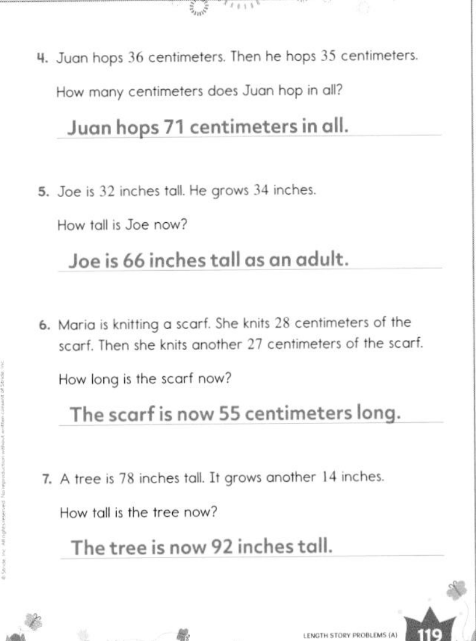

4. Juan hops 36 centimeters. Then he hops 35 centimeters.

   How many centimeters does Juan hop in all?

   Juan hops 71 centimeters in all.

5. Joe is 32 inches tall. He grows 34 inches.

   How tall is Joe now?

   Joe is 66 inches tall as an adult.

6. Maria is knitting a scarf. She knits 28 centimeters of the scarf. Then she knits another 27 centimeters of the scarf.

   How long is the scarf now?

   The scarf is now 55 centimeters long.

7. A tree is 78 inches tall. It grows another 14 inches.

   How tall is the tree now?

   The tree is now 92 inches tall.

LENGTH STORY PROBLEMS (A) 119

WRAP-UP

Adding to Solve Length Problems

Students will solve a problem to show that they understand how to add to solve a length problem involving inches or centimeters.

Length Story Problems (B)

Lesson Overview

ACTIVITY	ACTIVITY TITLE	TIME	ONLINE/OFFLINE
GET READY	Introduction to Length Story Problems (B)	**2** minutes	online
	Adding 9 Math Facts	**7** minutes	online
LEARN AND TRY IT	Subtracting to Solve Length Problems	**15** minutes	online
	Subtract to Solve Length Problems	**10** minutes	online
ALL ABOUT ME	Brain Break	**1** minute	online or offline
TRY IT	Practice Subtracting to Solve Length Problems	**20** minutes	online and offline
WRAP-UP	Subtracting to Solve Length Problems	**5** minutes	online

Content Background

Students will learn how to solve story problems involving lengths that decrease in inches or centimeters. Students will continue to follow the three steps for solving story problems: Understand it; Plan it; and Solve it. Each problem in this lesson can be solved by subtracting two lengths.

MATERIALS

Supplied

- *Math 2 Activity Book:* Practice Subtracting to Solve Length Problems

Lesson Goals

- Subtract to solve a length story problem.

GET READY

Introduction to Length Story Problems (B)

Students will get a glimpse of what they will learn about in the lesson. They will also read the lesson goals.

Adding 9 Math Facts

Students will practice adding 9.

LEARN AND TRY IT

LEARN Subtracting to Solve Length Problems

Students will learn how to subtract to solve length problems involving inches or centimeters.

TRY IT Subtract to Solve Length Problems

Students will practice subtracting to solve length problems involving inches or centimeters. Support will be provided to help students overcome misconceptions.

TRY IT Practice Subtracting to Solve Length Problems

Students will complete online practice problems. Then they will complete Practice Subtracting to Solve Length Problems from *Math 2 Activity Book*.

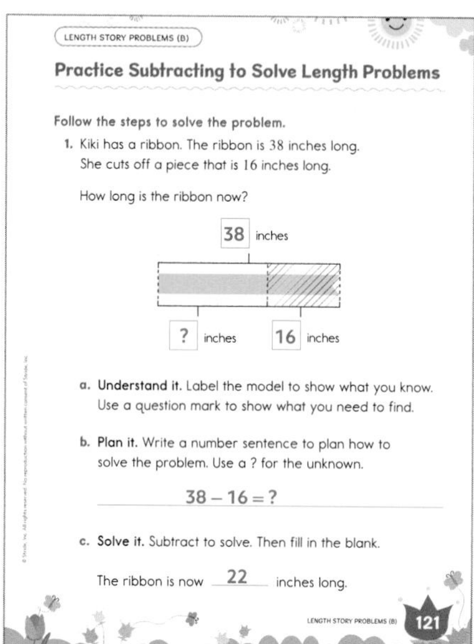

LENGTH STORY PROBLEMS (B)

Practice Subtracting to Solve Length Problems

Follow the steps to solve the problem.

1. Kiki has a ribbon. The ribbon is 38 inches long. She cuts off a piece that is 16 inches long.

   How long is the ribbon now?

   38 inches

   ? inches 16 inches

   a. **Understand it.** Label the model to show what you know. Use a question mark to show what you need to find.

   b. **Plan it.** Write a number sentence to plan how to solve the problem. Use a ? for the unknown.

   38 – 16 = ?

   c. **Solve it.** Subtract to solve. Then fill in the blank.

   The ribbon is now 22 inches long.

LENGTH STORY PROBLEMS (B) 121

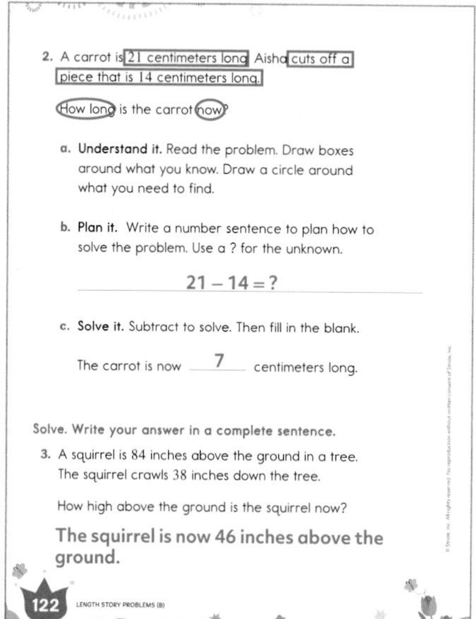

2. A carrot is 21 centimeters long. Aisha cuts off a piece that is 14 centimeters long.

   How long is the carrot now?

   a. **Understand it.** Read the problem. Draw boxes around what you know. Draw a circle around what you need to find.

   b. **Plan it.** Write a number sentence to plan how to solve the problem. Use a ? for the unknown.

   21 – 14 = ?

   c. **Solve it.** Subtract to solve. Then fill in the blank.

   The carrot is now 7 centimeters long.

Solve. Write your answer in a complete sentence.

3. A squirrel is 84 inches above the ground in a tree. The squirrel crawls 38 inches down the tree.

   How high above the ground is the squirrel now?

   The squirrel is now 46 inches above the ground.

122 LENGTH STORY PROBLEMS (B)

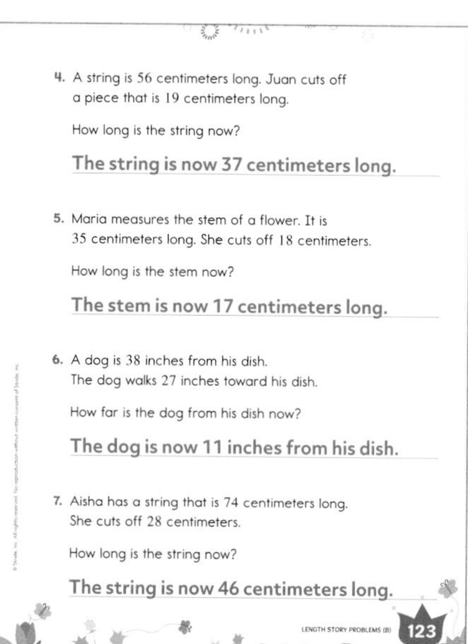

4. A string is 56 centimeters long. Juan cuts off a piece that is 19 centimeters long.

   How long is the string now?

   The string is now 37 centimeters long.

5. Maria measures the stem of a flower. It is 35 centimeters long. She cuts off 18 centimeters.

   How long is the stem now?

   The stem is now 17 centimeters long.

6. A dog is 38 inches from his dish. The dog walks 27 inches toward his dish.

   How far is the dog from his dish now?

   The dog is now 11 inches from his dish.

7. Aisha has a string that is 74 centimeters long. She cuts off 28 centimeters.

   How long is the string now?

   The string is now 46 centimeters long.

LENGTH STORY PROBLEMS (B) 123

WRAP-UP

Subtracting to Solve Length Problems

Students will solve a problem to show that they understand how to subtract to solve a length problem involving inches or centimeters.

Length Story Problems (C)

Lesson Overview

ACTIVITY	ACTIVITY TITLE	TIME	ONLINE/OFFLINE
GET READY	Introduction to Length Story Problems (C)	**2** minutes	online
	Adding 9 with Instant Recall	**8** minutes	online
LEARN AND **TRY IT**	Adding to Solve Longer Length Problems	**15** minutes	online
	Add to Solve Longer Length Problems	**10** minutes	online
	Practice Adding to Solve Longer Length Problems	**20** minutes	online and offline
WRAP-UP	Adding to Solve Longer Length Problems	**5** minutes	online

Content Background

Students will learn how to solve story problems involving lengths that increase in feet or meters. Students will continue to follow the three steps for solving story problems: Understand it; Plan it; and Solve it. Each problem in this lesson can be solved by adding two lengths.

MATERIALS

Supplied

- *Math 2 Activity Book:* Practice Adding to Solve Longer Length Problems

Lesson Goals

- Add to solve length story problems.

GET READY

Introduction to Length Story Problems (C)

Students will get a glimpse of what they will learn about in the lesson. They will also read the lesson goals.

Adding 9 with Instant Recall

Students will practice adding 9.

LEARN AND TRY IT

LEARN Adding to Solve Longer Length Problems

Students will learn how to add to solve length problems involving feet or meters.

TRY IT Add to Solve Longer Length Problems

Students will practice adding to solve length problems involving feet or meters. Support will be provided to help students overcome misconceptions.

TRY IT Practice Adding to Solve Longer Length Problems

Students will complete online practice problems. Then they will complete Practice Adding to Solve Longer Length Problems from *Math 2 Activity Book.Book*.

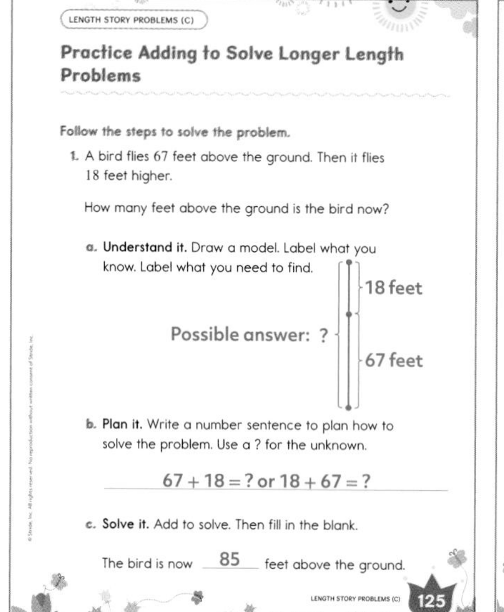

LENGTH STORY PROBLEMS (C)

Practice Adding to Solve Longer Length Problems

Follow the steps to solve the problem.

1. A bird flies 67 feet above the ground. Then it flies 18 feet higher.

   How many feet above the ground is the bird now?

   a. **Understand it.** Draw a model. Label what you know. Label what you need to find.

   Possible answer: ? 18 feet 67 feet

   b. **Plan it.** Write a number sentence to plan how to solve the problem. Use a ? for the unknown.

   67 + 18 = ? or 18 + 67 = ?

   c. **Solve it.** Add to solve. Then fill in the blank.

   The bird is now 85 feet above the ground.

LENGTH STORY PROBLEMS (C) 125

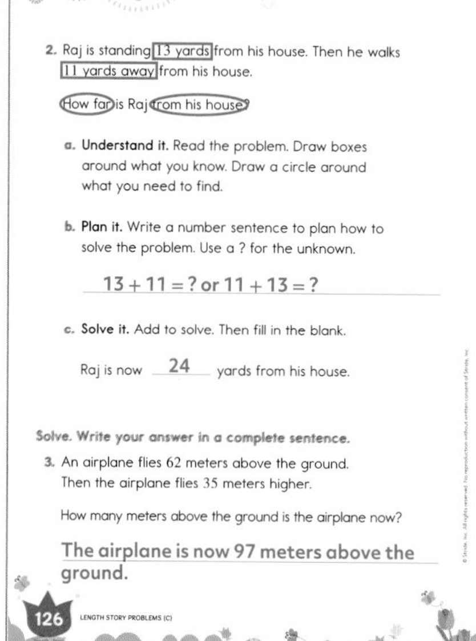

2. Raj is standing 13 yards from his house. Then he walks 11 yards away from his house.

   How far is Raj from his house?

   a. **Understand it.** Read the problem. Draw boxes around what you know. Draw a circle around what you need to find.

   b. **Plan it.** Write a number sentence to plan how to solve the problem. Use a ? for the unknown.

   13 + 11 = ? or 11 + 13 = ?

   c. **Solve it.** Add to solve. Then fill in the blank.

   Raj is now 24 yards from his house.

Solve. Write your answer in a complete sentence.

3. An airplane flies 62 meters above the ground. Then the airplane flies 35 meters higher.

   How many meters above the ground is the airplane now?

   The airplane is now 97 meters above the ground.

126 LENGTH STORY PROBLEMS (C)

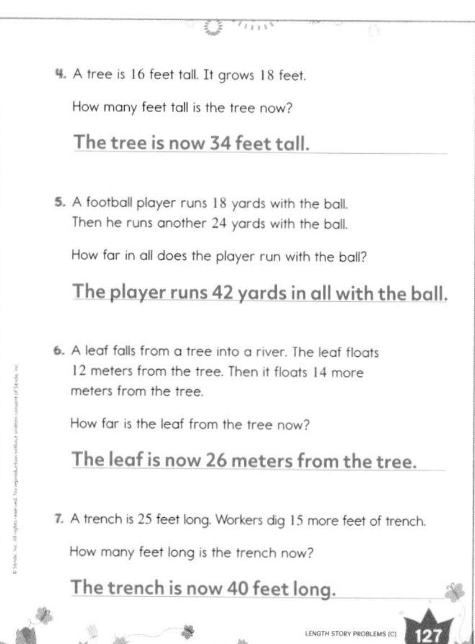

4. A tree is 16 feet tall. It grows 18 feet.

   How many feet tall is the tree now?

   The tree is now 34 feet tall.

5. A football player runs 18 yards with the ball. Then he runs another 24 yards with the ball.

   How far in all does the player run with the ball?

   The player runs 42 yards in all with the ball.

6. A leaf falls from a tree into a river. The leaf floats 12 meters from the tree. Then it floats 14 more meters from the tree.

   How far is the leaf from the tree now?

   The leaf is now 26 meters from the tree.

7. A trench is 25 feet long. Workers dig 15 more feet of trench.

   How many feet long is the trench now?

   The trench is now 40 feet long.

LENGTH STORY PROBLEMS (C) 127

WRAP-UP

Adding to Solve Longer Length Problems

Students will solve a problem to show that they understand how to add to solve a length problem involving feet or meters.

Length Story Problems (D)

Lesson Overview

ACTIVITY	ACTIVITY TITLE	TIME	ONLINE/OFFLINE
GET READY	Introduction to Length Story Problems (D)	**2** minutes	online
	Adding 9 Math Facts Game	**7** minutes	online
LEARN AND TRY IT	Subtracting to Solve Longer Length Problems	**15** minutes	online
	Subtract to Solve Longer Length Problems	**10** minutes	online
ALL ABOUT ME	Brain Break	**1** minute	online or offline
TRY IT	Practice Subtracting to Solve Longer Length Problems	**20** minutes	online and offline
WRAP-UP	Subtracting to Solve Longer Length Problems	**5** minutes	online

Content Background

Students will learn how to solve story problems involving lengths that decrease in feet or meters. Students will continue to follow the three steps for solving story problems: Understand it; Plan it; and Solve it. Each problem in this lesson can be solved by subtracting two lengths.

MATERIALS

Supplied

- *Math 2 Activity Book:* Practice Subtracting to Solve Longer Length Problems

Lesson Goals

- Subtract to solve length story problems.

GET READY

Introduction to Length Story Problems (D)

Students will get a glimpse of what they will learn about in the lesson. They will also read the lesson goals.

Adding 9 Math Facts Game

Students will play a game to practice adding 9.

LEARN AND TRY IT

LEARN Subtracting to Solve Longer Length Problems

Students will learn how to subtract to solve length problems involving feet or meters.

TRY IT Subtract to Solve Longer Length Problems

Students will practice subtracting to solve length problems involving feet or meters. Support will be provided to help students overcome misconceptions.

TRY IT Practice Subtracting to Solve Longer Length Problems

Students will complete online practice problems. Then they will complete Practice Subtracting to Solve Longer Length Problems from *Math 2 Activity Book*.

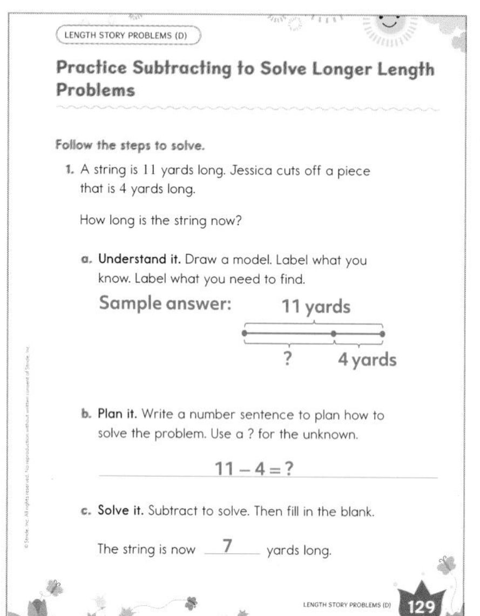

LENGTH STORY PROBLEMS (D)

Practice Subtracting to Solve Longer Length Problems

Follow the steps to solve.

1. A string is 11 yards long. Jessica cuts off a piece that is 4 yards long.

   How long is the string now?

   a. **Understand it.** Draw a model. Label what you know. Label what you need to find.

   Sample answer: 11 yards; ? 4 yards

   b. **Plan it.** Write a number sentence to plan how to solve the problem. Use a ? for the unknown.

   $11 - 4 = ?$

   c. **Solve it.** Subtract to solve. Then fill in the blank.

   The string is now __7__ yards long.

LENGTH STORY PROBLEMS (D) 129

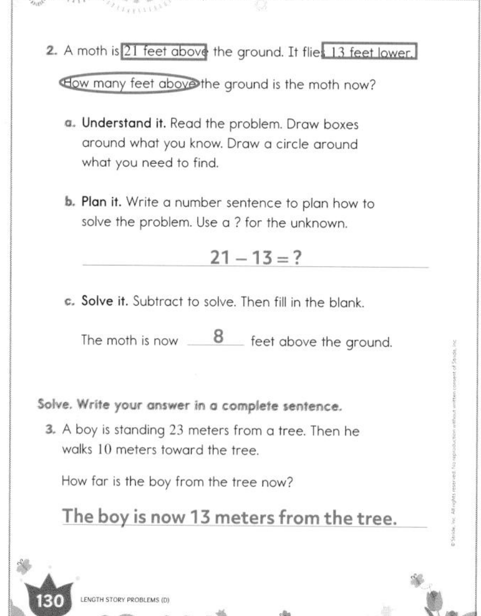

2. A moth is 21 feet above the ground. It flies 13 feet lower.

   How many feet above the ground is the moth now?

   a. **Understand it.** Read the problem. Draw boxes around what you know. Draw a circle around what you need to find.

   b. **Plan it.** Write a number sentence to plan how to solve the problem. Use a ? for the unknown.

   $21 - 13 = ?$

   c. **Solve it.** Subtract to solve. Then fill in the blank.

   The moth is now __8__ feet above the ground.

Solve. Write your answer in a complete sentence.

3. A boy is standing 23 meters from a tree. Then he walks 10 meters toward the tree.

   How far is the boy from the tree now?

   The boy is now 13 meters from the tree.

130 LENGTH STORY PROBLEMS (D)

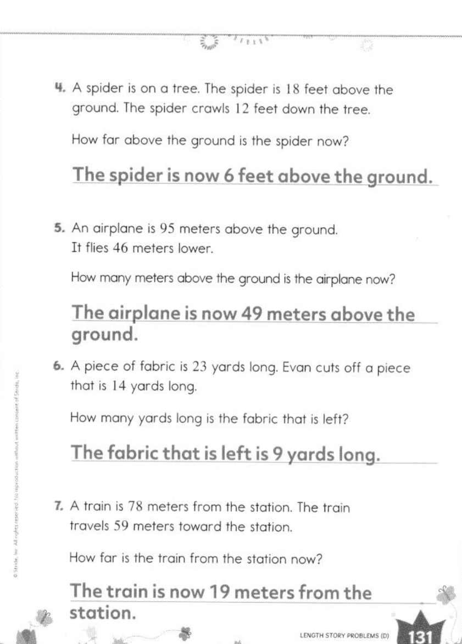

4. A spider is on a tree. The spider is 18 feet above the ground. The spider crawls 12 feet down the tree.

   How far above the ground is the spider now?

   The spider is now 6 feet above the ground.

5. An airplane is 95 meters above the ground. It flies 46 meters lower.

   How many meters above the ground is the airplane now?

   The airplane is now 49 meters above the ground.

6. A piece of fabric is 23 yards long. Evan cuts off a piece that is 14 yards long.

   How many yards long is the fabric that is left?

   The fabric that is left is 9 yards long.

7. A train is 78 meters from the station. The train travels 59 meters toward the station.

   How far is the train from the station now?

   The train is now 19 meters from the station.

LENGTH STORY PROBLEMS (D) 131

WRAP-UP

Subtracting to Solve Longer Length Problems

Students will solve a problem to show that they understand how to subtract to solve a length problem involving feet or meters.

Length Story Problems (E)

Lesson Overview

ACTIVITY	ACTIVITY TITLE	TIME	ONLINE/OFFLINE
GET READY	Introduction to Length Story Problems (E)	**2** minutes	online
TRY IT	Review Length Story Problems	**18** minutes	online
QUIZ	Length Story Problems	**25** minutes	online
WRAP-UP	More Math Practice	**15** minutes	online

Lesson Goals

- Review adding and subtracting to solve length story problems.
- Take a quiz.

MATERIALS

There are no materials to gather for this lesson.

GET READY

Introduction to Length Story Problems (E)

Students will read the lesson goals.

TRY IT

Review Length Story Problems

Students will answer questions to review what they have learned about solving length story problems.

QUIZ

Length Story Problems

Students will complete the Length Story Problems quiz.

WRAP-UP

More Math Practice

Students will practice skills according to their individual needs.

Compare Measurements (A)

Lesson Overview

ACTIVITY	ACTIVITY TITLE	TIME	ONLINE/OFFLINE
GET READY	Introduction to Compare Measurements (A)	**2** minutes	online
	Look Back at Comparing Measurements	**7** minutes	online
LEARN AND TRY IT	Comparing Customary Units	**7** minutes	online
	Compare Customary Units	**7** minutes	online
ALL ABOUT ME	Brain Break	**1** minute	online or offline
LEARN AND TRY IT	Comparing Metric Units	**7** minutes	online
	Compare Metric Units	**7** minutes	online
	Practice Comparing Units	**20** minutes	online and offline
WRAP-UP	Comparing Units	**2** minutes	online

Content Background

Students will learn to measure an object using more than one unit and compare those measurements. Students will measure one object in both a smaller unit and a larger unit, such as inches and feet or centimeters and meters.

Same Length, Different Units

More smaller units are needed to measure the same length in a larger unit. Fewer longer units are needed to measure the same length in a smaller unit. For example, 24 inches and 2 feet are the same length. More inches are needed to measure the same distance in feet because an inch is smaller than a foot. Three meters and 300 centimeters are the same length. Fewer meters are needed to measure the same distance in centimeters because a meter is longer than a centimeter.

MATERIALS

Supplied

- *Math 2 Activity Book:* Practice Comparing Units

Lesson Goals

- Measure one length with two units.
- Compare a length measured with two units.

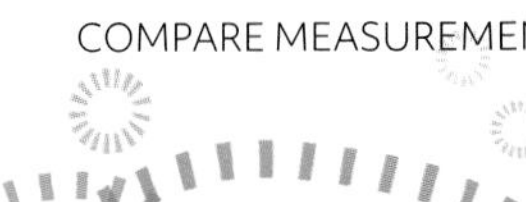

GET READY

Introduction to Compare Measurements (A)

Students will get a glimpse of what they will learn about in the lesson. They will also read the lesson goals.

Look Back at Comparing Measurements

Students will review and practice the prerequisite skill of comparing the length of an object measured in different nonstandard units.

LEARN AND TRY IT

LEARN Comparing Customary Units

Students will learn how to measure an object in more than one customary unit and describe how those units compare.

OPTIONAL Examples and exercises in the lesson use representations of measuring tools that are scaled down to fit the screen or workbook pages. Students will benefit from using a tape measure, 12-inch ruler, or yardstick to measure real objects in their own environment. Have them measure one object in two different units and then compare the measurements.

TRY IT Compare Customary Units

Students will practice comparing lengths they measure with customary units. Support will be provided to help students overcome misconceptions.

LEARN Comparing Metric Units

Students will learn how to measure an object in more than one metric unit and describe how those units compare.

OPTIONAL Examples and exercises in the lesson use representations of measuring tools that are scaled down to fit the screen or workbook pages. Students will benefit from using a centimeter tape measure or meterstick to measure real objects in their own environment. Have them measure one object in two different units and then compare the measurements.

TRY IT Compare Metric Units

Students will practice comparing lengths they measure with metric units. Support will be provided to help students overcome misconceptions.

TRY IT Practice Comparing Units

Students will complete online practice problems. Then they will complete Practice Comparing Units from *Math 2 Activity Book*.

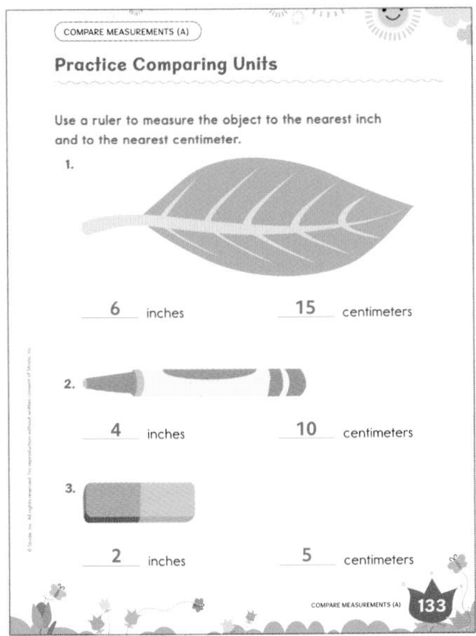
COMPARE MEASUREMENTS (A)

Practice Comparing Units

Use a ruler to measure the object to the nearest inch and to the nearest centimeter.

1. 6 inches 15 centimeters
2. 4 inches 10 centimeters
3. 2 inches 5 centimeters

COMPARE MEASUREMENTS (A) 133

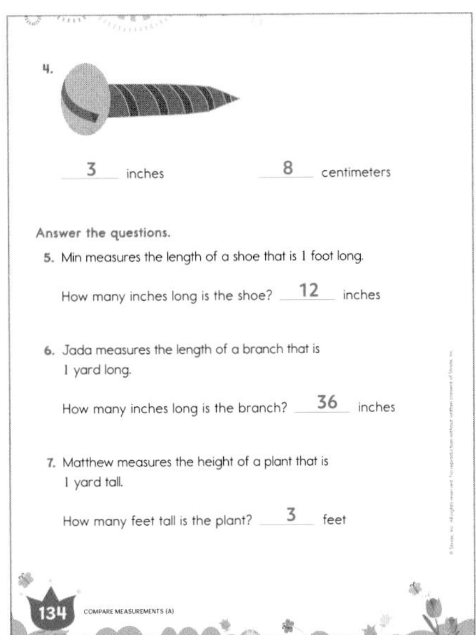
4. 3 inches 8 centimeters

Answer the questions.

5. Min measures the length of a shoe that is 1 foot long.
   How many inches long is the shoe? 12 inches
6. Jada measures the length of a branch that is 1 yard long.
   How many inches long is the branch? 36 inches
7. Matthew measures the height of a plant that is 1 yard tall.
   How many feet tall is the plant? 3 feet

134 COMPARE MEASUREMENTS (A)

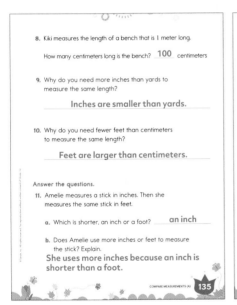

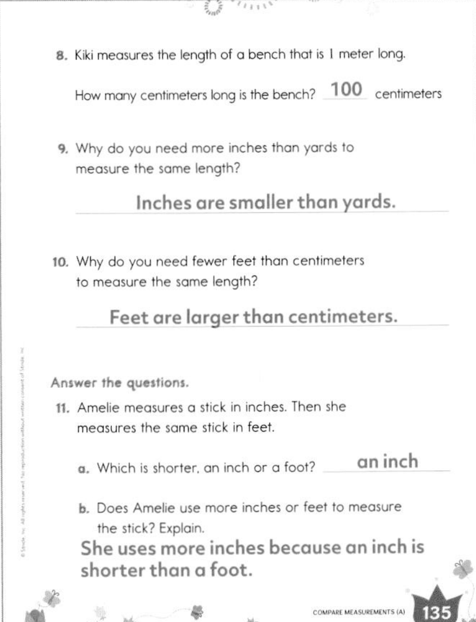
8. Kiki measures the length of a bench that is 1 meter long.
   How many centimeters long is the bench? 100 centimeters
9. Why do you need more inches than yards to measure the same length?
   Inches are smaller than yards.
10. Why do you need fewer feet than centimeters to measure the same length?
    Feet are larger than centimeters.

Answer the questions.

11. Amelie measures a stick in inches. Then she measures the same stick in feet.
    a. Which is shorter, an inch or a foot? an inch
    b. Does Amelie use more inches or feet to measure the stick? Explain.
    She uses more inches because an inch is shorter than a foot.

COMPARE MEASUREMENTS (A) 135

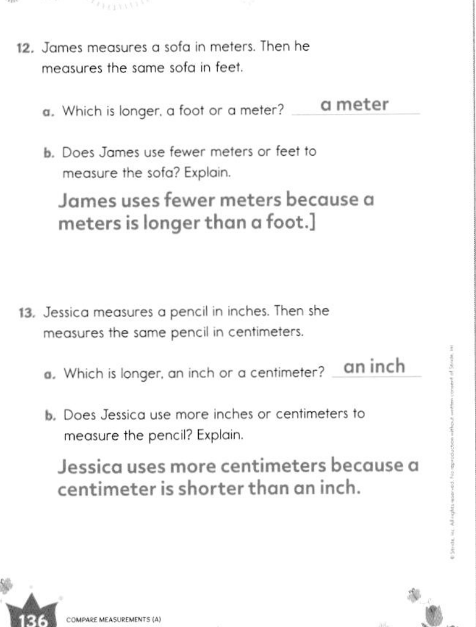
12. James measures a sofa in meters. Then he measures the same sofa in feet.
    a. Which is longer, a foot or a meter? a meter
    b. Does James use fewer meters or feet to measure the sofa? Explain.
    James uses fewer meters because a meters is longer than a foot.]
13. Jessica measures a pencil in inches. Then she measures the same pencil in centimeters.
    a. Which is longer, an inch or a centimeter? an inch
    b. Does Jessica use more inches or centimeters to measure the pencil? Explain.
    Jessica uses more centimeters because a centimeter is shorter than an inch.

136 COMPARE MEASUREMENTS (A)

WRAP-UP

Comparing Units

Students will solve problems to show that they understand how to compare measurements of the same length using different units.

Compare Measurements (B)

Lesson Overview

ACTIVITY	ACTIVITY TITLE	TIME	ONLINE/OFFLINE
GET READY	Introduction to Compare Measurements (B)	**2** minutes	online
	Subtracting 0 and 1 Math Facts	**7** minutes	online
LEARN AND **TRY IT**	Comparing Customary Lengths	**7** minutes	online
	Compare Customary Lengths	**7** minutes	online
ALL ABOUT ME	Brain Break	**1** minute	online or offline
LEARN AND **TRY IT**	Comparing Metric Lengths	**7** minutes	online
	Compare Metric Lengths	**7** minutes	online
	Practice Comparing Lengths of Two Objects	**20** minutes	online and offline
WRAP-UP	Comparing Lengths	**2** minutes	online

Content Background

Students will learn to compare the lengths of two objects measured using the same unit of measurement. Sometimes students will be given two objects that they must measure before comparing. Other times, lengths may be given in a story problem. For these problems, students will continue to follow the three steps for solving story problems: Understand it; Plan it; and Solve it.

Same Unit, Different Lengths

Lengths that are measured in the same unit can be compared to find how much longer or shorter one object is than the other. The difference between two lengths can be found by subtracting the smaller length from the larger length.

MATERIALS

Supplied

- *Math 2 Activity Book:* Practice Comparing Lengths of Two Objects

Lesson Goals

- Measure to compare two lengths.

GET READY

Introduction to Compare Measurements (B)

Students will get a glimpse of what they will learn about in the lesson. They will also read the lesson goals.

Subtracting 0 and 1 Math Facts

Students will practice subtracting 0 and 1.

LEARN AND TRY IT

LEARN Comparing Customary Lengths

Students will compare the lengths of two objects measured in customary units.

TRY IT Compare Customary Lengths

Students will practice comparing the lengths of two objects measured in customary units. Support will be provided to help students overcome misconceptions.

TIP Provide extra practice with this skill by having students measure objects at home with a ruler or tape measure. Then have students compare the lengths of different objects measured with the same unit.

LEARN Comparing Metric Lengths

Students will compare the lengths of two objects measured in metric units.

TRY IT Compare Metric Lengths

Students will practice comparing the lengths of two objects measured in metric units. Support will be provided to help students overcome misconceptions.

TIP Provide extra practice with this skill by having students measure objects at home with a ruler or meterstick. Then have students compare the lengths of different objects measured with the same unit.

TRY IT Practice Comparing Lengths of Two Objects

Students will complete online practice problems. Then they will complete Practice Comparing Lengths of Two Objects from *Math 2 Activity Book*.

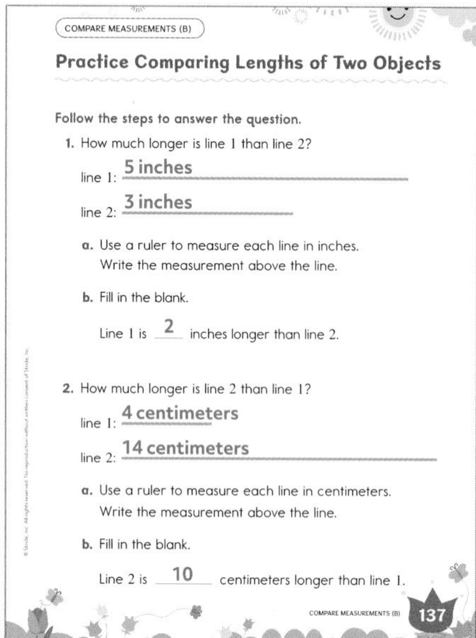

COMPARE MEASUREMENTS (B)

Practice Comparing Lengths of Two Objects

Follow the steps to answer the question.

1. How much longer is line 1 than line 2?

   line 1: 5 inches

   line 2: 3 inches

   a. Use a ruler to measure each line in inches. Write the measurement above the line.

   b. Fill in the blank.

   Line 1 is 2 inches longer than line 2.

2. How much longer is line 2 than line 1?

   line 1: 4 centimeters

   line 2: 14 centimeters

   a. Use a ruler to measure each line in centimeters. Write the measurement above the line.

   b. Fill in the blank.

   Line 2 is 10 centimeters longer than line 1.

COMPARE MEASUREMENTS (B) 137

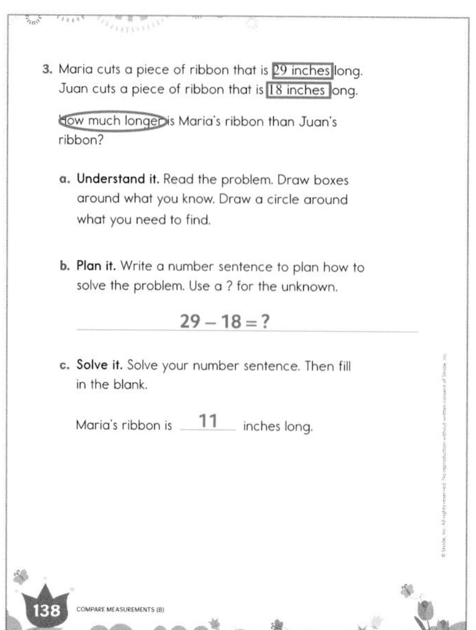

3. Maria cuts a piece of ribbon that is 29 inches long. Juan cuts a piece of ribbon that is 18 inches long.

   How much longer is Maria's ribbon than Juan's ribbon?

   a. Understand it. Read the problem. Draw boxes around what you know. Draw a circle around what you need to find.

   b. Plan it. Write a number sentence to plan how to solve the problem. Use a ? for the unknown.

   $29 - 18 = ?$

   c. Solve it. Solve your number sentence. Then fill in the blank.

   Maria's ribbon is 11 inches long.

138 COMPARE MEASUREMENTS (B)

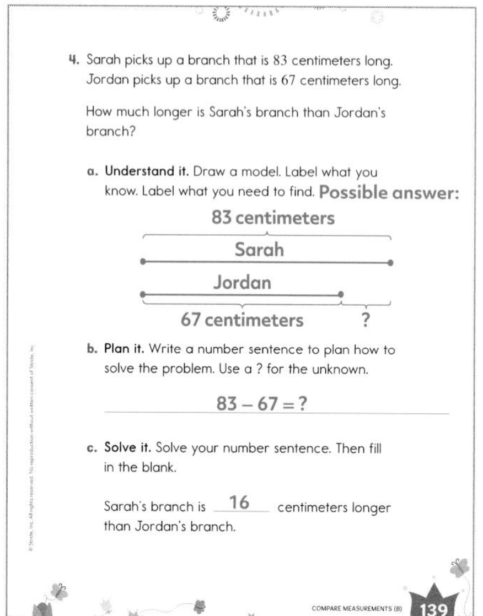

4. Sarah picks up a branch that is 83 centimeters long. Jordan picks up a branch that is 67 centimeters long.

   How much longer is Sarah's branch than Jordan's branch?

   a. Understand it. Draw a model. Label what you know. Label what you need to find. **Possible answer:**

   83 centimeters
   Sarah
   Jordan
   67 centimeters ?

   b. Plan it. Write a number sentence to plan how to solve the problem. Use a ? for the unknown.

   $83 - 67 = ?$

   c. Solve it. Solve your number sentence. Then fill in the blank.

   Sarah's branch is 16 centimeters longer than Jordan's branch.

COMPARE MEASUREMENTS (B) 139

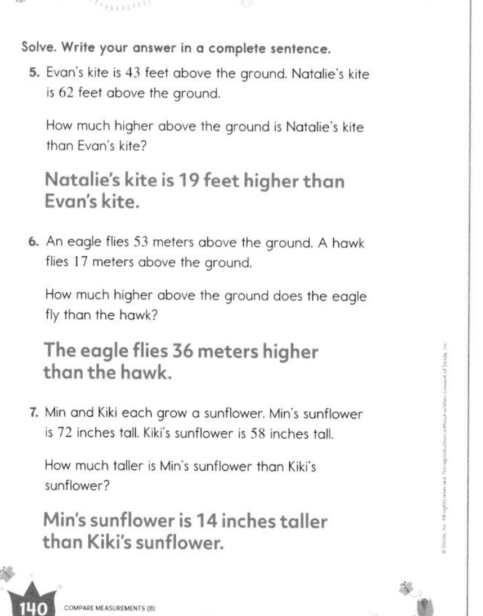

Solve. Write your answer in a complete sentence.

5. Evan's kite is 43 feet above the ground. Natalie's kite is 62 feet above the ground.

   How much higher above the ground is Natalie's kite than Evan's kite?

   Natalie's kite is 19 feet higher than Evan's kite.

6. An eagle flies 53 meters above the ground. A hawk flies 17 meters above the ground.

   How much higher above the ground does the eagle fly than the hawk?

   The eagle flies 36 meters higher than the hawk.

7. Min and Kiki each grow a sunflower. Min's sunflower is 72 inches tall. Kiki's sunflower is 58 inches tall.

   How much taller is Min's sunflower than Kiki's sunflower?

   Min's sunflower is 14 inches taller than Kiki's sunflower.

140 COMPARE MEASUREMENTS (B)

WRAP-UP

Comparing Lengths

Students will solve a problem to show that they understand how to compare lengths measured using the same unit.

Compare Measurements (C)

Lesson Overview

ACTIVITY	ACTIVITY TITLE	TIME	ONLINE/OFFLINE
GET READY	Introduction to Compare Measurements (C)	**2** minutes	
TRY IT	Review Compare Measurements	**18** minutes	
QUIZ	Compare Measurements	**25** minutes	
WRAP-UP	More Math Practice	**15** minutes	

Lesson Goals

- Review comparing units and lengths.
- Take a quiz.

MATERIALS

There are no materials to gather for this lesson.

GET READY

Introduction to Compare Measurements (C)

Students will read the lesson goals.

TRY IT

Review Compare Measurements

Students will answer questions to review what they have learned about how to compare measurements.

QUIZ

Compare Measurements

Students will complete the Compare Measurements quiz.

WRAP-UP

More Math Practice

Students will practice skills according to their individual needs.

Working with Length Wrap-Up

Lesson Overview

ACTIVITY	ACTIVITY TITLE	TIME	ONLINE/OFFLINE
GET READY	Introduction to Working with Length Wrap-Up	**2** minutes	
TRY IT	Review Working with Length	**23** minutes	
UNIT CHECKPOINT	Working with Length	**35** minutes	

Lesson Goals

- Review working with length.
- Show what you know about working with length.

MATERIALS

There are no materials to gather for this lesson.

GET READY

Introduction to Working with Length Wrap-Up

Students will read the lesson goals.

TRY IT

Review Working with Length

Students will answer questions to review what they have learned about working with length.

UNIT CHECKPOINT

Working with Length

Students will complete the Working with Length Unit Checkpoint.

LEARNING COACH CHECK-IN This is a graded assignment. Make sure students complete the online assessment.

Solve Story Problems with One Step

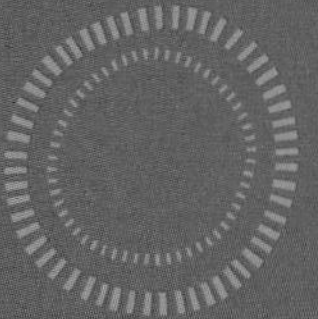

Solve Combine Story Problems (A)

Lesson Overview

ACTIVITY	ACTIVITY TITLE	TIME	ONLINE/OFFLINE
GET READY	Introduction to Solve Combine Story Problems (A)	**2** minutes	online
	Look Back at Solving Combine Story Problems	**7** minutes	online
LEARN AND TRY IT	Putting Together to Find the Total	**15** minutes	online
	Put Together to Find the Total	**10** minutes	online
ALL ABOUT ME	Brain Break	**1** minute	online or offline
TRY IT	Practice Putting Together to Find the Total	**20** minutes	online and offline
WRAP-UP	Putting Together to Find the Total	**5** minutes	online

Content Background

Students will be introduced to story problems that involve combining two amounts to find a total. The combine story problems in this lesson all follow the same pattern. Each problem will give two amounts that are combined, and students must find the total. This type of combine problem is sometimes called a *put-together* problem.

NOTE Students will not be expected to identify a story problem as a combine problem or a put-together problem. However, they will be expected to read a story problem and recognize that two amounts should be added to find a total.

Story Problem Steps

Students will learn to follow the three story problem steps to solve each problem.

Understand It: Students can put a box around facts given in the problem and circle what they need to find. Students can also draw and fill in a part-part-whole chart to organize the information in the story problem.

Plan It: Students can use the given information or the part-part-whole chart to write a number sentence that represents a plan to add or subtract in the next step.

Solve It: Students add or subtract to find the unknown value. Students may use any strategy they learned for adding and subtracting two-digit numbers. Remind students to write a complete sentence to answer the original question in the story problem.

MATERIALS

Supplied

- *Math 2 Activity Book:* Practice Putting Together to Find the Total

Find the Total

A part-part-whole chart is a convenient way to organize information given in combine story problems. It is a visual representation that the two parts combined are the same as the total or whole amount. Here is an example of finding the total in a put-together story problem and the related part-part-whole chart.

Jan has 38 buttons.
Kelly has 15 buttons.
How many buttons do they have in all?

?	
38	15

Notice that a question mark represents the total or whole amount that students must find. Students could use this chart to write the number sentence $38 + 15 = ?$ as a plan to solve the problem.

NOTE A question mark is not the only symbol that can be used to represent the unknown. Students can use other symbols, such as a small square or triangle.

Lesson Goals

- Find the total in a put-together story problem.

GET READY

Introduction to Solve Combine Story Problems (A)

Students will get a glimpse of what they will learn about in the lesson. They will also read the lesson goals.

Look Back at Solving Combine Story Problems

Students will review and practice the prerequisite skill of solving put-together and take-apart story problems.

LEARN AND TRY IT

LEARN Putting Together to Find the Total

Students will learn how to solve story problems by putting amounts together to find the total.

TRY IT Put Together to Find the Total

Students will practice solving story problems by putting amounts together to find the total. Support will be provided to help students overcome misconceptions.

TIP Discourage students from trying to solve the problems in their heads. Encourage them to work out each problem on paper. This will help students develop good habits, as well as help them solve the problems correctly.

TRY IT Practice Putting Together to Find the Total

Students will complete online practice problems. Then they will complete Practice Putting Together to Find the Total from *Math 2 Activity Book*.

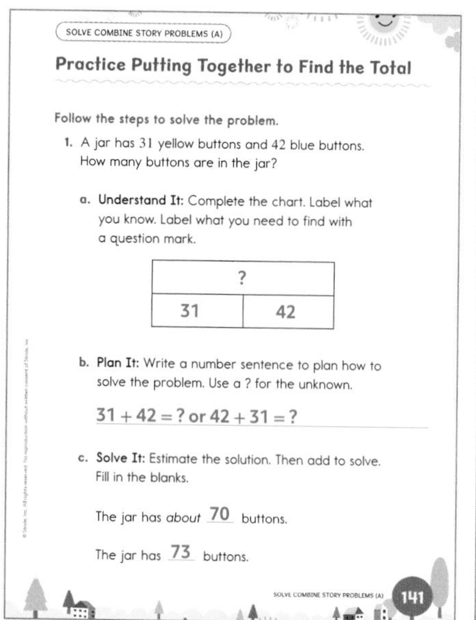

SOLVE COMBINE STORY PROBLEMS (A)

Practice Putting Together to Find the Total

Follow the steps to solve the problem.

1. A jar has 31 yellow buttons and 42 blue buttons. How many buttons are in the jar?

   a. **Understand It:** Complete the chart. Label what you know. Label what you need to find with a question mark.

?	
31	42

   b. **Plan It:** Write a number sentence to plan how to solve the problem. Use a ? for the unknown.

   31 + 42 = ? or 42 + 31 = ?

   c. **Solve It:** Estimate the solution. Then add to solve. Fill in the blanks.

   The jar has *about* 70 buttons.

   The jar has 73 buttons.

SOLVE COMBINE STORY PROBLEMS (A) 141

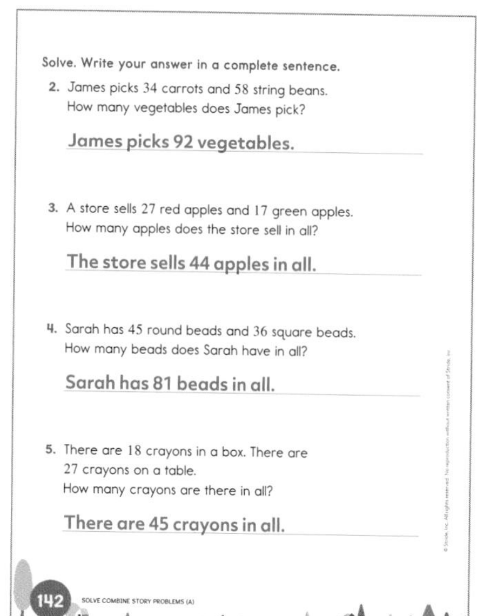

Solve. Write your answer in a complete sentence.

2. James picks 34 carrots and 58 string beans. How many vegetables does James pick?

   James picks 92 vegetables.

3. A store sells 27 red apples and 17 green apples. How many apples does the store sell in all?

   The store sells 44 apples in all.

4. Sarah has 45 round beads and 36 square beads. How many beads does Sarah have in all?

   Sarah has 81 beads in all.

5. There are 18 crayons in a box. There are 27 crayons on a table. How many crayons are there in all?

   There are 45 crayons in all.

142 SOLVE COMBINE STORY PROBLEMS (A)

WRAP-UP

Putting Together to Find the Total

Students will solve a problem to show that they understand how to solve a story problem by putting amounts together to find the total.

Solve Combine Story Problems (B)

Lesson Overview

ACTIVITY	ACTIVITY TITLE	TIME	ONLINE/OFFLINE
GET READY	Introduction to Solve Combine Story Problems (B)	**2** minutes	online
	Subtracting 0 and 1 with Instant Recall	**8** minutes	online
LEARN AND TRY IT	Taking Apart to Find a Part	**15** minutes	online
	Take Apart to Find a Part	**10** minutes	online
	Practice Taking Apart to Find a Part	**20** minutes	online and offline
WRAP-UP	Taking Apart to Find a Part	**5** minutes	online

Content Background

Students will encounter more story problems that involve combining two amounts to find a total. The combine story problems in this lesson all follow a pattern. Each problem will give a total and one of the two amounts that are being combined, and students must find the other amount. This type of combine problem is sometimes called a *take-apart* problem because one amount is taken from the total to find the other amount.

NOTE Students will not be expected to identify a story problem as a combine problem or a take-apart problem. However, they will be expected to read a story problem and recognize that one part should be subtracted from the total to find the other part.

Find One Part

Students will continue to follow the three story problem steps to solve each combine story problem. They can also continue to organize the information in a part-part-whole chart. Here is an example of finding one part in a take-apart story problem and the related part-part-whole chart.

Jordan has 93 apples.
He puts 56 of the apples in a bowl.
He puts the rest in a bag.
How many apples does Jordan put in the bag?

93	
56	?

MATERIALS

Supplied

- *Math 2 Activity Book:* Practice Taking Apart to Find a Part

Notice that a symbol represents one of the parts. In this case, the symbol is a question mark. It doesn't matter whether students write the question mark in the right or the left box. Some students may write the number sentence $56 + ? = 93$ as a plan. To solve this sentence, students must subtract 56 from 93, so the number sentence $93 - 56 = ?$ is also correct. Students may write both number sentences or just the subtraction sentence.

Lesson Goals

- Find a part in a take-apart story problem.

GET READY

Introduction to Solve Combine Story Problems (B)

Students will get a glimpse of what they will learn about in the lesson. They will also read the lesson goals.

Subtracting 0 and 1 with Instant Recall

Students will practice subtracting 0 and 1.

LEARN AND TRY IT

LEARN Taking Apart to Find a Part

Students will learn how to solve story problems by taking amounts apart to find the missing part.

TRY IT Take Apart to Find a Part

Students will practice solving story problems by taking amounts apart to find the missing part. Support will be provided to help students overcome misconceptions.

TRY IT Practice Taking Apart to Find a Part

Students will complete online practice problems. Then they will complete Practice Taking Apart to Find a Part from *Math 2 Activity Book*.

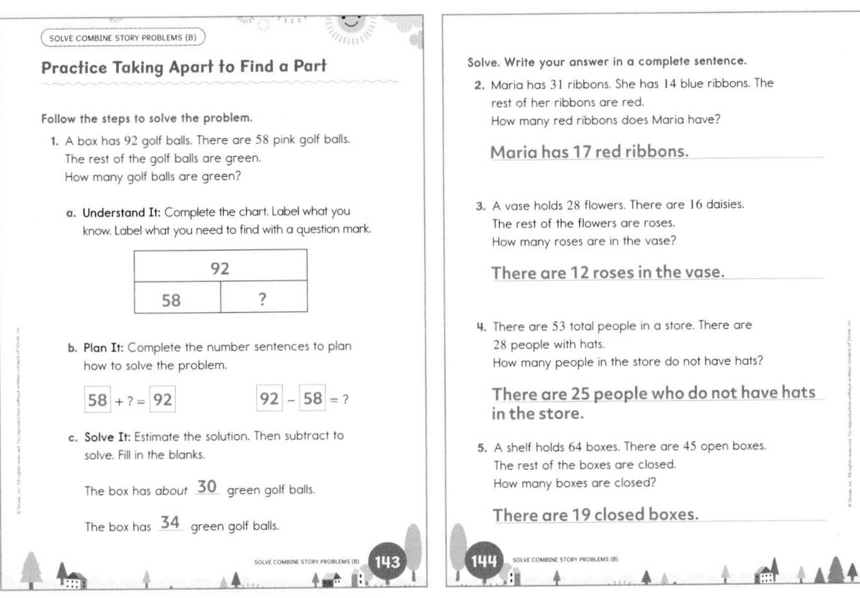

SOLVE COMBINE STORY PROBLEMS (B)

Practice Taking Apart to Find a Part

Follow the steps to solve the problem.

1. A box has 92 golf balls. There are 58 pink golf balls. The rest of the golf balls are green. How many golf balls are green?

   a. **Understand It:** Complete the chart. Label what you know. Label what you need to find with a question mark.

92	
58	?

   b. **Plan It:** Complete the number sentences to plan how to solve the problem.

   58 + ? = 92   92 − 58 = ?

   c. **Solve It:** Estimate the solution. Then subtract to solve. Fill in the blanks.

   The box has *about* 30 green golf balls.

   The box has 34 green golf balls.

SOLVE COMBINE STORY PROBLEMS (B) 143

Solve. Write your answer in a complete sentence.

2. Maria has 31 ribbons. She has 14 blue ribbons. The rest of her ribbons are red. How many red ribbons does Maria have?

   Maria has 17 red ribbons.

3. A vase holds 28 flowers. There are 16 daisies. The rest of the flowers are roses. How many roses are in the vase?

   There are 12 roses in the vase.

4. There are 53 total people in a store. There are 28 people with hats. How many people in the store do not have hats?

   There are 25 people who do not have hats in the store.

5. A shelf holds 64 boxes. There are 45 open boxes. The rest of the boxes are closed. How many boxes are closed?

   There are 19 closed boxes.

144 SOLVE COMBINE STORY PROBLEMS (B)

WRAP-UP

Taking Apart to Find a Part

Students will solve a problem to show that they understand how to solve a story problem by taking amounts apart to find one of the parts.

Solve Combine Story Problems (C)

Lesson Overview

ACTIVITY	ACTIVITY TITLE	TIME	ONLINE/OFFLINE
GET READY	Introduction to Solve Combine Story Problems (C)	**2** minutes	online
	Subtracting 0 and 1 Math Facts Game	**7** minutes	online
LEARN AND TRY IT	Solving for Both Parts	**15** minutes	online
	Solve for Both Parts	**10** minutes	online
ALL ABOUT ME	Brain Break	**1** minute	online or offline
TRY IT	Practice Solving for Both Parts	**20** minutes	online and offline
WRAP-UP	Solving for Both Parts	**5** minutes	online

Content Background

Students will encounter another type of story problem that also involves combining two amounts to find a total. The combine story problems in this lesson give only the total. Students must find both amounts that could be combined to get that total. Sometimes the answer will be a list of all the possible combinations. Other times the answer is just one possible combination, and there are many correct answers.

Find Both Parts

Students will continue to follow the three story problem steps to solve each combine story problem. They can also continue to organize the information in a part-part-whole chart. Here is an example of finding both parts in a combine story problem.

Jordan has 46 beads.
He puts some of the beads in a jar.
He puts the rest in a box.
How many beads could Jordan put in each place?

46	
?	?

Notice that a symbol represents *each* part. Students may write the number sentence $? + ? = 46$ as a plan. Students solve the problem by finding two numbers that add to 46. Any two numbers that add to 46 are a correct solution. Jordan could put 5 beads in a jar and 41 in a box. Another correct solution is 20 beads in the jar and 26 in the box.

NOTE Students can use two question marks, or they can use two different symbols, such as one question mark and one small square.

MATERIALS

Supplied

- *Math 2 Activity Book:* Practice Solving for Both Parts

Lesson Goals

- Find both parts in a combine story problem.

GET READY

Introduction to Solve Combine Story Problems (C)

Students will get a glimpse of what they will learn about in the lesson. They will also read the lesson goals.

Subtracting 0 and 1 Math Facts Game

Students will play a game to practice subtracting 0 and 1.

LEARN AND TRY IT

LEARN Solving for Both Parts

Students will learn how to solve story problems by solving for both parts when given a total amount.

TRY IT Solve for Both Parts

Students will practice solving story problems by solving for both parts when given a total amount. Support will be provided to help students overcome misconceptions.

TRY IT Practice Solving for Both Parts

Students will complete online practice problems. Then they will complete Practice Solving for Both Parts from *Math 2 Activity Book.*

SOLVE COMBINE STORY PROBLEMS (C)

Practice Solving for Both Parts

Follow the steps to solve the problem.

1. There are 5 bunnies in a field. Some of the bunnies are white. The rest of the bunnies are tan. How many of each color bunny could be in the field?

   a. **Understand It:** Complete the chart. Label what you know. Label what you need to find with question marks.

5	
?	?

   b. **Plan It:** Write a number sentence to plan how to solve the problem. Use a ? for each unknown.

   $? + ? = 5$

   c. **Solve It:** Find all the pairs of numbers that add to 5.

   1 white and 4 tan 4 white and 1 tan

   2 white and 3 tan 3 white and 2 tan

   Students can list the pairs in any order.

SOLVE COMBINE STORY PROBLEMS (C) 145

Answers will vary. Possible answers are shown. Accept all reasonable answers that add to the total amount given in the problem.

Solve. Find one pair of numbers for each problem.

2. Some children and adults are at the park. There are 18 people in all at the park. How many children and adults could be at the park?

   13 children and 5 adults

3. There are 34 plants in a garden. Some of the plants are pansies. The rest are lilies. How many of each flower could be in the garden?

   20 pansies and 14 lilies

4. Jessica does schoolwork for 45 minutes. She works on math and science only. How many minutes could Jessica work on each subject?

   30 minutes on math and 15 minutes on science

5. There are 25 animals at a shelter. Some of the animals are dogs. The rest are cats. How many dogs and cats could be at the shelter?

   12 dogs and 13 cats

146 SOLVE COMBINE STORY PROBLEMS (C)

WRAP-UP

Solving for Both Parts

Students will solve a problem to show that they understand how to solve a story problem by solving for both parts when given a total amount.

Solve Combine Story Problems (D)

Lesson Overview

ACTIVITY	ACTIVITY TITLE	TIME	ONLINE/OFFLINE
GET READY	Introduction to Solve Combine Story Problems (D)	**2** minutes	
TRY IT	Review Solve Combine Story Problems	**18** minutes	
QUIZ	Solve Combine Story Problems	**25** minutes	
WRAP-UP	More Math Practice	**15** minutes	

Lesson Goals

- Review solving combine story problems.
- Take a quiz.

MATERIALS

There are no materials to gather for this lesson.

GET READY

Introduction to Solve Combine Story Problems (D)

Students will read the lesson goals.

TRY IT

Review Solve Combine Story Problems

Students will answer questions to review what they have learned about how to solve combine story problems.

QUIZ

Solve Combine Story Problems

Students will complete the Solve Combine Story Problems quiz.

WRAP-UP

More Math Practice

Students will practice skills according to their individual needs.

Solve Change Story Problems (A)

Lesson Overview

ACTIVITY	ACTIVITY TITLE	TIME	ONLINE/OFFLINE
GET READY	Introduction to Solve Change Story Problems (A)	**2** minutes	online
	Look Back at Solving Add-To Problems	**7** minutes	online
LEARN AND TRY IT	Finding the End in an Add-To Problem	**7** minutes	online
	Find the End in an Add-To Problem	**7** minutes	online
ALL ABOUT ME	Brain Break	**1** minute	online or offline
LEARN AND TRY IT	Finding the Change or Start in an Add-To Problem	**7** minutes	online
	Find the Change or Start in an Add-To Problem	**7** minutes	online
	Practice Solving an Add-To Problem	**20** minutes	online and offline
WRAP-UP	Solving an Add-To Problem	**2** minutes	online

Content Background

Students will be introduced to story problems that involve amounts that change. The change story problems in this lesson are called "add-to" problems because one amount changes when another amount is added to it.

NOTE Students will not be expected to identify a story problem as a change problem or an "add-to" problem. However, they will be expected to read a story problem and recognize that one amount is added to another amount to get a final or ending amount.

Story Problem Steps

Students will learn to follow the three story problem steps to solve each problem.

Understand It: Students can put a box around facts given in the problem and circle what they need to find.

Plan It: Students can draw and fill in a start-change-end chart to organize the information in the story problem. Students can use the chart to create a number sentence they can use to solve the problem in the next step.

Solve It: When students are solving for the ending amount, they can solve the problem using the number sentence directly. When students are solving for the change or start amount, they may need to use the number sentence

MATERIALS

Supplied

- *Math 2 Activity Book:* Practice Solving an Add-To Problem

in the chart to write a related number sentence in order to solve the problem. Students may use any strategy they learned for adding and subtracting two-digit numbers to find the unknown amount. Remind students to write a complete sentence to answer the original question in the story problem.

Find the Ending Amount

A start-change-end chart is a convenient way to organize the information given in a change story problem. Here is an example of finding the ending amount in an add-to story problem.

Maria has 27 pennies.
She finds 53 more pennies.
How many pennies does Maria have in all?

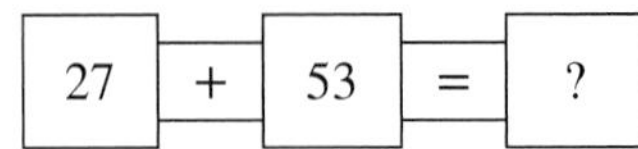

Notice that a question mark represents the final or ending amount. Students should recognize the number sentence $27 + 53 = ?$ in this chart and apply an addition strategy to add 27 and 53.

Find the Change or Start Amount

Here is an example of finding the amount of change in an add-to story problem.

Santiago has 15 toy cars.
He buys some more toy cars.
Now he has 38 toy cars.
How many toy cars does Santiago buy?

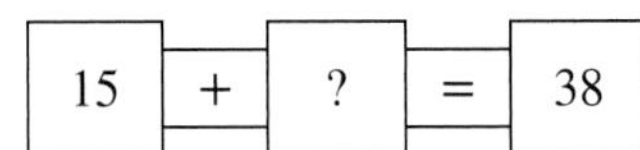

Notice that a ? represents the change amount. This is still an add-to problem because some toy cars are added to the original amount. However, we must subtract to solve this add-to problem. Students can use the related subtraction sentence $38 - 15 = ?$ to solve this problem. Students will also need to use a related subtraction sentence to find the starting amount in an add-to story problem.

NOTE As in all story problems, a question mark is just one of the symbols that can be used to represent the unknown.

Lesson Goals

- Find the ending amount in an add-to problem.
- Find the change amount in an add-to problem.
- Find the starting amount in an add-to problem.

GET READY

Introduction to Solve Change Story Problems (A)

Students will get a glimpse of what they will learn about in the lesson. They will also read the lesson goals.

Look Back at Solving Add-To Problems

Students will review and practice the prerequisite skill of solving one-step add-to problems using drawings or pictures.

LEARN AND TRY IT

LEARN Finding the End in an Add-To Problem

Students will learn how to solve add-to story problems by finding the ending amount.

TRY IT Find the End in an Add-To Problem

Students will practice solving add-to story problems by finding the ending amount. Support will be provided to help students overcome misconceptions.

LEARN Finding the Change or Start in an Add-To Problem

Students will learn how to solve add-to story problems by finding the change or start amount.

TRY IT Find the Change or Start in an Add-To Problem

Students will practice solving add-to story problems by finding the change or start amount. Support will be provided to help students overcome misconceptions.

TRY IT Practice Solving an Add-To Problem

Students will complete online practice problems. Then they will complete Practice Solving an Add-To Problem from *Math 2 Activity Book*.

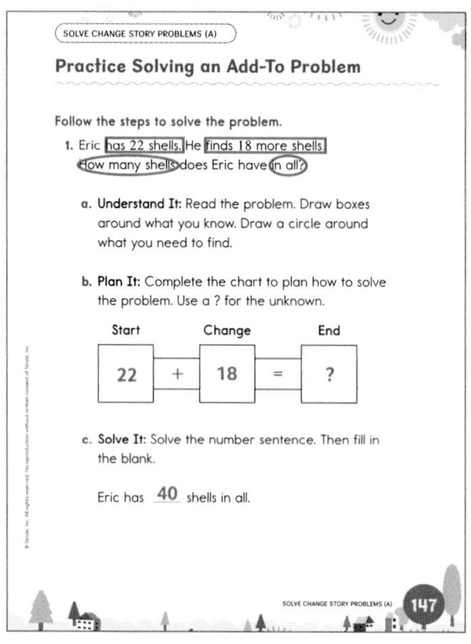

SOLVE CHANGE STORY PROBLEMS (A)

Practice Solving an Add-To Problem

Follow the steps to solve the problem.

1. Eric has 22 shells. He finds 18 more shells. How many shells does Eric have in all?

   a. **Understand It:** Read the problem. Draw boxes around what you know. Draw a circle around what you need to find.

   b. **Plan It:** Complete the chart to plan how to solve the problem. Use a ? for the unknown.

Start		Change		End
22	+	18	=	?

   c. **Solve It:** Solve the number sentence. Then fill in the blank.

   Eric has 40 shells in all.

SOLVE CHANGE STORY PROBLEMS (A) 147

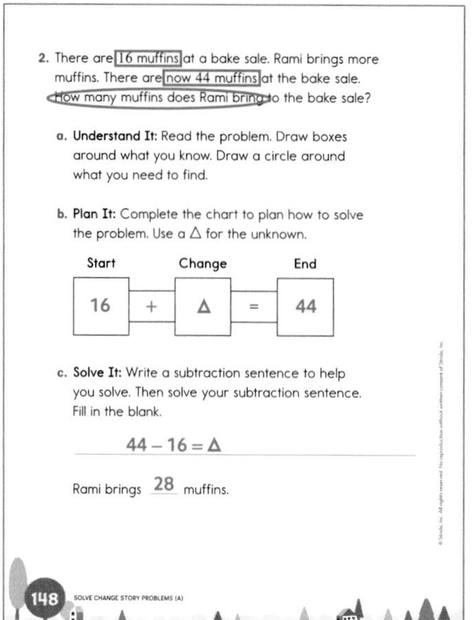

2. There are 16 muffins at a bake sale. Rami brings more muffins. There are now 44 muffins at the bake sale. How many muffins does Rami bring to the bake sale?

   a. **Understand It:** Read the problem. Draw boxes around what you know. Draw a circle around what you need to find.

   b. **Plan It:** Complete the chart to plan how to solve the problem. Use a △ for the unknown.

Start		Change		End
16	+	△	=	44

   c. **Solve It:** Write a subtraction sentence to help you solve. Then solve your subtraction sentence. Fill in the blank.

   44 – 16 = △

   Rami brings 28 muffins.

148 SOLVE CHANGE STORY PROBLEMS (A)

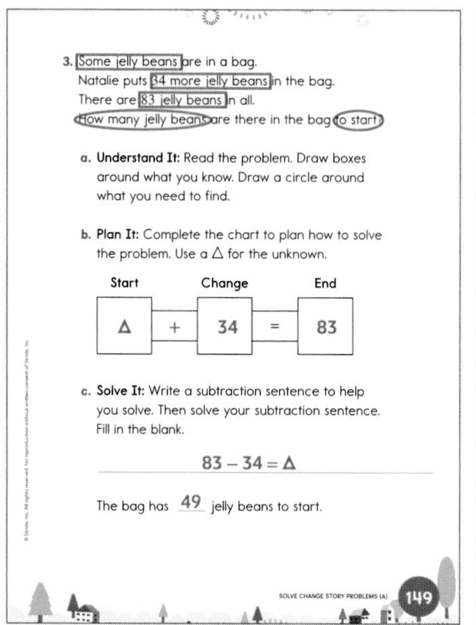

3. Some jelly beans are in a bag. Natalie puts 34 more jelly beans in the bag. There are 83 jelly beans in all. How many jelly beans are there in the bag to start?

   a. **Understand It:** Read the problem. Draw boxes around what you know. Draw a circle around what you need to find.

   b. **Plan It:** Complete the chart to plan how to solve the problem. Use a △ for the unknown.

Start		Change		End
△	+	34	=	83

   c. **Solve It:** Write a subtraction sentence to help you solve. Then solve your subtraction sentence. Fill in the blank.

   83 – 34 = △

   The bag has 49 jelly beans to start.

SOLVE CHANGE STORY PROBLEMS (A) 149

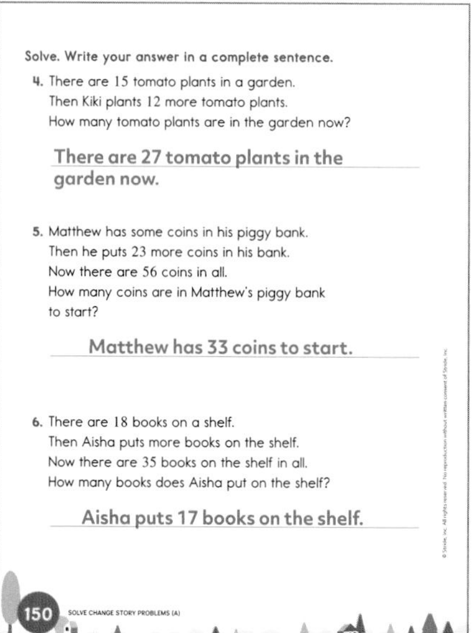

Solve. Write your answer in a complete sentence.

4. There are 15 tomato plants in a garden. Then Kiki plants 12 more tomato plants. How many tomato plants are in the garden now?

   There are 27 tomato plants in the garden now.

5. Matthew has some coins in his piggy bank. Then he puts 23 more coins in his bank. Now there are 56 coins in all. How many coins are in Matthew's piggy bank to start?

   Matthew has 33 coins to start.

6. There are 18 books on a shelf. Then Aisha puts more books on the shelf. Now there are 35 books on the shelf in all. How many books does Aisha put on the shelf?

   Aisha puts 17 books on the shelf.

150 SOLVE CHANGE STORY PROBLEMS (A)

WRAP-UP

Solving an Add-To Problem

Students will solve problems to show that they understand how to solve add-to story problems.

Solve Change Story Problems (B)

Lesson Overview

ACTIVITY	ACTIVITY TITLE	TIME	ONLINE/OFFLINE
GET READY	Introduction to Solve Change Story Problems (B)	**2** minutes	online
	Subtracting 2 and 3 Math Facts	**7** minutes	online
LEARN AND **TRY IT**	Finding the End or Change in a Take-From Problem	**7** minutes	online
	Find the End or Change in a Take-From Problem	**7** minutes	online
ALL ABOUT ME	Brain Break	**1** minute	online or offline
LEARN AND **TRY IT**	Finding the Start in a Take-From Problem	**7** minutes	online
	Find the Start in a Take-From Problem	**7** minutes	online
	Practice Solving a Take-From Problem	**20** minutes	online and offline
WRAP-UP	Solving a Take-From Problem	**2** minutes	online

Content Background

Students will encounter more story problems that involve amounts that change. The change problems in this lesson are called "take-from" problems because one amount changes when another amount is taken from it.

NOTE Students will not be expected to identify a story problem as a change problem or a "take-from" problem. However, they will be expected to read a story problem and recognize that one amount is taken from another amount to get a final or ending amount.

Find the Ending or Change Amount

Students will continue to follow the three story problem steps to solve each change story problem. They can also continue to organize the information in a start-change-end chart. Here is an example of finding the ending amount in a take-from story problem.

Thomas has 53 grapes.
He eats 31 grapes.
How many grapes does Thomas have left?

53	–	31	=	?

Notice that a question mark represents the final or ending amount. Students should recognize the number sentence $53 - 31 = ?$ in this chart and apply a subtraction strategy to subtract 31 from 53.

MATERIALS

Supplied

- *Math 2 Activity Book:* Practice Solving a Take-From Problem

Students can use a related subtraction sentence to solve when the change amount is unknown.

Find the Starting Amount

Here is an example of finding the starting amount in a take-from story problem.

Harriet has some coins.
She donates 44 coins.
Now she has 12 coins left.
How many coins does Harriet start with?

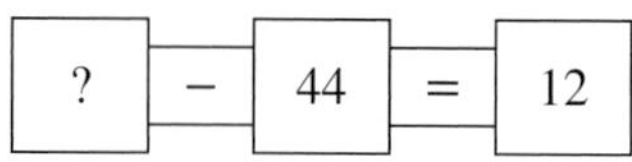

Notice that a question mark represents the starting amount. This is still a take-from problem because some coins are taken from the original amount. However, we must add to solve this take-from problem. Students can write the related addition sentence $12 + 44 = ?$ to solve this problem.

Lesson Goals

- Find the ending amount in a take-from problem.
- Find the change amount in a take-from problem.
- Find the starting amount in a take-from problem.

GET READY

Introduction to Solve Change Story Problems (B)

Students will get a glimpse of what they will learn about in the lesson. They will also read the lesson goals.

Subtracting 2 and 3 Math Facts

Students will practice subtracting 2 and 3.

LEARN AND TRY IT

LEARN Finding the End or Change in a Take-From Problem

Students will learn how to solve take-from story problems by finding the ending or change amount.

TRY IT Find the End or Change in a Take-From Problem

Students will practice solving take-from story problems by finding the ending or change amount. Support will be provided to help students overcome misconceptions.

LEARN **Finding the Start in a Take-From Problem**

Students will learn how to solve take-from story problems by finding the starting amount.

TRY IT **Find the Start in a Take-From Problem**

Students will practice solving take-from story problems by finding the starting amount. Support will be provided to help students overcome misconceptions.

TRY IT **Practice Solving a Take-From Problem**

Students will complete online practice problems. Then they will complete Practice Solving a Take-From Problem from *Math 2 Activity Book*.

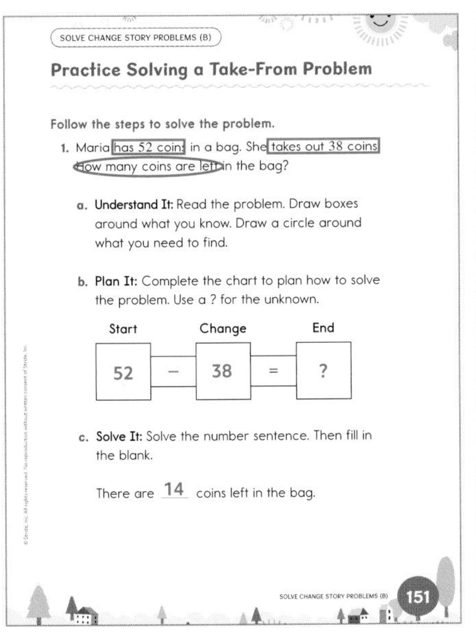

SOLVE CHANGE STORY PROBLEMS (B)

Practice Solving a Take-From Problem

Follow the steps to solve the problem.

1. Maria has 52 coins in a bag. She takes out 38 coins. How many coins are left in the bag?

   a. **Understand It:** Read the problem. Draw boxes around what you know. Draw a circle around what you need to find.

   b. **Plan It:** Complete the chart to plan how to solve the problem. Use a ? for the unknown.

Start		Change		End
52	–	38	=	?

   c. **Solve It:** Solve the number sentence. Then fill in the blank.

   There are 14 coins left in the bag.

SOLVE CHANGE STORY PROBLEMS (B) 151

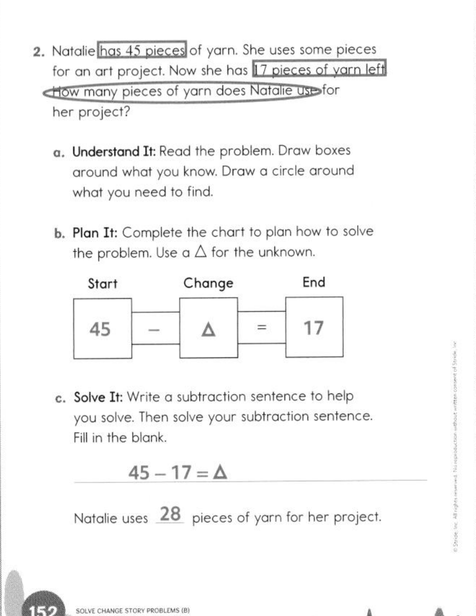

2. Natalie has 45 pieces of yarn. She uses some pieces for an art project. Now she has 17 pieces of yarn left. How many pieces of yarn does Natalie use for her project?

   a. **Understand It:** Read the problem. Draw boxes around what you know. Draw a circle around what you need to find.

   b. **Plan It:** Complete the chart to plan how to solve the problem. Use a △ for the unknown.

Start		Change		End
45	–	△	=	17

   c. **Solve It:** Write a subtraction sentence to help you solve. Then solve your subtraction sentence. Fill in the blank.

   $45 - 17 = \triangle$

   Natalie uses 28 pieces of yarn for her project.

152 SOLVE CHANGE STORY PROBLEMS (B)

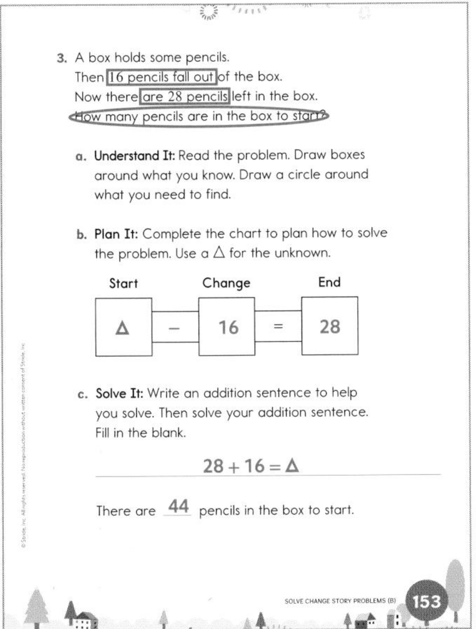

3. A box holds some pencils. Then 16 pencils fall out of the box. Now there are 28 pencils left in the box. How many pencils are in the box to start?

   a. **Understand It:** Read the problem. Draw boxes around what you know. Draw a circle around what you need to find.

   b. **Plan It:** Complete the chart to plan how to solve the problem. Use a △ for the unknown.

Start		Change		End
△	–	16	=	28

   c. **Solve It:** Write an addition sentence to help you solve. Then solve your addition sentence. Fill in the blank.

   $28 + 16 = \triangle$

   There are 44 pencils in the box to start.

SOLVE CHANGE STORY PROBLEMS (B) 153

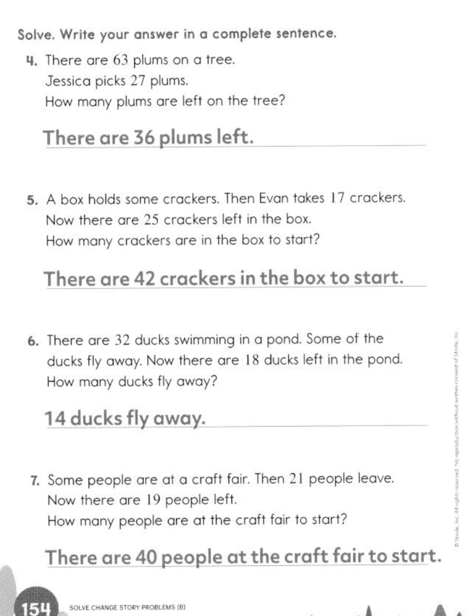

Solve. Write your answer in a complete sentence.

4. There are 63 plums on a tree. Jessica picks 27 plums. How many plums are left on the tree?

   There are 36 plums left.

5. A box holds some crackers. Then Evan takes 17 crackers. Now there are 25 crackers left in the box. How many crackers are in the box to start?

   There are 42 crackers in the box to start.

6. There are 32 ducks swimming in a pond. Some of the ducks fly away. Now there are 18 ducks left in the pond. How many ducks fly away?

   14 ducks fly away.

7. Some people are at a craft fair. Then 21 people leave. Now there are 19 people left. How many people are at the craft fair to start?

   There are 40 people at the craft fair to start.

154 SOLVE CHANGE STORY PROBLEMS (B)

WRAP-UP

Solving a Take-From Problem

Students will solve problems to show that they understand how to solve take-from story problems.

Solve Change Story Problems (C)

Lesson Overview

ACTIVITY	ACTIVITY TITLE	TIME	ONLINE/OFFLINE
GET READY	Introduction to Solve Change Story Problems (C)	**2** minutes	online
	Subtracting 2 and 3 with Instant Recall	**7** minutes	online
LEARN AND TRY IT	Adding to Solve a Money Problem	**7** minutes	online
	Add to Solve a Money Problem	**7** minutes	online
ALL ABOUT ME	Brain Break	**1** minute	online or offline
LEARN AND TRY IT	Subtracting to Solve a Money Problem	**7** minutes	online
	Subtract to Solve a Money Problem	**7** minutes	online
	Practice Solving a Money Problem	**20** minutes	online and offline
WRAP-UP	Solving a Money Problem	**2** minutes	online

Content Background

Students will apply what they have learned about add-to and take-from problems in order to solve story problems involving dollars or cents. Students will continue to follow the three story problem steps. Some students may find it helpful to continue to use start-change-end charts to plan how to solve each problem. Other students may be able to simply write a number sentence instead of filling out the chart each time. Encourage students to apply addition and subtraction strategies rather than counting on strategies to solve each story problem.

NOTE Students will not be expected to identify a story problem as a change problem, an "add-to" problem, or a "take-from" problem. However, they will be expected to read a story problem and recognize that one amount is added to or taken from another amount. Then they must use that information to determine whether they must add or subtract in order to solve the problem.

MATERIALS

Supplied

- *Math 2 Activity Book:* Practice Solving a Money Problem

Lesson Goals

- Add or subtract cents to solve a story problem.
- Add or subtract dollars to solve a story problem.

GET READY

Introduction to Solve Change Story Problems (C)

Students will get a glimpse of what they will learn about in the lesson. They will also read the lesson goals.

Subtracting 2 and 3 with Instant Recall

Students will practice subtracting 2 and 3.

LEARN AND TRY IT

LEARN Adding to Solve a Money Problem

Students will learn how to solve money story problems by adding dollars or cents.

TRY IT Add to Solve a Money Problem

Students will practice solving money story problems by adding dollars or cents. Support will be provided to help students overcome misconceptions.

LEARN Subtracting to Solve a Money Problem

Students will learn how to solve money story problems by subtracting dollars or cents.

TRY IT Subtract to Solve a Money Problem

Students will practice solving money story problems by subtracting dollars or cents. Support will be provided to help students overcome misconceptions.

TRY IT Practice Solving a Money Problem

Students will complete online practice problems. Then they will complete Practice Solving a Money Problem from *Math 2 Activity Book*.

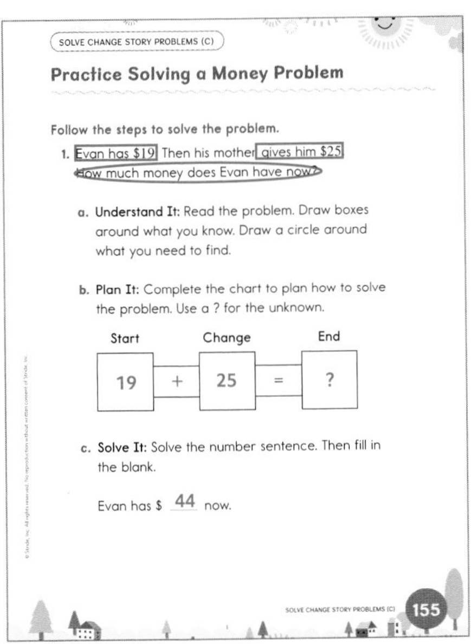
SOLVE CHANGE STORY PROBLEMS (C)

Practice Solving a Money Problem

Follow the steps to solve the problem.

1. Evan has $19. Then his mother gives him $25. How much money does Evan have now?

   a. **Understand It:** Read the problem. Draw boxes around what you know. Draw a circle around what you need to find.

   b. **Plan It:** Complete the chart to plan how to solve the problem. Use a ? for the unknown.

Start		Change		End
19	+	25	=	?

   c. **Solve It:** Solve the number sentence. Then fill in the blank.

   Evan has $ 44 now.

SOLVE CHANGE STORY PROBLEMS (C) 155

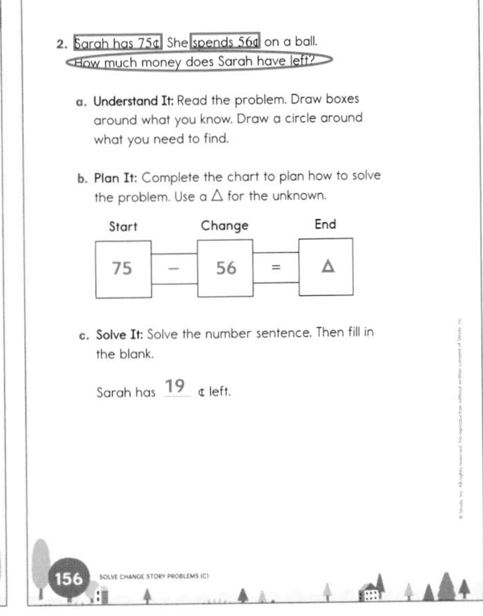
2. Sarah has 75¢. She spends 56¢ on a ball. How much money does Sarah have left?

   a. **Understand It:** Read the problem. Draw boxes around what you know. Draw a circle around what you need to find.

   b. **Plan It:** Complete the chart to plan how to solve the problem. Use a △ for the unknown.

Start		Change		End
75	−	56	=	△

   c. **Solve It:** Solve the number sentence. Then fill in the blank.

   Sarah has 19 ¢ left.

156 SOLVE CHANGE STORY PROBLEMS (C)

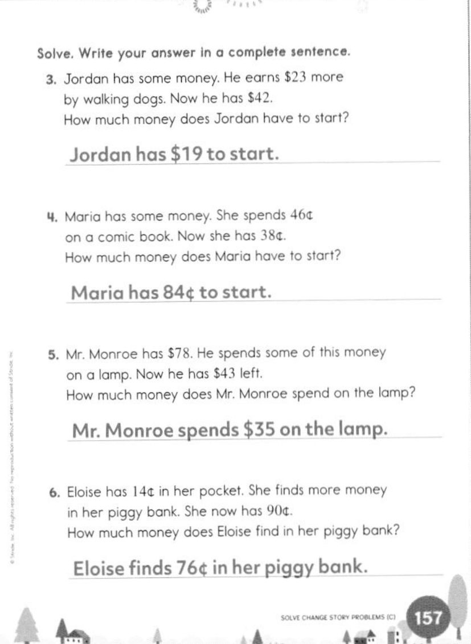
Solve. Write your answer in a complete sentence.

3. Jordan has some money. He earns $23 more by walking dogs. Now he has $42. How much money does Jordan have to start?

   Jordan has $19 to start.

4. Maria has some money. She spends 46¢ on a comic book. Now she has 38¢. How much money does Maria have to start?

   Maria has 84¢ to start.

5. Mr. Monroe has $78. He spends some of this money on a lamp. Now he has $43 left. How much money does Mr. Monroe spend on the lamp?

   Mr. Monroe spends $35 on the lamp.

6. Eloise has 14¢ in her pocket. She finds more money in her piggy bank. She now has 90¢. How much money does Eloise find in her piggy bank?

   Eloise finds 76¢ in her piggy bank.

SOLVE CHANGE STORY PROBLEMS (C) 157

WRAP-UP

Solving a Money Problem

Students will solve problems to show that they understand how to solve money story problems.

Solve Change Story Problems (D)

Lesson Overview

ACTIVITY	ACTIVITY TITLE	TIME	ONLINE/OFFLINE
GET READY	Introduction to Solve Change Story Problems (D)	**2** minutes	online
TRY IT	Review Solve Change Story Problems	**18** minutes	online
QUIZ	Solve Change Story Problems	**25** minutes	online
WRAP-UP	More Math Practice	**15** minutes	online

Lesson Goals

- Review solving change story problems.
- Take a quiz.

MATERIALS

There are no materials to gather for this lesson.

GET READY

Introduction to Solve Change Story Problems (D)

Students will read the lesson goals.

TRY IT

Review Solve Change Story Problems

Students will answer questions to review what they have learned about how to solve change story problems.

QUIZ

Solve Change Story Problems

Students will complete the Solve Change Story Problems quiz.

WRAP-UP

More Math Practice

Students will practice skills according to their individual needs.

Solve Compare Story Problems (A)

Lesson Overview

ACTIVITY	ACTIVITY TITLE	TIME	ONLINE/OFFLINE
GET READY	Introduction to Solve Compare Story Problems (A)	**2** minutes	online
	Look Back at Solving Compare Story Problems	**7** minutes	online
LEARN AND TRY IT	Comparing to Find a Difference	**15** minutes	online
	Compare to Find a Difference	**10** minutes	online
ALL ABOUT ME	Brain Break	**1** minute	online or offline
TRY IT	Practice Comparing to Find a Difference	**20** minutes	online and offline
WRAP-UP	Comparing to Find a Difference	**5** minutes	online

Content Background

Students will be introduced to story problems that involve comparing two amounts to find how many more or fewer. Each problem in this lesson will give two amounts that are compared, and then students must subtract to find the difference.

NOTE Students will not be expected to identify a story problem as a compare problem. However, they will be expected to read a story problem and recall the relationship between the greater amount, the lesser amount, and the difference.

Story Problem Steps

Students will learn to follow the three story problem steps to solve each problem.

Understand It: Students can put a box around facts given in the problem and circle what they need to find. Students can also draw and fill in a greater-lesser-difference chart to organize the information in the story problem.

Plan It: Students can use the given information or their completed chart to write a number sentence that represents a plan to add or subtract in the next step.

Solve It: Students add or subtract to find the unknown value. Students may use any of the strategies they learned for adding and subtracting two-digit numbers. Remind students to write a complete sentence to answer the original question in the story problem.

MATERIALS

Supplied

- *Math 2 Activity Book:* Practice Comparing to Find a Difference

Find the Difference

A greater-lesser-difference chart is a convenient way to organize information given in compare story problem. It is similar to the part-part-whole chart students use to solve combine story problems. Here is an example of a compare story problem and the related chart.

Jan has 38 buttons.
Kelly has 15 buttons.
How many more buttons does Jan have than Kelly?

Greater 38	
Lesser 15	**Difference** ?

Notice that a question mark represents the difference. Students could use this chart to write the number sentence $38 - 15 = ?$ as a plan to solve the problem.

Lesson Goals

- Find the difference in a compare story problem.

GET READY

Introduction to Solve Compare Story Problems (A)

Students will get a glimpse of what they will learn about in the lesson. They will also read the lesson goals.

Look Back at Solving Compare Story Problems

Students will review and practice the prerequisite skill of drawing a model to solve a compare problem.

LEARN AND TRY IT

LEARN Comparing to Find a Difference

Students will learn how to solve story problems by comparing to find the difference between two amounts.

TIP Remind students that in a part-part-whole chart, the difference is one of the parts. The whole and the other part are the numbers being compared.

TRY IT Compare to Find a Difference

Students will practice solving story problems by comparing to find the difference between two amounts. Support will be provided to help students overcome misconceptions.

TRY IT Practice Comparing to Find a Difference

Students will complete online practice problems. Then they will complete Practice Comparing to Find a Difference from *Math 2 Activity Book*.

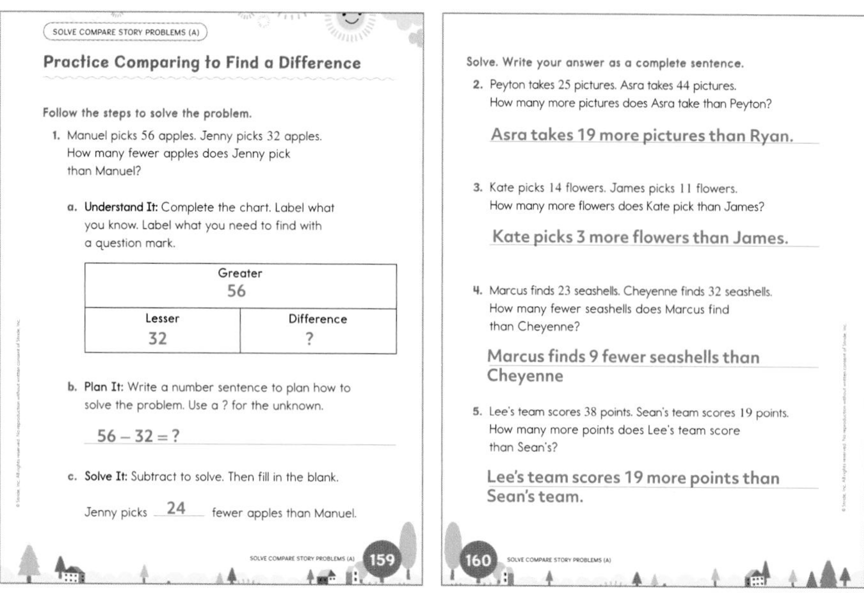

SOLVE COMPARE STORY PROBLEMS (A)

Practice Comparing to Find a Difference

Follow the steps to solve the problem.

1. Manuel picks 56 apples. Jenny picks 32 apples. How many fewer apples does Jenny pick than Manuel?

   a. **Understand It:** Complete the chart. Label what you know. Label what you need to find with a question mark.

Greater 56	
Lesser 32	Difference ?

   b. **Plan It:** Write a number sentence to plan how to solve the problem. Use a ? for the unknown.

   56 – 32 = ?

   c. **Solve It:** Subtract to solve. Then fill in the blank.

   Jenny picks 24 fewer apples than Manuel.

SOLVE COMPARE STORY PROBLEMS (A) 159

Solve. Write your answer as a complete sentence.

2. Peyton takes 25 pictures. Asra takes 44 pictures. How many more pictures does Asra take than Peyton?

   Asra takes 19 more pictures than Ryan.

3. Kate picks 14 flowers. James picks 11 flowers. How many more flowers does Kate pick than James?

   Kate picks 3 more flowers than James.

4. Marcus finds 23 seashells. Cheyenne finds 32 seashells. How many fewer seashells does Marcus find than Cheyenne?

   Marcus finds 9 fewer seashells than Cheyenne

5. Lee's team scores 38 points. Sean's team scores 19 points. How many more points does Lee's team score than Sean's?

   Lee's team scores 19 more points than Sean's team.

160 SOLVE COMPARE STORY PROBLEMS (A)

WRAP-UP

Comparing to Find a Difference

Students will solve problems to show that they understand how to solve a story problem by comparing to find the difference between two amounts.

Solve Compare Story Problems (B)

Lesson Overview

ACTIVITY	ACTIVITY TITLE	TIME	ONLINE/OFFLINE
GET READY	Introduction to Solve Compare Story Problems (B)	**2** minutes	online
	Subtracting 2 and 3 Math Facts Game	**8** minutes	online
LEARN AND TRY IT	Comparing to Find the Lesser Amount	**15** minutes	online
	Compare to Find the Lesser Amount	**10** minutes	online
	Practice Comparing to Find the Lesser Amount	**20** minutes	online and offline
WRAP-UP	Comparing to Find the Lesser Amount	**5** minutes	online

Content Background

Students will encounter more story problems that involve comparing two amounts. Each problem in this lesson will give the greater of the two amounts and the difference. Students must subtract to find the lesser amount.

NOTE Students will not be expected to identify a story problem as a compare problem. However, they will be expected to read a story problem and recall the relationship between the greater amount, the lesser amount, and the difference.

Find the Lesser Amount

Students will continue to follow the three story problem steps to solve each compare story problem. They can also continue to organize the information in a greater-lesser-difference chart. Here is an example of finding the lesser amount in a compare story problem.

Mary and Jane both have stickers.
Mary has 76 stickers.
Jane has 40 fewer stickers than Mary.
How many stickers does Jane have?

<table>
<tr><td colspan="2">Greater
76</td></tr>
<tr><td>Lesser
?</td><td>Difference
40</td></tr>
</table>

Notice that a question mark represents the lesser amount. Students could use this chart to write the number sentence $76 - ? = 40$ as a plan to solve the problem. The next step is to write the related subtraction sentence $76 - 40 = ?$ and subtract.

MATERIALS

Supplied

- *Math 2 Activity Book:* Practice Comparing to Find the Lesser Amount

Lesson Goals

- Find the lesser amount in a compare story problem.

GET READY

Introduction to Solve Compare Story Problems (B)

Students will get a glimpse of what they will learn about in the lesson. They will also read the lesson goals.

Subtracting 2 and 3 Math Facts Game

Students will play a game to practice subtracting 2 and 3.

LEARN AND TRY IT

LEARN Comparing to Find the Lesser Amount

Students will learn how to solve story problems by comparing to find the lesser amount.

TRY IT Compare to Find the Lesser Amount

Students will practice solving story problems by comparing to find the lesser amount. Support will be provided to help students overcome misconceptions.

TRY IT Practice Comparing to Find the Lesser Amount

Students will complete online practice problems. Then they will complete Practice Comparing to Find the Lesser Amount from *Math 2 Activity Book*.

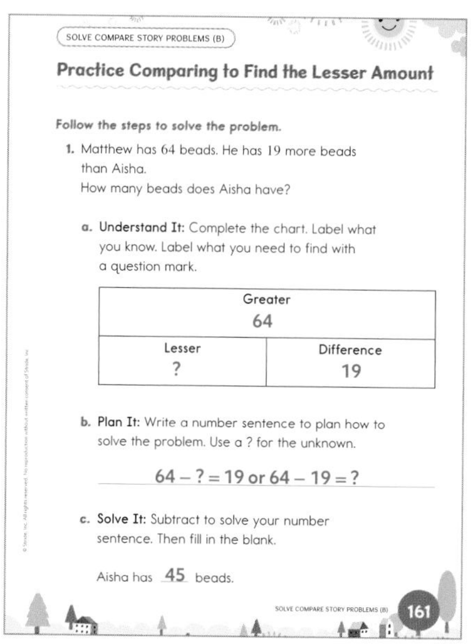
SOLVE COMPARE STORY PROBLEMS (B)

Practice Comparing to Find the Lesser Amount

Follow the steps to solve the problem.

1. Matthew has 64 beads. He has 19 more beads than Aisha. How many beads does Aisha have?

a. **Understand It:** Complete the chart. Label what you know. Label what you need to find with a question mark.

Greater 64	
Lesser ?	Difference 19

b. **Plan It:** Write a number sentence to plan how to solve the problem. Use a ? for the unknown.

64 – ? = 19 or 64 – 19 = ?

c. **Solve It:** Subtract to solve your number sentence. Then fill in the blank.

Aisha has 45 beads.

SOLVE COMPARE STORY PROBLEMS (B) 161

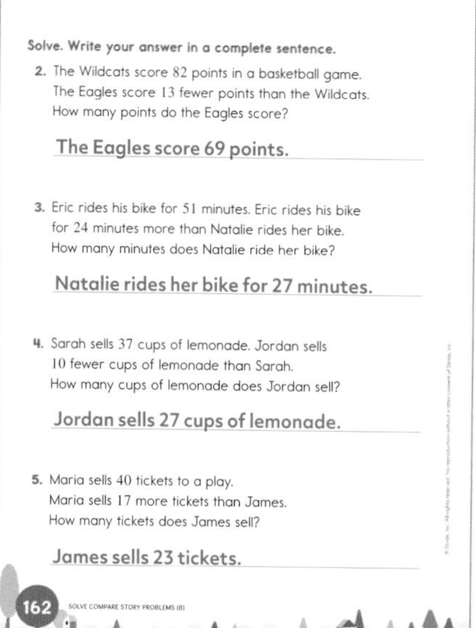
Solve. Write your answer in a complete sentence.

2. The Wildcats score 82 points in a basketball game. The Eagles score 13 fewer points than the Wildcats. How many points do the Eagles score?

The Eagles score 69 points.

3. Eric rides his bike for 51 minutes. Eric rides his bike for 24 minutes more than Natalie rides her bike. How many minutes does Natalie ride her bike?

Natalie rides her bike for 27 minutes.

4. Sarah sells 37 cups of lemonade. Jordan sells 10 fewer cups of lemonade than Sarah. How many cups of lemonade does Jordan sell?

Jordan sells 27 cups of lemonade.

5. Maria sells 40 tickets to a play. Maria sells 17 more tickets than James. How many tickets does James sell?

James sells 23 tickets.

162 SOLVE COMPARE STORY PROBLEMS (B)

WRAP-UP

Comparing to Find the Lesser Amount

Students will solve a problem to show that they understand how to solve a story problem by comparing to find the lesser amount.

Solve Compare Story Problems (C)

Lesson Overview

ACTIVITY	ACTIVITY TITLE	TIME	ONLINE/OFFLINE
GET READY	Introduction to Solve Compare Story Problems (C)	**2** minutes	online
	Subtracting 4 and 5 Math Facts	**7** minutes	online
LEARN AND TRY IT	Comparing to Find the Greater Amount	**15** minutes	online
	Compare to Find the Greater Amount	**10** minutes	online
ALL ABOUT ME	Brain Break	**1** minute	online or offline
TRY IT	Practice Comparing to Find the Greater Amount	**20** minutes	online and offline
WRAP-UP	Comparing to Find the Greater Amount	**5** minutes	online

Content Background

Students will encounter more story problems that involve comparing two amounts. Each problem in this lesson will give the lesser of the two amounts and the difference. Students must add to find the greater amount.

NOTE Students will not be expected to identify a story problem as a compare problem. However, they will be expected to read a story problem and recall the relationship between the greater amount, the lesser amount, and the difference.

Find the Greater Amount

Students will continue to follow the three story problem steps to solve each compare story problem. They can also continue to organize the information in a greater-lesser-difference chart. Here is an example of finding the greater amount in a compare story problem.

Max does 55 jumping jacks.
Sean does 32 more jumping jacks than Max.
How many jumping jacks does Sean do?

<table>
<tr><td colspan="2">Greater
?</td></tr>
<tr><td>Lesser
55</td><td>Difference
32</td></tr>
</table>

Notice that a question mark represents the greater amount. Students could use this chart to write the number sentence $? - 55 = 32$ as a plan to solve the problem. The next step is to write the related addition sentence $55 + 32 = ?$ and add.

MATERIALS

Supplied

- *Math 2 Activity Book:* Practice Comparing to Find the Greater Amount

Lesson Goals

- Find the greater amount in a compare story problem.

GET READY

Introduction to Solve Compare Story Problems (C)

Students will get a glimpse of what they will learn about in the lesson. They will also read the lesson goals.

Subtracting 4 and 5 Math Facts

Students will practice subtracting 4 and 5.

LEARN AND TRY IT

LEARN Comparing to Find the Greater Amount

Students will learn how to solve story problems by comparing to find the greater amount.

TRY IT Compare to Find the Greater Amount

Students will practice solving story problems by comparing to find the greater amount. Support will be provided to help students overcome misconceptions.

TRY IT Practice Comparing to Find the Greater Amount

Students will complete online practice problems. Then they will complete Practice Comparing to Find the Greater Amount from *Math 2 Activity Book*.

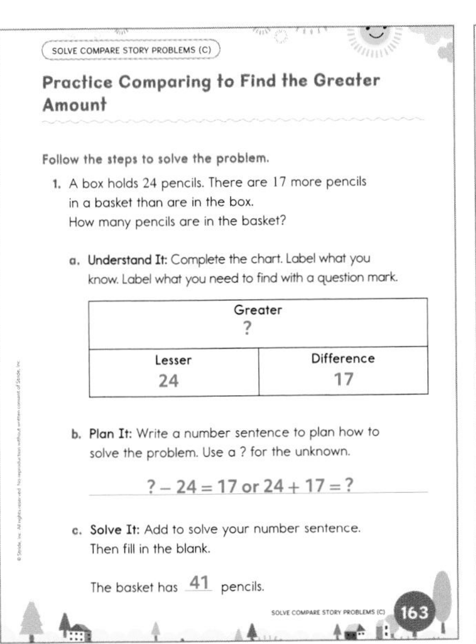

SOLVE COMPARE STORY PROBLEMS (C)

Practice Comparing to Find the Greater Amount

Follow the steps to solve the problem.

1. A box holds 24 pencils. There are 17 more pencils in a basket than are in the box. How many pencils are in the basket?

   a. Understand It: Complete the chart. Label what you know. Label what you need to find with a question mark.

Greater ?	
Lesser 24	Difference 17

   b. Plan It: Write a number sentence to plan how to solve the problem. Use a ? for the unknown.

   ? – 24 = 17 or 24 + 17 = ?

   c. Solve It: Add to solve your number sentence. Then fill in the blank.

   The basket has 41 pencils.

SOLVE COMPARE STORY PROBLEMS (C) 163

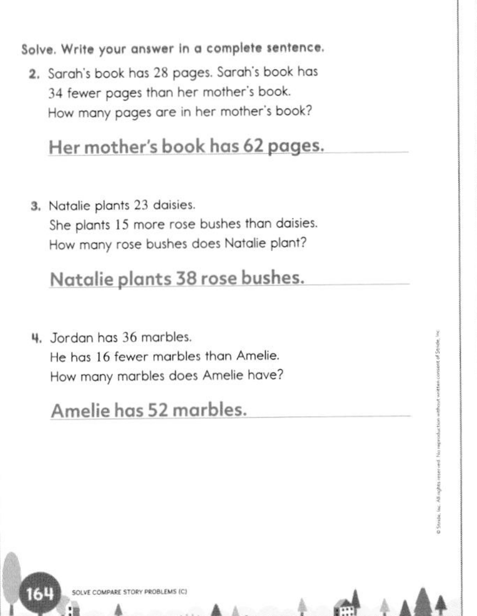

Solve. Write your answer in a complete sentence.

2. Sarah's book has 28 pages. Sarah's book has 34 fewer pages than her mother's book. How many pages are in her mother's book?

   Her mother's book has 62 pages.

3. Natalie plants 23 daisies. She plants 15 more rose bushes than daisies. How many rose bushes does Natalie plant?

   Natalie plants 38 rose bushes.

4. Jordan has 36 marbles. He has 16 fewer marbles than Amelie. How many marbles does Amelie have?

   Amelie has 52 marbles.

164 SOLVE COMPARE STORY PROBLEMS (C)

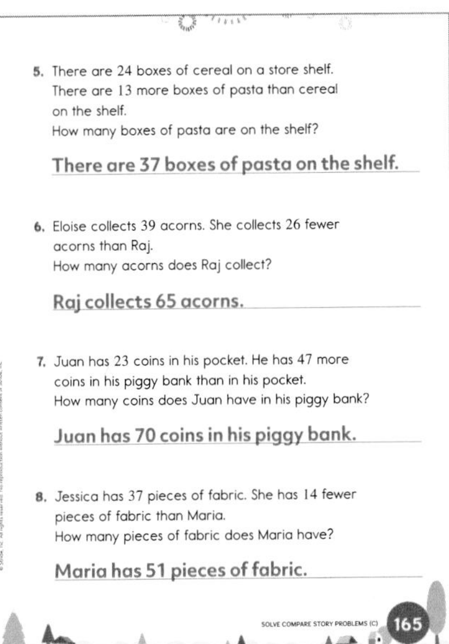

5. There are 24 boxes of cereal on a store shelf. There are 13 more boxes of pasta than cereal on the shelf. How many boxes of pasta are on the shelf?

   There are 37 boxes of pasta on the shelf.

6. Eloise collects 39 acorns. She collects 26 fewer acorns than Raj. How many acorns does Raj collect?

   Raj collects 65 acorns.

7. Juan has 23 coins in his pocket. He has 47 more coins in his piggy bank than in his pocket. How many coins does Juan have in his piggy bank?

   Juan has 70 coins in his piggy bank.

8. Jessica has 37 pieces of fabric. She has 14 fewer pieces of fabric than Maria. How many pieces of fabric does Maria have?

   Maria has 51 pieces of fabric.

SOLVE COMPARE STORY PROBLEMS (C) 165

WRAP-UP

Comparing to Find the Greater Amount

Students will solve a problem to show that they understand how to solve a story problem by comparing to find the greater amount.

Solve Compare Story Problems (D)

Lesson Overview

ACTIVITY	ACTIVITY TITLE	TIME	ONLINE/OFFLINE
GET READY	Introduction to Solve Compare Story Problems (D)	**2** minutes	
TRY IT	Review Solve Compare Story Problems	**18** minutes	
QUIZ	Solve Compare Story Problems	**25** minutes	
WRAP-UP	More Math Practice	**15** minutes	

Lesson Goals

- Review solving compare story problems.
- Take a quiz.

MATERIALS

There are no materials to gather for this lesson.

GET READY

Introduction to Solve Compare Story Problems (D)

Students will read the lesson goals.

TRY IT

Review Solve Compare Story Problems

Students will answer questions to review what they have learned about how to solve compare story problems.

QUIZ

Solve Compare Story Problems

Students will complete the Solve Compare Story Problems quiz.

WRAP-UP

More Math Practice

Students will practice skills according to their individual needs.

Solve Story Problems with One Step Wrap-Up

Lesson Overview

ACTIVITY	ACTIVITY TITLE	TIME	ONLINE/OFFLINE
GET READY	Introduction to Solve Story Problems with One Step Wrap-Up	2 minutes	online
TRY IT	Review Solve Story Problems with One Step	18 minutes	online
UNIT CHECKPOINT	Solve Story Problems with One Step Online Checkpoint	18 minutes	online
	Solve Story Problems with One Step Offline Checkpoint	20 minutes	offline
WRAP-UP	Turn in Your Offline Checkpoint	2 minutes	offline

Lesson Goals

- Review solving story problems with one step.
- Show what you know about solving story problems with one step.

MATERIALS

Supplied

- Solve Story Problems with One Step Offline Checkpoint (printout)

GET READY

Introduction to Solve Story Problems with One Step Wrap-Up

Students will read the lesson goals.

TRY IT

Review Solve Story Problems with One Step

Students will answer questions to review what they have learned about solving story problems with one step.

UNIT CHECKPOINT

Solve Story Problems with One Step Online Checkpoint

Students will complete the Solve Story Problems with One Step Unit Checkpoint.

LEARNING COACH CHECK-IN This is a graded assignment. Make sure students complete the online assessment.

Solve Story Problems with One Step Offline Checkpoint

Students will complete multistep problems that go beyond the short answer and multiple choice problems in their regular lessons. These problems give students an opportunity to demonstrate problem solving, reasoning, communication, and modeling skills. Students will need to use paper and pencil and/or technology to show their work.

Materials are linked online. The materials are not provided in this lesson guide or the activity book.

LEARNING COACH CHECK-IN This is a graded assignment. Make sure students complete, review, and submit their assignment to the teacher. If you are unsure how to do this, ask students' teacher.

WRAP-UP

Turn in Your Offline Checkpoint

Students will turn in their graded assignment.

Mid-Year Project

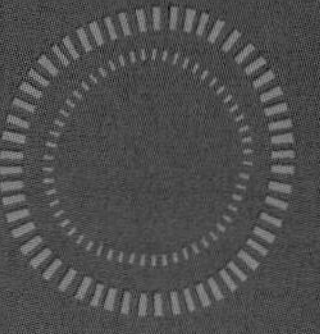

Mid-Year Project

Project Overview

The mid-year project gives students the opportunity to further apply the knowledge and skills acquired in previous units.

1. **Learn and Try It:** Students learn more about selected topics.
2. **Putting It All Together:** Students complete a small, creative project designed to extend concepts and skills they have encountered across units. This project is designed to emphasize a real-world application that connects mathematics to everyday life. Students will need to use pencil and paper and/or technology to show their work.

   LEARNING COACH CHECK-IN This is a graded assignment. Make sure students complete, review, and submit the assignment to their teacher.

Students will be presented with two project options. They will choose and complete one project. All materials needed for this lesson are linked online. The materials are not provided in this lesson guide or the activity book.

MATERIALS

Supplied

- Earning Money Project (printout)
- Measuring Distances Project (printout)

Solve Story Problems

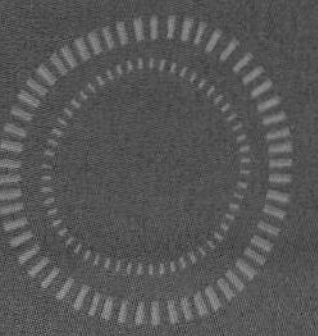

Add-Add Story Problems (A)

Lesson Overview

ACTIVITY	ACTIVITY TITLE	TIME	ONLINE/OFFLINE
GET READY	Introduction to Add-Add Story Problems (A)	**2** minutes	online
	Look Back at Strategies for Adding	**7** minutes	online
LEARN AND **TRY IT**	Solving Add-Add Story Problems	**15** minutes	online
	Solve Add-Add Story Problems	**10** minutes	online
ALL ABOUT ME	Brain Break	**1** minute	online or offline
TRY IT	Practice Solving Add-Add Story Problems	**20** minutes	online and offline
WRAP-UP	Solving Add-Add Story Problems	**5** minutes	online

Content Background

Students will learn how to solve story problems with two addition steps. The problems can involve amounts that are combined, amounts that change, or amounts that are compared. Regardless of the particular situation, each problem involves amounts that must be added. Some problems must be solved by adding two numbers and then adding that sum to a third number. Other problems can be solved by adding three amounts in one number sentence. Students will continue to apply the three story problem steps to solve each problem.

MATERIALS

Supplied

- *Math 2 Activity Book:* Practice Solving Add-Add Story Problems

Lesson Goals

- Solve add-add story problems.

GET READY

Introduction to Add-Add Story Problems (A)

Students will get a glimpse of what they will learn about in the lesson. They will also read the lesson goals.

Look Back at Strategies for Adding

Students will review and practice the prerequisite skill of applying strategies for adding two-digit numbers.

LEARN AND TRY IT

LEARN Solving Add-Add Story Problems

Students will learn how to solve story problems with two addition steps.

TIP Eventually students must determine whether to add or subtract to solve one- or two-step story problems. As students read each story problem, encourage them to notice specific words that indicate addition. For example, words like *and*, *more than*, *in all*, or *total* are clues to add.

TRY IT Solve Add-Add Story Problems

Students will practice solving story problems with two addition steps. Support will be provided to help students overcome misconceptions.

TRY IT Practice Solving Add-Add Story Problems

Students will complete online practice problems. Then they will complete Practice Solving Add-Add Story Problems from *Math 2 Activity Book*.

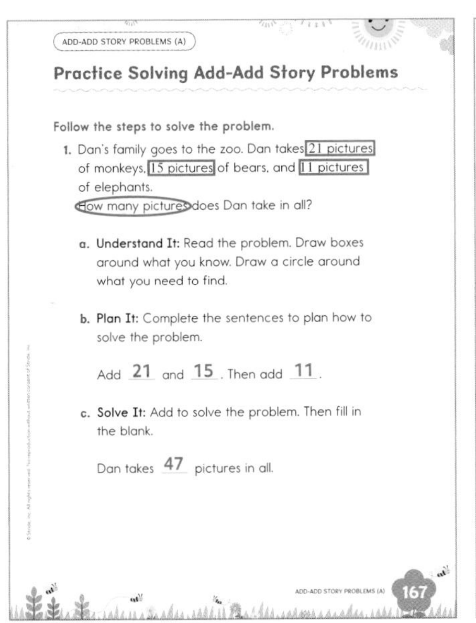

ADD-ADD STORY PROBLEMS (A)

Practice Solving Add-Add Story Problems

Follow the steps to solve the problem.

1. Dan's family goes to the zoo. Dan takes 21 pictures of monkeys, 15 pictures of bears, and 11 pictures of elephants. How many pictures does Dan take in all?

   a. **Understand It:** Read the problem. Draw boxes around what you know. Draw a circle around what you need to find.

   b. **Plan It:** Complete the sentences to plan how to solve the problem.

   Add 21 and 15. Then add 11.

   c. **Solve It:** Add to solve the problem. Then fill in the blank.

   Dan takes 47 pictures in all.

ADD-ADD STORY PROBLEMS (A) 167

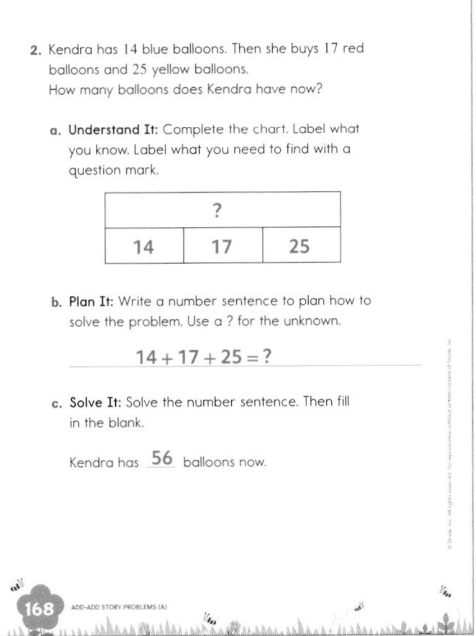

2. Kendra has 14 blue balloons. Then she buys 17 red balloons and 25 yellow balloons. How many balloons does Kendra have now?

   a. **Understand It:** Complete the chart. Label what you know. Label what you need to find with a question mark.

?		
14	17	25

   b. **Plan It:** Write a number sentence to plan how to solve the problem. Use a ? for the unknown.

   $14 + 17 + 25 = ?$

   c. **Solve It:** Solve the number sentence. Then fill in the blank.

   Kendra has 56 balloons now.

168 ADD-ADD STORY PROBLEMS (A)

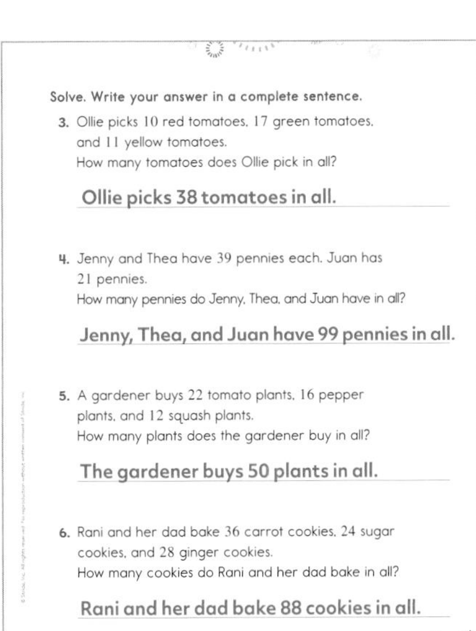

Solve. Write your answer in a complete sentence.

3. Ollie picks 10 red tomatoes, 17 green tomatoes, and 11 yellow tomatoes. How many tomatoes does Ollie pick in all?

   Ollie picks 38 tomatoes in all.

4. Jenny and Thea have 39 pennies each. Juan has 21 pennies. How many pennies do Jenny, Thea, and Juan have in all?

   Jenny, Thea, and Juan have 99 pennies in all.

5. A gardener buys 22 tomato plants, 16 pepper plants, and 12 squash plants. How many plants does the gardener buy in all?

   The gardener buys 50 plants in all.

6. Rani and her dad bake 36 carrot cookies, 24 sugar cookies, and 28 ginger cookies. How many cookies do Rani and her dad bake in all?

   Rani and her dad bake 88 cookies in all.

ADD-ADD STORY PROBLEMS (A) 169

WRAP-UP

Solving Add-Add Story Problems

Students will solve a problem to show that they understand how to solve story problems with two addition steps.

Add-Add Story Problems (B)

Lesson Overview

ACTIVITY	ACTIVITY TITLE	TIME	ONLINE/OFFLINE
GET READY	Introduction to Add-Add Story Problems (B)	**2** minutes	online
	Subtracting 4 and 5 with Instant Recall	**7** minutes	online
LEARN AND TRY IT	Solving Add-Add Money Problems	**7** minutes	online
	Solve Add-Add Money Problems	**7** minutes	online
ALL ABOUT ME	Brain Break	**1** minute	online or offline
LEARN AND TRY IT	Solving Add-Add Length Problems	**7** minutes	online
	Solve Add-Add Length Problems	**7** minutes	online
	Practice Solving Add-Add Money and Length Problems	**20** minutes	online and offline
WRAP-UP	Solving Add-Add Money and Length Problems	**2** minutes	online

Content Background

Students will learn how to solve money and length story problems with two addition steps. Money story problems involve problems about either dollars or cents. Length story problems involve lengths given in the same unit. Students will continue to apply the three story problem steps to solve each problem.

MATERIALS

Supplied

- *Math 2 Activity Book:* Practice Solving Add-Add Money and Length Problems

Lesson Goals

- Solve add-add story problems about money.
- Solve add-add story problems about length.

GET READY

Introduction to Add-Add Story Problems (B)

Students will get a glimpse of what they will learn about in the lesson. They will also read the lesson goals.

Subtracting 4 and 5 with Instant Recall

Students will practice subtracting 4 and 5.

LEARN AND TRY IT

LEARN Solving Add-Add Money Problems

Students will learn how to solve money story problems with two addition steps.

TRY IT Solve Add-Add Money Problems

Students will practice solving money story problems with two addition steps. Support will be provided to help students overcome misconceptions.

LEARN Solving Add-Add Length Problems

Students will learn how to solve length story problems with two addition steps.

TRY IT Solve Add-Add Length Problems

Students will practice solving length story problems with two addition steps. Support will be provided to help students overcome misconceptions.

TRY IT Practice Solving Add-Add Money and Length Problems

Students will complete online practice problems. Then they will complete Practice Solving Add-Add Money and Length Problems from *Math 2 Activity Book*.

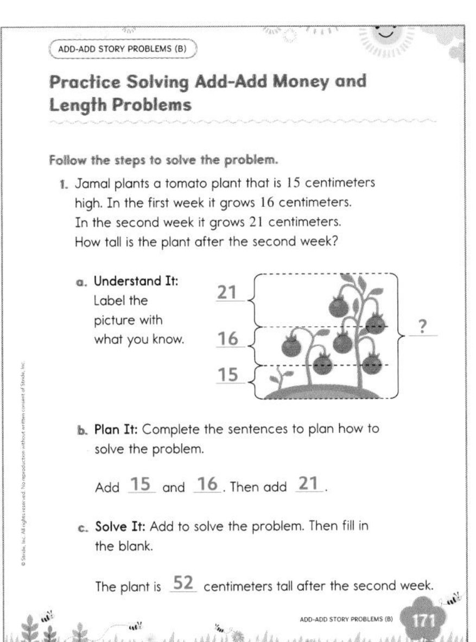

ADD-ADD STORY PROBLEMS (B)

Practice Solving Add-Add Money and Length Problems

Follow the steps to solve the problem.

1. Jamal plants a tomato plant that is 15 centimeters high. In the first week it grows 16 centimeters. In the second week it grows 21 centimeters. How tall is the plant after the second week?

   a. **Understand It:** Label the picture with what you know.

   b. **Plan It:** Complete the sentences to plan how to solve the problem.

   Add 15 and 16. Then add 21.

   c. **Solve It:** Add to solve the problem. Then fill in the blank.

   The plant is 52 centimeters tall after the second week.

ADD-ADD STORY PROBLEMS (B) 171

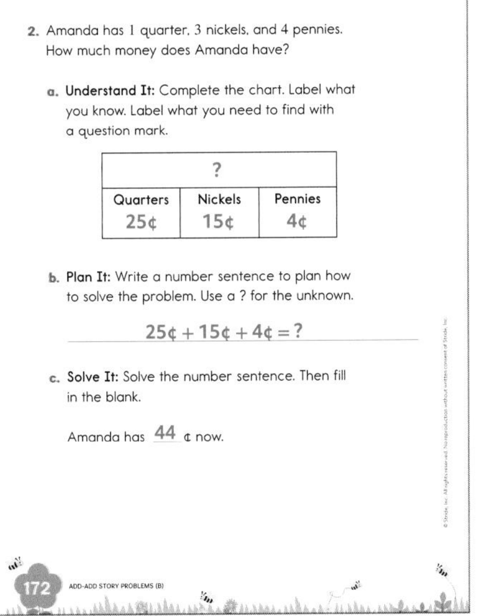

2. Amanda has 1 quarter, 3 nickels, and 4 pennies. How much money does Amanda have?

   a. **Understand It:** Complete the chart. Label what you know. Label what you need to find with a question mark.

?		
Quarters 25¢	Nickels 15¢	Pennies 4¢

   b. **Plan It:** Write a number sentence to plan how to solve the problem. Use a ? for the unknown.

   25¢ + 15¢ + 4¢ = ?

   c. **Solve It:** Solve the number sentence. Then fill in the blank.

   Amanda has 44 ¢ now.

172 ADD-ADD STORY PROBLEMS (B)

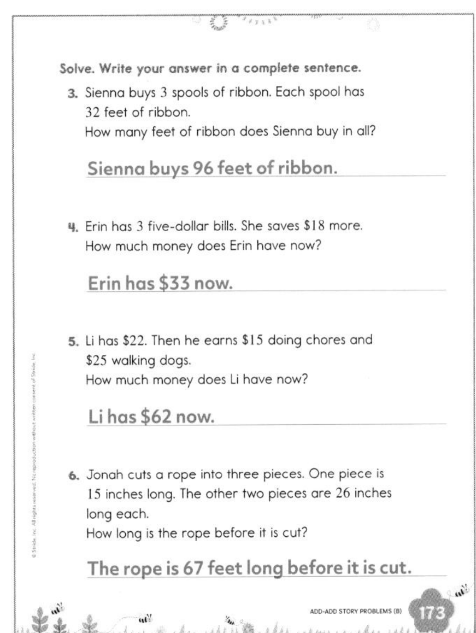

Solve. Write your answer in a complete sentence.

3. Sienna buys 3 spools of ribbon. Each spool has 32 feet of ribbon. How many feet of ribbon does Sienna buy in all?

   Sienna buys 96 feet of ribbon.

4. Erin has 3 five-dollar bills. She saves $18 more. How much money does Erin have now?

   Erin has $33 now.

5. Li has $22. Then he earns $15 doing chores and $25 walking dogs. How much money does Li have now?

   Li has $62 now.

6. Jonah cuts a rope into three pieces. One piece is 15 inches long. The other two pieces are 26 inches long each. How long is the rope before it is cut?

   The rope is 67 feet long before it is cut.

ADD-ADD STORY PROBLEMS (B) 173

WRAP-UP

Solving Add-Add Money and Length Problems

Students will solve problems to show that they understand how to solve money and length story problems with two addition steps.

Add-Add Story Problems (C)

Lesson Overview

ACTIVITY	ACTIVITY TITLE	TIME	ONLINE/OFFLINE
GET READY	Introduction to Add-Add Story Problems (C)	**2** minutes	online
TRY IT	Review Add-Add Story Problems	**18** minutes	online
QUIZ	Add-Add Story Problems	**25** minutes	online
WRAP-UP	More Math Practice	**15** minutes	online

Lesson Goals

- Review solving add-add story problems.
- Take a quiz.

MATERIALS

There are no materials to gather for this lesson.

GET READY

Introduction to Add-Add Story Problems (C)

Students will read the lesson goals.

TRY IT

Review Add-Add Story Problems

Students will answer questions to review what they have learned about solving add-add story problems.

QUIZ

Add-Add Story Problems

Students will complete the Add-Add Story Problems quiz.

WRAP-UP

More Math Practice

Students will practice skills according to their individual needs.

Subtract-Subtract Story Problems (A)

Lesson Overview

ACTIVITY	ACTIVITY TITLE	TIME	ONLINE/OFFLINE
GET READY	Introduction to Subtract-Subtract Story Problems (A)	**2** minutes	online
	Look Back at Using a Part-Part-Whole Chart	**7** minutes	online
LEARN AND TRY IT	Solving Subtract-Subtract Story Problems	**15** minutes	online
	Solve Subtract-Subtract Story Problems	**10** minutes	online
ALL ABOUT ME	Brain Break	**1** minute	online or offline
TRY IT	Practice Solving Subtract-Subtract Story Problems	**20** minutes	online and offline
WRAP-UP	Solving Subtract-Subtract Story Problems	**5** minutes	online

Content Background

Students will learn how to solve story problems with two subtraction steps. The problems can involve amounts that are combined, amounts that change, or amounts that are compared. Regardless of the particular situation, each problem involves amounts that must be subtracted. Students will continue to apply the three story problem steps to solve each problem.

MATERIALS

Supplied

- *Math 2 Activity Book:* Practice Solving Subtract-Subtract Story Problems

Lesson Goals

- Solve subtract-subtract story problems.

GET READY

Introduction to Subtract-Subtract Story Problems (A)

Students will get a glimpse of what they will learn about in the lesson. They will also read the lesson goals.

Look Back at Using a Part-Part-Whole Chart

Students will review and practice the prerequisite skill of using a part-part-whole chart to solve a story problem.

LEARN AND TRY IT

LEARN Solving Subtract-Subtract Story Problems

Students will learn how to solve story problems with two subtraction steps.

TIP Eventually students must determine whether to add or subtract to solve one- or two-step story problems. As students read each story problem, encourage them to notice specific words that indicate subtraction. For example, words like *or*, *less than*, *fewer*, or *have left* are clues to subtract.

TRY IT Solve Subtract-Subtract Story Problems

Students will practice solving story problems with two subtraction steps. Support will be provided to help students overcome misconceptions.

TRY IT Practice Solving Subtract-Subtract Story Problems

Students will complete online practice problems. Then they will complete Practice Solving Subtract-Subtract Story Problems from *Math 2 Activity Book*.

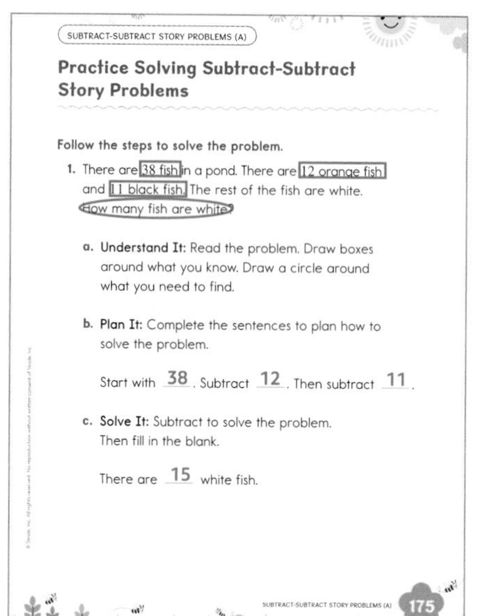

SUBTRACT-SUBTRACT STORY PROBLEMS (A)

Practice Solving Subtract-Subtract Story Problems

Follow the steps to solve the problem.

1. There are 38 fish in a pond. There are 12 orange fish and 11 black fish. The rest of the fish are white. How many fish are white?
   a. **Understand It:** Read the problem. Draw boxes around what you know. Draw a circle around what you need to find.
   b. **Plan It:** Complete the sentences to plan how to solve the problem.
   Start with 38. Subtract 12. Then subtract 11.
   c. **Solve It:** Subtract to solve the problem. Then fill in the blank.
   There are 15 white fish.

SUBTRACT-SUBTRACT STORY PROBLEMS (A) 175

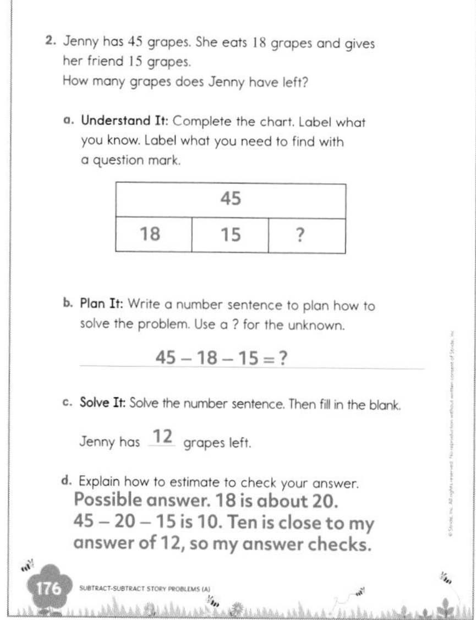

2. Jenny has 45 grapes. She eats 18 grapes and gives her friend 15 grapes. How many grapes does Jenny have left?
   a. **Understand It:** Complete the chart. Label what you know. Label what you need to find with a question mark.

45		
18	15	?

   b. **Plan It:** Write a number sentence to plan how to solve the problem. Use a ? for the unknown.
   $45 - 18 - 15 = ?$
   c. **Solve It:** Solve the number sentence. Then fill in the blank.
   Jenny has 12 grapes left.
   d. Explain how to estimate to check your answer.
   Possible answer. 18 is about 20. 45 – 20 – 15 is 10. Ten is close to my answer of 12, so my answer checks.

176 SUBTRACT-SUBTRACT STORY PROBLEMS (A)

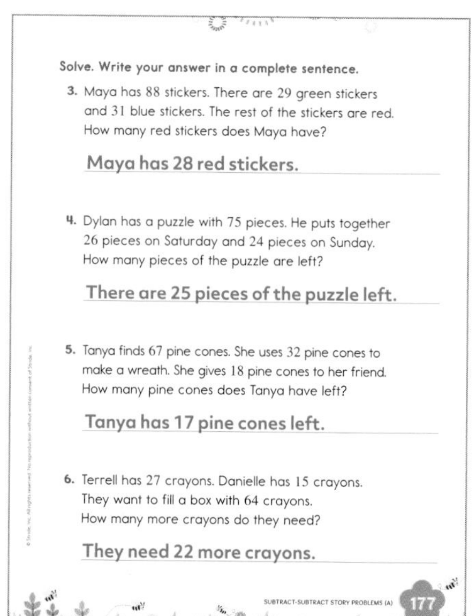

Solve. Write your answer in a complete sentence.

3. Maya has 88 stickers. There are 29 green stickers and 31 blue stickers. The rest of the stickers are red. How many red stickers does Maya have?
   Maya has 28 red stickers.
4. Dylan has a puzzle with 75 pieces. He puts together 26 pieces on Saturday and 24 pieces on Sunday. How many pieces of the puzzle are left?
   There are 25 pieces of the puzzle left.
5. Tanya finds 67 pine cones. She uses 32 pine cones to make a wreath. She gives 18 pine cones to her friend. How many pine cones does Tanya have left?
   Tanya has 17 pine cones left.
6. Terrell has 27 crayons. Danielle has 15 crayons. They want to fill a box with 64 crayons. How many more crayons do they need?
   They need 22 more crayons.

SUBTRACT-SUBTRACT STORY PROBLEMS (A) 177

WRAP-UP

Solving Subtract-Subtract Story Problems

Students will solve a problem to show that they understand how to solve story problems with two subtraction steps.

Subtract-Subtract Story Problems (B)

Lesson Overview

ACTIVITY	ACTIVITY TITLE	TIME	ONLINE/OFFLINE
GET READY	Introduction to Subtract-Subtract Story Problems (B)	2 minutes	online
	Subtracting 4 and 5 Math Facts Game	7 minutes	online
LEARN AND TRY IT	Solving Subtract-Subtract Money and Length Problems	15 minutes	online
	Solve Subtract-Subtract Money and Length Problems	10 minutes	online
ALL ABOUT ME	Brain Break	1 minute	online or offline
TRY IT	Practice Solving Subtract-Subtract Money and Length Problems	20 minutes	online and offline
WRAP-UP	Solving Subtract-Subtract Money and Length Problems	5 minutes	online

Content Background

Students will learn how to solve money and length story problems with two subtraction steps. Money story problems involve problems about either dollars or cents. Length story problems involve lengths given in the same unit. Students will continue to apply the three story problem steps to solve each problem.

MATERIALS

Supplied

- *Math 2 Activity Book:* Practice Solving Subtract-Subtract Money and Length Problems

Lesson Goals

- Solve subtract-subtract story problems about money.
- Solve subtract-subtract story problems about length.

GET READY

Introduction to Subtract-Subtract Story Problems (B)

Students will get a glimpse of what they will learn about in the lesson. They will also read the lesson goals.

Subtracting 4 and 5 Math Facts Game

Students will play a game to practice subtracting 4 and 5.

LEARN AND TRY IT

LEARN Solving Subtract-Subtract Money and Length Problems

Students will learn how to solve story problems about money and length with two subtraction steps.

TRY IT Solve Subtract-Subtract Money and Length Problems

Students will practice solving story problems about money and length with two subtraction steps. Support will be provided to help students overcome misconceptions.

TRY IT Practice Solving Subtract-Subtract Money and Length Problems

Students will complete online practice problems. Then they will complete Practice Solving Subtract-Subtract Money and Length Problems from *Math 2 Activity Book*.

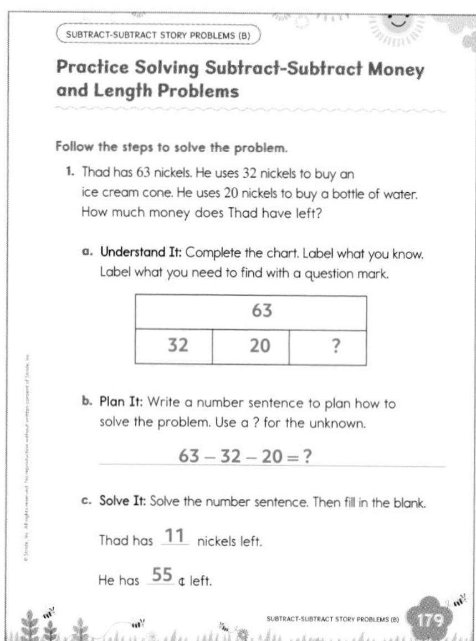

SUBTRACT-SUBTRACT STORY PROBLEMS (B)

Practice Solving Subtract-Subtract Money and Length Problems

Follow the steps to solve the problem.

1. Thad has 63 nickels. He uses 32 nickels to buy an ice cream cone. He uses 20 nickels to buy a bottle of water. How much money does Thad have left?

   a. **Understand It:** Complete the chart. Label what you know. Label what you need to find with a question mark.

63		
32	20	?

   b. **Plan It:** Write a number sentence to plan how to solve the problem. Use a ? for the unknown.

   63 – 32 – 20 = ?

   c. **Solve It:** Solve the number sentence. Then fill in the blank.

   Thad has 11 nickels left.

   He has 55 ¢ left.

SUBTRACT-SUBTRACT STORY PROBLEMS (B) 179

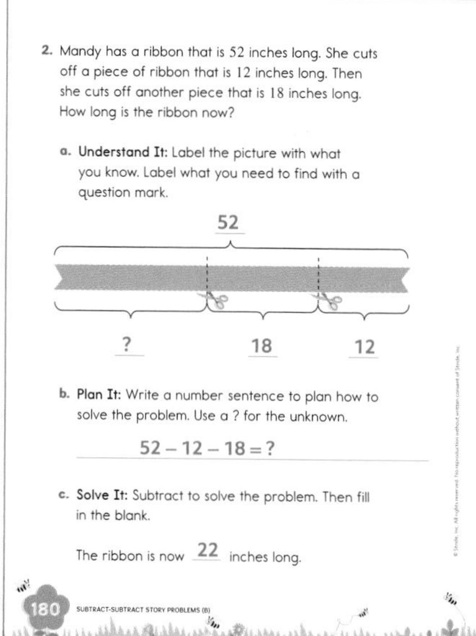

2. Mandy has a ribbon that is 52 inches long. She cuts off a piece of ribbon that is 12 inches long. Then she cuts off another piece that is 18 inches long. How long is the ribbon now?

   a. **Understand It:** Label the picture with what you know. Label what you need to find with a question mark.

   b. **Plan It:** Write a number sentence to plan how to solve the problem. Use a ? for the unknown.

   52 – 12 – 18 = ?

   c. **Solve It:** Subtract to solve the problem. Then fill in the blank.

   The ribbon is now 22 inches long.

180 SUBTRACT-SUBTRACT STORY PROBLEMS (B)

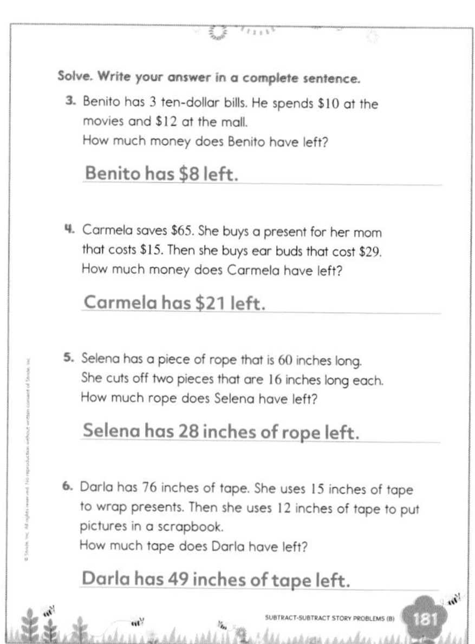

Solve. Write your answer in a complete sentence.

3. Benito has 3 ten-dollar bills. He spends $10 at the movies and $12 at the mall. How much money does Benito have left?

   Benito has $8 left.

4. Carmela saves $65. She buys a present for her mom that costs $15. Then she buys ear buds that cost $29. How much money does Carmela have left?

   Carmela has $21 left.

5. Selena has a piece of rope that is 60 inches long. She cuts off two pieces that are 16 inches long each. How much rope does Selena have left?

   Selena has 28 inches of rope left.

6. Darla has 76 inches of tape. She uses 15 inches of tape to wrap presents. Then she uses 12 inches of tape to put pictures in a scrapbook. How much tape does Darla have left?

   Darla has 49 inches of tape left.

SUBTRACT-SUBTRACT STORY PROBLEMS (B) 181

WRAP-UP

Solving Subtract-Subtract Story Problems

Students will solve problems to show that they understand how to solve money and length story problems with two subtraction steps.

Subtract-Subtract Story Problems (C)

Lesson Overview

ACTIVITY	ACTIVITY TITLE	TIME	ONLINE/OFFLINE
GET READY	Introduction to Subtract-Subtract Story Problems (C)	**2** minutes	
TRY IT	Review Subtract-Subtract Story Problems	**18** minutes	
QUIZ	Subtract-Subtract Story Problems	**25** minutes	
WRAP-UP	More Math Practice	**15** minutes	

Lesson Goals

- Review solving subtract-subtract story problems.
- Take a quiz.

MATERIALS

There are no materials to gather for this lesson.

GET READY

Introduction to Subtract-Subtract Story Problems (C)

Students will read the lesson goals.

TRY IT

Review Subtract-Subtract Story Problems

Students will answer questions to review what they have learned about solving subtract-subtract story problems.

QUIZ

Subtract-Subtract Story Problems

Students will complete the Subtract-Subtract Story Problems quiz.

WRAP-UP

More Math Practice

Students will practice skills according to their individual needs.

Add and Subtract Story Problems (A)

Lesson Overview

ACTIVITY	ACTIVITY TITLE	TIME	ONLINE/OFFLINE
GET READY	Introduction to Add and Subtract Story Problems (A)	**2** minutes	
	Look Back at Using Friendly Numbers to Add and Subtract	**7** minutes	
LEARN AND **TRY IT**	Solving Add and Subtract Story Problems	**15** minutes	
	Solve Add and Subtract Story Problems	**10** minutes	
ALL ABOUT ME	Brain Break	**1** minute	or
TRY IT	Practice Solving Add and Subtract Story Problems	**20** minutes	and
WRAP-UP	Solving Add and Subtract Story Problems	**5** minutes	

Content Background

Students will learn how to solve story problems with one addition step and one subtraction step. The problems can involve amounts that are combined, amounts that change, or amounts that are compared. Sometimes the subtraction step must be completed first, while other times the addition step must be completed first. Encourage students to read each problem carefully to determine how to solve the problem. Students will continue to apply the three story problem steps to solve each problem.

MATERIALS

Supplied

- *Math 2 Activity Book:* Practice Solving Add and Subtract Story Problems

Lesson Goals

- Solve two-step addition and subtraction story problems.

GET READY

Introduction to Add and Subtract Story Problems (A)

Students will get a glimpse of what they will learn about in the lesson. They will also read the lesson goals

Look Back at Using Friendly Numbers to Add and Subtract

Students will review and practice the prerequisite skill of using friendly numbers to add and subtract.

LEARN AND TRY IT

LEARN Solving Add and Subtract Story Problems

Students will learn how to solve story problems with an addition step and a subtraction step.

TIP Students must determine whether to add or subtract first to solve these story problems. They can apply what they have learned about words in add-add and subtract-subtract story problems to determine whether to add or subtract first.

TRY IT Solve Add and Subtract Story Problems

Students will practice solving story problems with an addition step and a subtraction step. Support will be provided to help students overcome misconceptions.

TRY IT Practice Solving Add and Subtract Story Problems

Students will complete online practice problems. Then they will complete Practice Solving Add and Subtract Story Problems from *Math 2 Activity Book*.

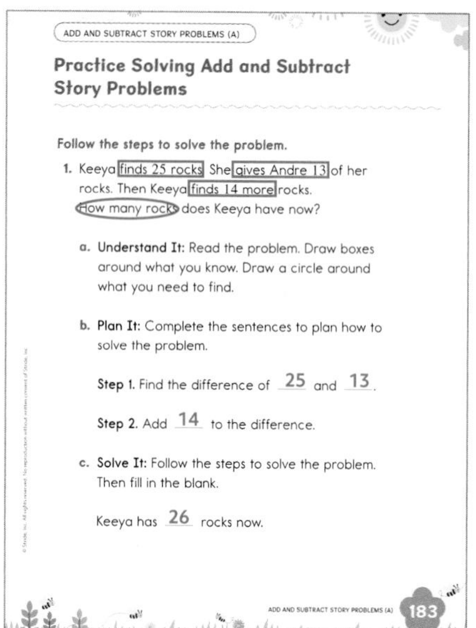

ADD AND SUBTRACT STORY PROBLEMS (A)

Practice Solving Add and Subtract Story Problems

Follow the steps to solve the problem.

1. Keeya finds 25 rocks. She gives Andre 13 of her rocks. Then Keeya finds 14 more rocks. How many rocks does Keeya have now?

   a. **Understand It:** Read the problem. Draw boxes around what you know. Draw a circle around what you need to find.

   b. **Plan It:** Complete the sentences to plan how to solve the problem.

   Step 1. Find the difference of 25 and 13.

   Step 2. Add 14 to the difference.

   c. **Solve It:** Follow the steps to solve the problem. Then fill in the blank.

   Keeya has 26 rocks now.

ADD AND SUBTRACT STORY PROBLEMS (A) 183

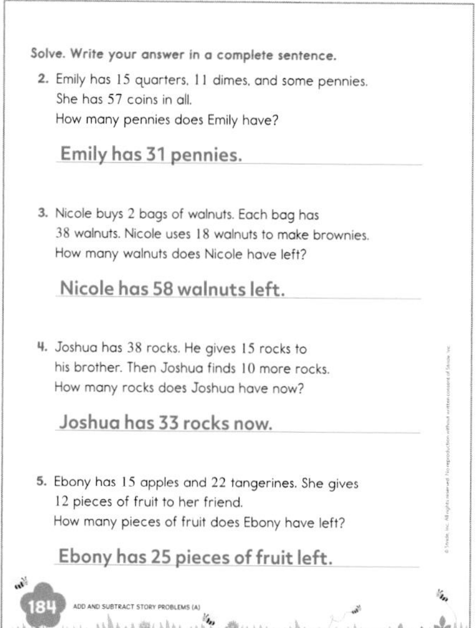

Solve. Write your answer in a complete sentence.

2. Emily has 15 quarters, 11 dimes, and some pennies. She has 57 coins in all. How many pennies does Emily have?

   Emily has 31 pennies.

3. Nicole buys 2 bags of walnuts. Each bag has 38 walnuts. Nicole uses 18 walnuts to make brownies. How many walnuts does Nicole have left?

   Nicole has 58 walnuts left.

4. Joshua has 38 rocks. He gives 15 rocks to his brother. Then Joshua finds 10 more rocks. How many rocks does Joshua have now?

   Joshua has 33 rocks now.

5. Ebony has 15 apples and 22 tangerines. She gives 12 pieces of fruit to her friend. How many pieces of fruit does Ebony have left?

   Ebony has 25 pieces of fruit left.

184 ADD AND SUBTRACT STORY PROBLEMS (A)

WRAP-UP

Solving Add and Subtract Story Problems

Students will solve a problem to show that they understand how to solve story problems with an addition step and a subtraction step.

Add and Subtract Story Problems (B)

Lesson Overview

ACTIVITY	ACTIVITY TITLE	TIME	ONLINE/OFFLINE
GET READY	Introduction to Add and Subtract Story Problems (B)	**2** minutes	online
	Subtracting 6 and 7 Math Facts	**7** minutes	online
LEARN AND TRY IT	Solving Money and Length Add and Subtract Problems	**15** minutes	online
	Solve Money and Length Add and Subtract Problems	**10** minutes	online
ALL ABOUT ME	Brain Break	**1** minute	online or offline
TRY IT	Practice Solving Money and Length Add and Subtract Problems	**20** minutes	online and offline
WRAP-UP	Solving Money and Length Add and Subtract Problems	**5** minutes	online

Content Background

Students will learn how to solve money and length story problems with one addition step and one subtraction step. Money story problems involve problems about either dollars or cents. Length story problems involve lengths given in the same unit. Sometimes the subtraction step must be completed first, while other times the addition step must be completed first. Encourage students to read each problem carefully to determine how to solve the problem. Students will continue to apply the three story problem steps to solve each problem.

MATERIALS

Supplied

- *Math 2 Activity Book:* Practice Solving Subtract-Subtract Money and Length Problems

Lesson Goals

- Solve two-step addition and subtraction story problems about money.
- Solve two-step addition and subtraction story problems about length.

GET READY

Introduction to Add and Subtract Story Problems (B)

Students will get a glimpse of what they will learn about in the lesson. They will also read the lesson goals.

Subtracting 6 and 7 Math Facts

Students will practice subtracting 6 and 7.

LEARN AND TRY IT

LEARN Solving Money and Length Add and Subtract Problems

Students will learn how to solve story problems about money and length with an addition step and a subtraction step.

TRY IT Solve Money and Length Add and Subtract Problems

Students will practice solving story problems about money and length with an addition step and a subtraction step. Support will be provided to help students overcome misconceptions.

TRY IT Practice Solving Money and Length Add and Subtract Problems

Students will complete online practice problems. Then they will complete Practice Solving Money and Length Add and Subtract Problems from *Math 2 Activity Book*.

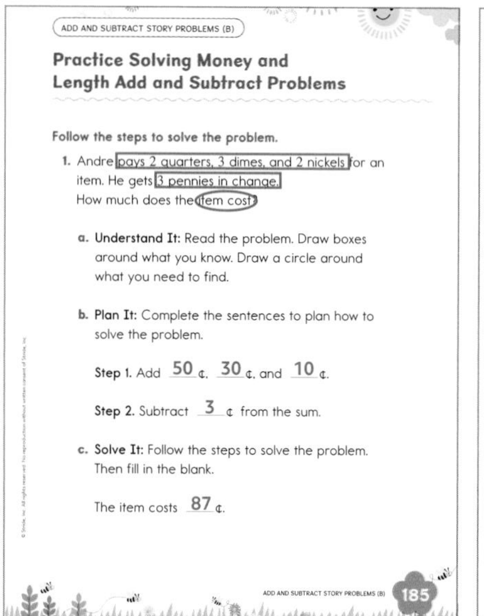

ADD AND SUBTRACT STORY PROBLEMS (B)

Practice Solving Money and Length Add and Subtract Problems

Follow the steps to solve the problem.

1. Andre pays 2 quarters, 3 dimes, and 2 nickels for an item. He gets 3 pennies in change. How much does the item cost?

   a. **Understand It:** Read the problem. Draw boxes around what you know. Draw a circle around what you need to find.

   b. **Plan It:** Complete the sentences to plan how to solve the problem.

   Step 1. Add 50 ¢, 30 ¢, and 10 ¢.

   Step 2. Subtract 3 ¢ from the sum.

   c. **Solve It:** Follow the steps to solve the problem. Then fill in the blank.

   The item costs 87 ¢.

ADD AND SUBTRACT STORY PROBLEMS (B) 185

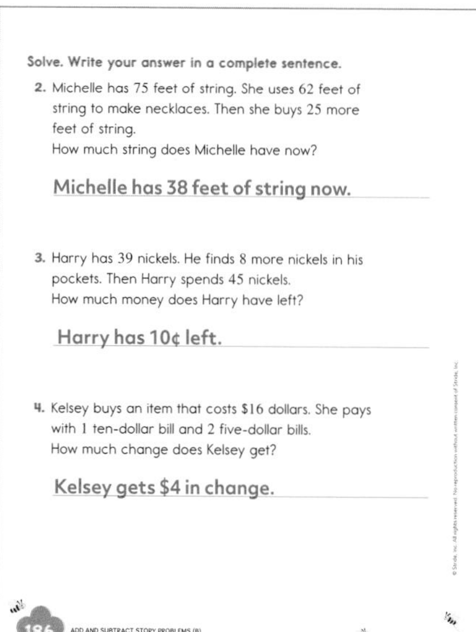

Solve. Write your answer in a complete sentence.

2. Michelle has 75 feet of string. She uses 62 feet of string to make necklaces. Then she buys 25 more feet of string. How much string does Michelle have now?

   Michelle has 38 feet of string now.

3. Harry has 39 nickels. He finds 8 more nickels in his pockets. Then Harry spends 45 nickels. How much money does Harry have left?

   Harry has 10¢ left.

4. Kelsey buys an item that costs $16 dollars. She pays with 1 ten-dollar bill and 2 five-dollar bills. How much change does Kelsey get?

   Kelsey gets $4 in change.

186 ADD AND SUBTRACT STORY PROBLEMS (B)

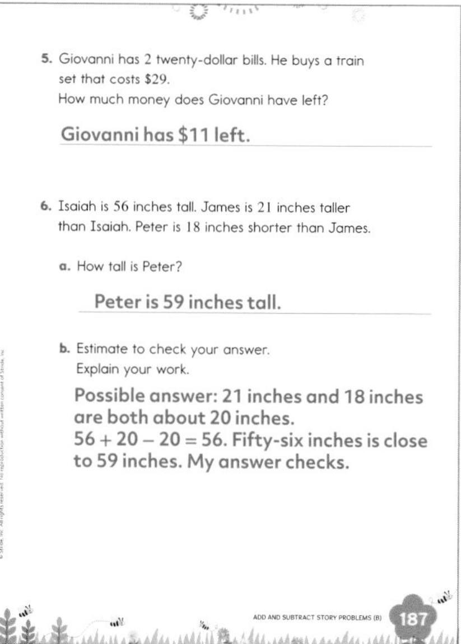

5. Giovanni has 2 twenty-dollar bills. He buys a train set that costs $29. How much money does Giovanni have left?

   Giovanni has $11 left.

6. Isaiah is 56 inches tall. James is 21 inches taller than Isaiah. Peter is 18 inches shorter than James.

   a. How tall is Peter?

   Peter is 59 inches tall.

   b. Estimate to check your answer. Explain your work.

   Possible answer: 21 inches and 18 inches are both about 20 inches. 56 + 20 − 20 = 56. Fifty-six inches is close to 59 inches. My answer checks.

ADD AND SUBTRACT STORY PROBLEMS (B) 187

WRAP-UP

Solving Money and Length Add and Subtract Problems

Students will solve problems to show that they understand how to solve money and length story problems with an addition step and a subtraction step.

Add and Subtract Story Problems (C)

Lesson Overview

ACTIVITY	ACTIVITY TITLE	TIME	ONLINE/OFFLINE
GET READY	Introduction to Add and Subtract Story Problems (C)	**2** minutes	
TRY IT	Review Add and Subtract Story Problems	**18** minutes	
QUIZ	Add and Subtract Story Problems	**25** minutes	
WRAP-UP	More Math Practice	**15** minutes	

Lesson Goals

- Review solving two-step addition and subtraction story problems.
- Take a quiz.

MATERIALS

There are no materials to gather for this lesson.

GET READY

Introduction to Add and Subtract Story Problems (C)

Students will read the lesson goals.

TRY IT

Review Add and Subtract Story Problems

Students will answer questions to review what they have learned about solving two-step addition and subtraction story problems.

QUIZ

Add and Subtract Story Problems

Students will complete the Add and Subtract Story Problems quiz.

WRAP-UP

More Math Practice

Students will practice skills according to their individual needs.

Thinking About Story Problems (A)

Lesson Overview

ACTIVITY	ACTIVITY TITLE	TIME	ONLINE/OFFLINE
GET READY	Introduction to Thinking About Story Problems (A)	**2** minutes	online
	Look Back at Clue Words	**7** minutes	online
LEARN AND **TRY IT**	Solving One-Step Story Problems	**7** minutes	online
	Solve One-Step Story Problems	**7** minutes	online
ALL ABOUT ME	Brain Break	**1** minute	online or offline
LEARN AND **TRY IT**	Writing One-Step Story Problems	**7** minutes	online
	Write One-Step Story Problems	**7** minutes	online
	Practice Thinking About One-Step Story Problems	**20** minutes	online and offline
WRAP-UP	Thinking About One-Step Story Problems	**2** minutes	online

Content Background

Students will learn how to solve and write one-step story problems. The problems can involve amounts that are combined, amounts that change, or amounts that are compared. Students will continue to apply the three story problem steps.

Solving Story Problems

Students have learned to solve combine, change, and compare story problems. The one-step story problems were separated into specific categories in each lesson. In this lesson, students must figure out what type of problem they are solving. They will learn to identify words that indicate whether to add or subtract. Here are some common addition and subtraction clue words.

Addition Clue Words: and, more, in all, altogether, total, sum

Subtraction Clue Words: fewer than, less than, more than, difference, has left

Students should be encouraged to read each problem carefully to identify clue words during the Understand It step of the story problem steps.

MATERIALS

Supplied

- *Math 2 Activity Book:* Practice Thinking About One-Step Story Problems

Writing Story Problems

Story problems start with facts about a situation and end with a question about those facts. In this lesson, students will create story problems that can be solved in one step. Sometimes they will be given facts in a picture , and they can choose how the facts are related. Other times they will be given a relationship in a number sentence, and they can choose what amounts the numbers represent. Students should be encouraged to use their creativity and curiosity to create their own story problems.

Lesson Goals

- Solve one-step story problems.
- Write one-step story problems.

GET READY

Introduction to Thinking About Story Problems (A)

Students will get a glimpse of what they will learn about in the lesson. They will also read the lesson goals.

Look Back at Clue Words

Students will review and practice the prerequisite skill of using clue words to solve story problems.

LEARN AND TRY IT

LEARN Solving One-Step Story Problems

Students will learn how to solve a variety of one-step story problems by identifying clue words.

TRY IT Solve One-Step Story Problems

Students will practice solving a variety of one-step story problems. Support will be provided to help students overcome misconceptions.

LEARN Writing One-Step Story Problems

Students will learn how to write one-step story problems.

TRY IT Write One-Step Story Problems

Students will practice writing one-step story problems. Support will be provided to help students overcome misconceptions.

TRY IT Practice Thinking About One-Step Story Problems

Students will complete online practice problems. Then they will complete Practice Thinking About One-Step Story Problems from *Math 2 Activity Book*.

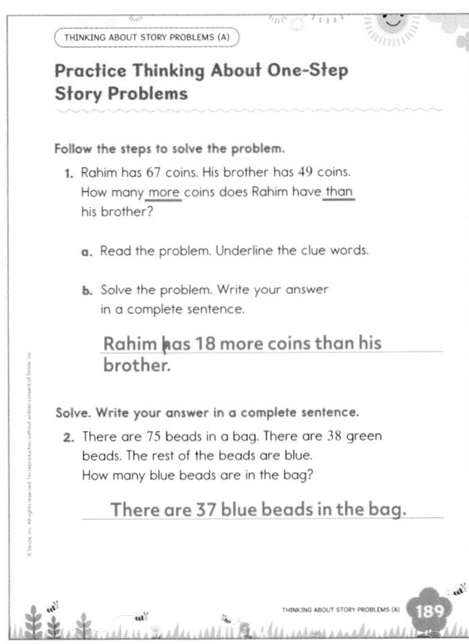

THINKING ABOUT STORY PROBLEMS (A)

Practice Thinking About One-Step Story Problems

Follow the steps to solve the problem.

1. Rahim has 67 coins. His brother has 49 coins. How many more coins does Rahim have than his brother?
   a. Read the problem. Underline the clue words.
   b. Solve the problem. Write your answer in a complete sentence.

   Rahim has 18 more coins than his brother.

Solve. Write your answer in a complete sentence.

2. There are 75 beads in a bag. There are 38 green beads. The rest of the beads are blue. How many blue beads are in the bag?

   There are 37 blue beads in the bag.

THINKING ABOUT STORY PROBLEMS (A) 189

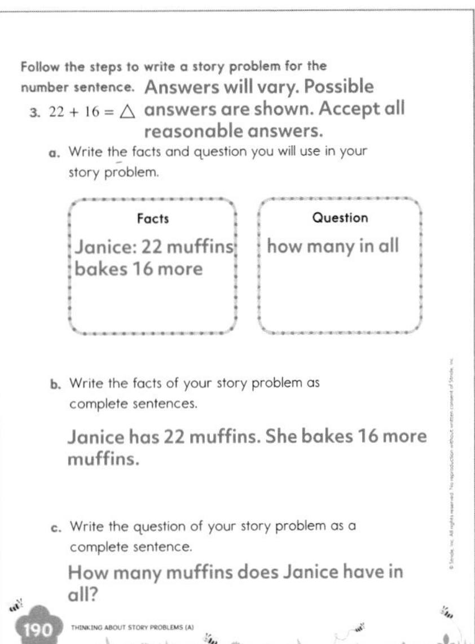

Follow the steps to write a story problem for the number sentence. Answers will vary. Possible answers are shown. Accept all reasonable answers.

3. $22 + 16 = \triangle$
   a. Write the facts and question you will use in your story problem.

Facts	Question
Janice: 22 muffins bakes 16 more	how many in all

   b. Write the facts of your story problem as complete sentences.

   Janice has 22 muffins. She bakes 16 more muffins.

   c. Write the question of your story problem as a complete sentence.

   How many muffins does Janice have in all?

190 THINKING ABOUT STORY PROBLEMS (A)

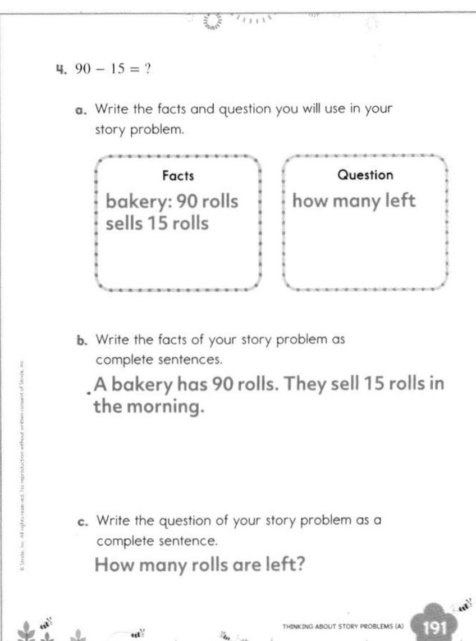

4. $90 - 15 = ?$
   a. Write the facts and question you will use in your story problem.

Facts	Question
bakery: 90 rolls sells 15 rolls	how many left

   b. Write the facts of your story problem as complete sentences.

   A bakery has 90 rolls. They sell 15 rolls in the morning.

   c. Write the question of your story problem as a complete sentence.

   How many rolls are left?

THINKING ABOUT STORY PROBLEMS (A) 191

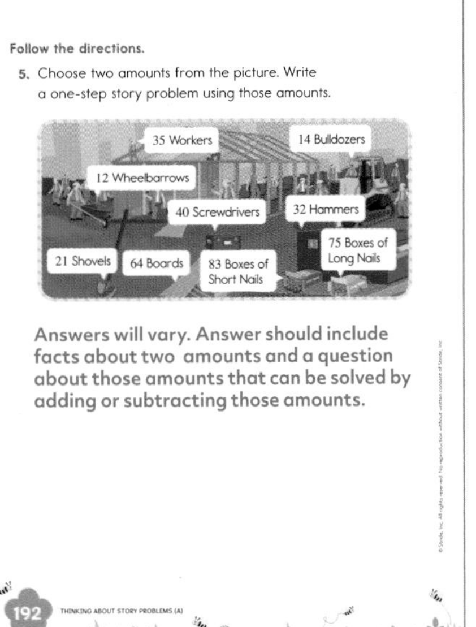

Follow the directions.

5. Choose two amounts from the picture. Write a one-step story problem using those amounts.

Answers will vary. Answer should include facts about two amounts and a question about those amounts that can be solved by adding or subtracting those amounts.

192 THINKING ABOUT STORY PROBLEMS (A)

WRAP-UP

Thinking About One-Step Story Problems

Students will solve a problem to show that they understand how to solve a one-step story problem.

Thinking About Story Problems (B)

Lesson Overview

ACTIVITY	ACTIVITY TITLE	TIME	ONLINE/OFFLINE
GET READY	Introduction to Thinking About Story Problems (B)	**2** minutes	online
	Subtracting 6 and 7 with Instant Recall	**7** minutes	online
LEARN AND **TRY IT**	Solving Two-Step Story Problems	**7** minutes	online
	Solve Two-Step Story Problems	**7** minutes	online
ALL ABOUT ME	Brain Break	**1** minute	online or offline
LEARN AND **TRY IT**	Writing Two-Step Story Problems	**7** minutes	online
	Write Two-Step Story Problems	**7** minutes	online
	Practice Thinking About Two-Step Story Problems	**20** minutes	online and offline
WRAP-UP	Thinking About Two-Step Story Problems	**2** minutes	online

Content Background

Students will learn how to solve and write two-step story problems. The problems can involve adding twice, subtracting twice, or both adding and subtracting. In this lesson, students must figure out what type of problem they are solving by identifying clue words. Students will continue to apply the three story problem steps. When students write their own story problems, they must give enough facts so that the problem can be solved by adding twice, subtracting twice, or adding once and subtracting once.

MATERIALS

Supplied

- *Math 2 Activity Book:* Practice Thinking About Two-Step Story Problems

Lesson Goals

- Solve two-step story problems.
- Write two-step story problems.

GET READY

Introduction to Thinking About Story Problems (B)

Students will get a glimpse of what they will learn about in the lesson. They will also read the lesson goals.

Subtracting 6 and 7 with Instant Recall

Students will practice subtracting 6 and 7.

LEARN AND TRY IT

LEARN Solving Two-Step Story Problems

Students will learn how to solve a variety of two-step story problems by identifying clue words.

TRY IT Solve Two-Step Story Problems

Students will practice solving a variety of two-step story problems. Support will be provided to help students overcome misconceptions.

LEARN Writing Two-Step Story Problems

Students will learn how to write two-step story problems.

TRY IT Write Two-Step Story Problems

Students will practice writing two-step story problems. Support will be provided to help students overcome misconceptions.

TRY IT Practice Thinking About Two-Step Story Problems

Students will complete online practice problems. Then they will complete Practice Thinking About Two-Step Story Problems from *Math 2 Activity Book*.

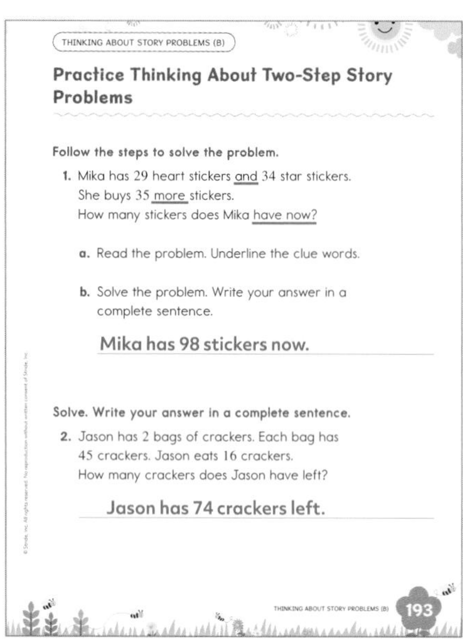
THINKING ABOUT STORY PROBLEMS (B)

Practice Thinking About Two-Step Story Problems

Follow the steps to solve the problem.

1. Mika has 29 heart stickers and 34 star stickers. She buys 35 more stickers. How many stickers does Mika have now?

   a. Read the problem. Underline the clue words.

   b. Solve the problem. Write your answer in a complete sentence.

   Mika has 98 stickers now.

Solve. Write your answer in a complete sentence.

2. Jason has 2 bags of crackers. Each bag has 45 crackers. Jason eats 16 crackers. How many crackers does Jason have left?

   Jason has 74 crackers left.

THINKING ABOUT STORY PROBLEMS (B) 193

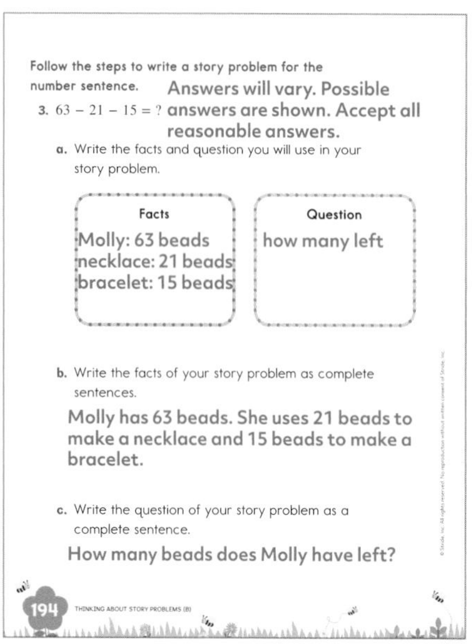
Follow the steps to write a story problem for the number sentence.

Answers will vary. Possible answers are shown. Accept all reasonable answers.

3. 63 − 21 − 15 = ?

   a. Write the facts and question you will use in your story problem.

Facts	Question
Molly: 63 beads necklace: 21 beads bracelet: 15 beads	how many left

   b. Write the facts of your story problem as complete sentences.

   Molly has 63 beads. She uses 21 beads to make a necklace and 15 beads to make a bracelet.

   c. Write the question of your story problem as a complete sentence.

   How many beads does Molly have left?

194 THINKING ABOUT STORY PROBLEMS (B)

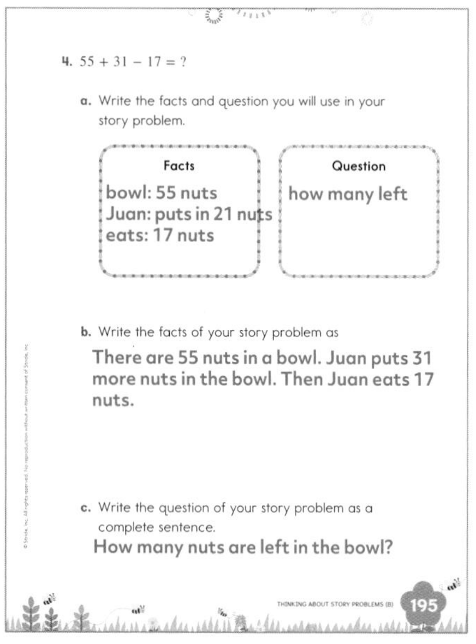
4. 55 + 31 − 17 = ?

   a. Write the facts and question you will use in your story problem.

Facts	Question
bowl: 55 nuts Juan: puts in 21 nuts eats: 17 nuts	how many left

   b. Write the facts of your story problem as

   There are 55 nuts in a bowl. Juan puts 31 more nuts in the bowl. Then Juan eats 17 nuts.

   c. Write the question of your story problem as a complete sentence.

   How many nuts are left in the bowl?

THINKING ABOUT STORY PROBLEMS (B) 195

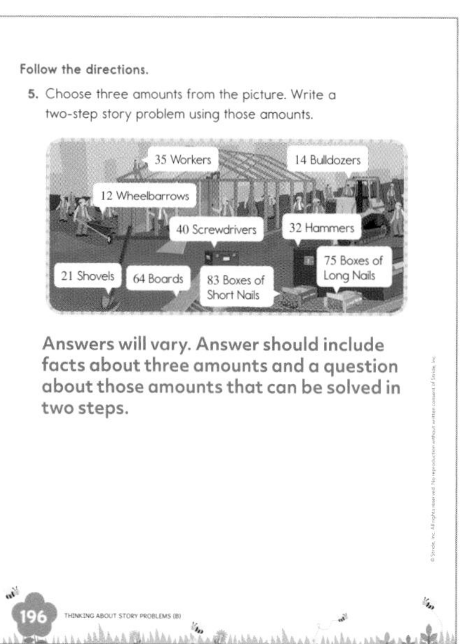
Follow the directions.

5. Choose three amounts from the picture. Write a two-step story problem using those amounts.

Answers will vary. Answer should include facts about three amounts and a question about those amounts that can be solved in two steps.

196 THINKING ABOUT STORY PROBLEMS (B)

WRAP-UP

Thinking About Two-Step Story Problems

Students will solve a problem to show that they understand how to solve a two-step story problem.

Thinking About Story Problems (C)

Lesson Overview

ACTIVITY	ACTIVITY TITLE	TIME	ONLINE/OFFLINE
GET READY	Introduction to Thinking About Story Problems (C)	2 minutes	online
	Subtracting 6 and 7 Math Facts Game	7 minutes	online
LEARN AND TRY IT	Solving Length and Money Story Problems	7 minutes	online
	Solve Length and Money Story Problems	7 minutes	online
ALL ABOUT ME	Brain Break	1 minute	online or offline
LEARN AND TRY IT	Writing Length and Money Story Problems	7 minutes	online
	Write Length and Money Story Problems	7 minutes	online
	Practice Thinking About Length and Money Story Problems	20 minutes	online and offline
WRAP-UP	Thinking About Length and Money Story Problems	2 minutes	online

Content Background

Students will learn how to solve and write story problems about length and money. Students will solve two-step story problems with dollar amounts, cent amounts, or lengths measured in the same units. Students will continue to apply the three story problem steps and determine whether to add twice, subtract twice, or add once and subtract once. When students write their own problems, they must give enough facts about dollar amounts, cent amounts, or lengths measured in the same units so that the problem can be solved in two steps.

MATERIALS

Supplied

- *Math 2 Activity Book:* Practice Thinking About Length and Money Story Problems

Lesson Goals

- Solve two-step story problems about length or money.
- Write two-step story problems about length or money.

GET READY

Introduction to Thinking About Story Problems (C)

Students will get a glimpse of what they will learn about in the lesson. They will also read the lesson goals.

Subtracting 6 and 7 Math Facts Game

Students will play a game to practice subtracting 6 and 7.

LEARN AND TRY IT

LEARN Solving Length and Money Story Problems

Students will learn how to solve a variety of two-step story problems about length and money by identifying clue words.

TRY IT Solve Length and Money Story Problems

Students will practice solving a variety of two-step story problems about length and money. Support will be provided to help students overcome misconceptions.

LEARN Writing Length and Money Story Problems

Students will learn how to write story problems about length and money.

TRY IT Write Length and Money Story Problems

Students will practice writing story problems about length and money. Support will be provided to help students overcome misconceptions.

TRY IT Practice Thinking About Length and Money Story Problems

Students will complete online practice problems. Then they will complete Practice Thinking About Length and Money Story Problems from *Math 2 Activity Book.*

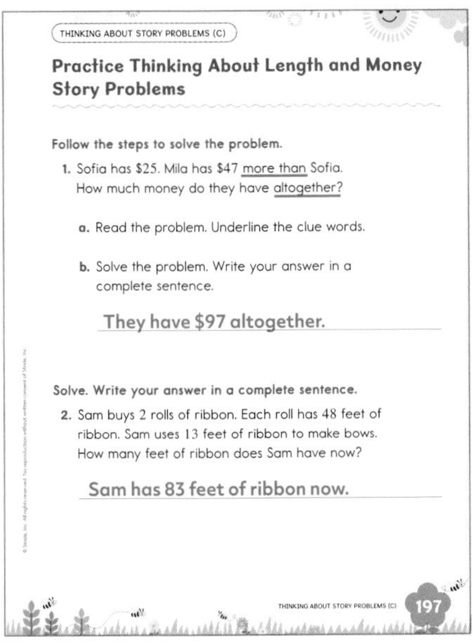

THINKING ABOUT STORY PROBLEMS (C)

Practice Thinking About Length and Money Story Problems

Follow the steps to solve the problem.

1. Sofia has $25. Mila has $47 more than Sofia. How much money do they have altogether?

   a. Read the problem. Underline the clue words.

   b. Solve the problem. Write your answer in a complete sentence.

   They have $97 altogether.

Solve. Write your answer in a complete sentence.

2. Sam buys 2 rolls of ribbon. Each roll has 48 feet of ribbon. Sam uses 13 feet of ribbon to make bows. How many feet of ribbon does Sam have now?

   Sam has 83 feet of ribbon now.

THINKING ABOUT STORY PROBLEMS (C) 197

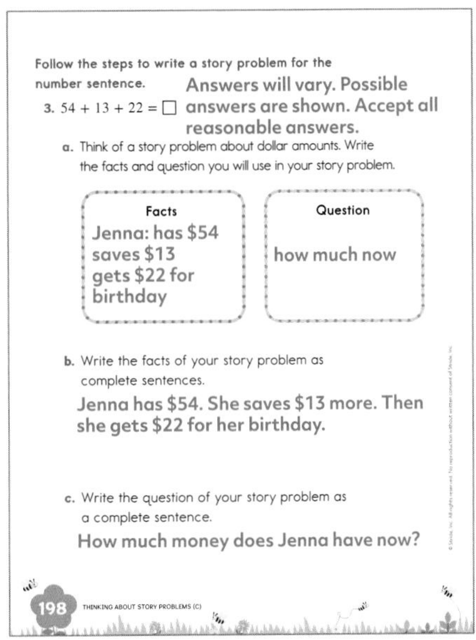

Follow the steps to write a story problem for the number sentence.

Answers will vary. Possible answers are shown. Accept all reasonable answers.

3. 54 + 13 + 22 = □

   a. Think of a story problem about dollar amounts. Write the facts and question you will use in your story problem.

Facts	Question
Jenna: has $54 saves $13 gets $22 for birthday	how much now

   b. Write the facts of your story problem as complete sentences.

   Jenna has $54. She saves $13 more. Then she gets $22 for her birthday.

   c. Write the question of your story problem as a complete sentence.

   How much money does Jenna have now?

198 THINKING ABOUT STORY PROBLEMS (C)

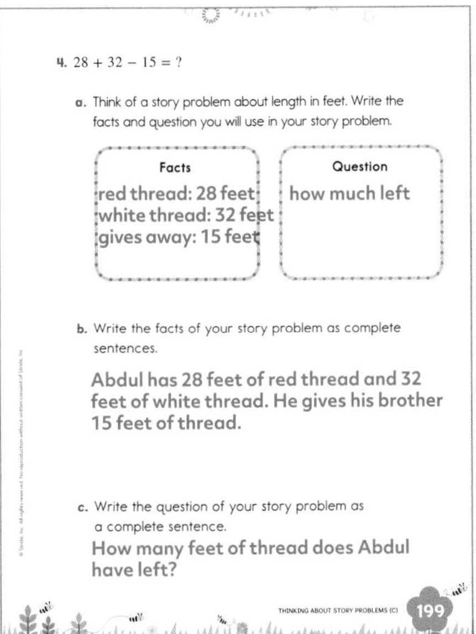

4. 28 + 32 − 15 = ?

   a. Think of a story problem about length in feet. Write the facts and question you will use in your story problem.

Facts	Question
red thread: 28 feet white thread: 32 feet gives away: 15 feet	how much left

   b. Write the facts of your story problem as complete sentences.

   Abdul has 28 feet of red thread and 32 feet of white thread. He gives his brother 15 feet of thread.

   c. Write the question of your story problem as a complete sentence.

   How many feet of thread does Abdul have left?

THINKING ABOUT STORY PROBLEMS (C) 199

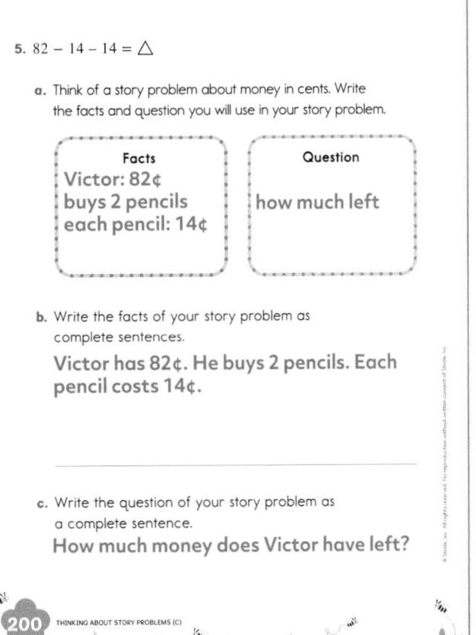

5. 82 − 14 − 14 = △

   a. Think of a story problem about money in cents. Write the facts and question you will use in your story problem.

Facts	Question
Victor: 82¢ buys 2 pencils each pencil: 14¢	how much left

   b. Write the facts of your story problem as complete sentences.

   Victor has 82¢. He buys 2 pencils. Each pencil costs 14¢.

   c. Write the question of your story problem as a complete sentence.

   How much money does Victor have left?

200 THINKING ABOUT STORY PROBLEMS (C)

WRAP-UP

Thinking About Length and Money Story Problems

Students will solve problems to show that they understand how to solve two-step story problems about length and money.

Thinking About Story Problems (D)

Lesson Overview

ACTIVITY	ACTIVITY TITLE	TIME	ONLINE/OFFLINE
GET READY	Introduction to Thinking About Story Problems (D)	**2** minutes	
TRY IT	Review Thinking About Story Problems	**18** minutes	
QUIZ	Thinking About Story Problems	**25** minutes	
WRAP-UP	More Math Practice	**15** minutes	

Lesson Goals

- Review solving and writing story problems.
- Take a quiz.

MATERIALS

There are no materials to gather for this lesson.

GET READY

Introduction to Thinking About Story Problems (D)

Students will read the lesson goals.

TRY IT

Review Thinking About Story Problems

Students will answer questions to review what they have learned about thinking about story problems.

QUIZ

Thinking About Story Problems

Students will complete the Thinking About Story Problems quiz.

WRAP-UP

More Math Practice

Students will practice skills according to their individual needs.

Solve Story Problems Wrap-Up

Lesson Overview

ACTIVITY	ACTIVITY TITLE	TIME	ONLINE/OFFLINE
GET READY	Introduction to Solve Story Problems Wrap-Up	**2** minutes	
TRY IT	Review Solve Story Problems	**23** minutes	
UNIT CHECKPOINT	Solve Story Problems	**35** minutes	

Lesson Goals

- Review solving story problems.
- Show what you know about solving story problems.

MATERIALS

There are no materials to gather for this lesson.

GET READY

Introduction to Solve Story Problems Wrap-Up

Students will read the lesson goals.

TRY IT

Review Solve Story Problems

Students will answer questions to review what they have learned about solving story problems.

UNIT CHECKPOINT

Solve Story Problems

Students will complete the Solve Story Problems Unit Checkpoint.

LEARNING COACH CHECK-IN This is a graded assignment. Make sure students complete the online assessment.

Numbers Through 1,000

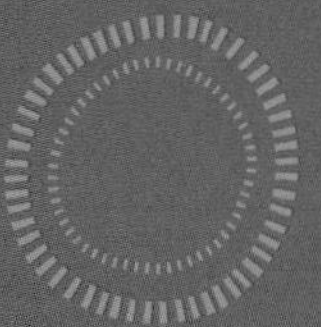

Count and Represent Larger Numbers (A)

Lesson Overview

ACTIVITY	ACTIVITY TITLE	TIME	ONLINE/OFFLINE
GET READY	Introduction to Count and Represent Larger Numbers (A)	**2** minutes	online
	Look Back at Reading and Writing Numbers to 500	**7** minutes	online
LEARN AND TRY IT	Counting by 1s up to 1,000	**15** minutes	online
	Count by 1s up to 1,000	**10** minutes	online
ALL ABOUT ME	Brain Break	**1** minute	online or offline
TRY IT	Practice Counting by 1s up to 1,000	**20** minutes	online and offline
WRAP-UP	Counting by 1s up to 1,000	**5** minutes	online

Content Background

Students will review counting to 500 and will learn to count through 1,000. The biggest challenge when counting above 100 is remembering to change to the next hundred after a number ending in 99. Students will be introduced to the thousands place when they learn that the number after 999 is 1,000, or one thousand.

MATERIALS

Supplied

- *Math 2 Activity Book:* Practice Counting by 1s up to 1,000

Lesson Goals

- Count by 1s up to 1,000.

GET READY

Introduction to Count and Represent Larger Numbers (A)

Students will get a glimpse of what they will learn about in the lesson. They will also read the lesson goals.

Look Back at Reading and Writing Numbers to 500

Students will review and practice the prerequisite skill of reading and writing numbers up to 500.

LEARN AND TRY IT

LEARN Counting by 1s up to 1,000

Students will learn to count by 1s up to 1,000.

OPTIONAL Encourage students to count aloud, making sure they change to the next hundred after a number ending in ninety-nine.

TRY IT Count by 1s up to 1,000

Students will practice counting by 1s up to 1,000. Support will be provided to help students overcome misconceptions.

TRY IT Practice Counting by 1s up to 1,000

Students will complete online practice problems. Then they will complete Practice Counting by 1s up to 1,000 from *Math 2 Activity Book*.

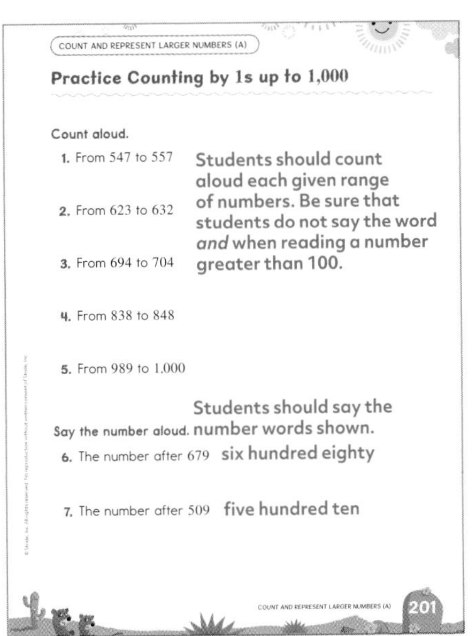
COUNT AND REPRESENT LARGER NUMBERS (A)

Practice Counting by 1s up to 1,000

Count aloud.

1. From 547 to 557
2. From 623 to 632
3. From 694 to 704
4. From 838 to 848
5. From 989 to 1,000

Students should count aloud each given range of numbers. Be sure that students do not say the word *and* when reading a number greater than 100.

Say the number aloud. **Students should say the number words shown.**

6. The number after 679 **six hundred eighty**
7. The number after 509 **five hundred ten**

COUNT AND REPRESENT LARGER NUMBERS (A) 201

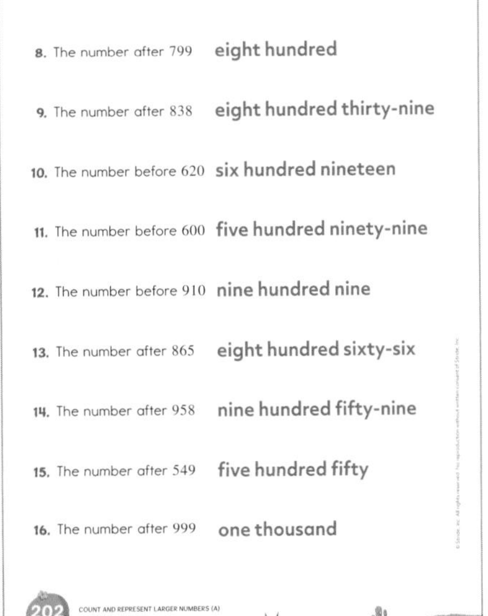
8. The number after 799 **eight hundred**
9. The number after 838 **eight hundred thirty-nine**
10. The number before 620 **six hundred nineteen**
11. The number before 600 **five hundred ninety-nine**
12. The number before 910 **nine hundred nine**
13. The number after 865 **eight hundred sixty-six**
14. The number after 958 **nine hundred fifty-nine**
15. The number after 549 **five hundred fifty**
16. The number after 999 **one thousand**

202 COUNT AND REPRESENT LARGER NUMBERS (A)

WRAP-UP

Counting by 1s up to 1,000

Students will solve a problem to show that they understand how to count by 1s up to 1,000.

Count and Represent Larger Numbers (B)

Lesson Overview

ACTIVITY	ACTIVITY TITLE	TIME	ONLINE/OFFLINE
GET READY	Introduction to Count and Represent Larger Numbers (B)	**2** minutes	online
	Subtracting 8 and 9 Math Facts	**8** minutes	online
LEARN AND **TRY IT**	Reading Numbers up to 1,000	**15** minutes	online
	Read Numbers up to 1,000	**10** minutes	online
	Practice Reading Numbers up to 1,000	**20** minutes	online and offline
WRAP-UP	Reading Numbers up to 1,000	**5** minutes	online

Content Background

Students will learn to read numbers up to 1,000 by reading the numbers in the hundreds, tens, and ones places. They will specifically learn that the number 1,000 is read *one thousand.*

MATERIALS

- *Math 2 Activity Book:* Practice Reading Numbers up to 1,000

Lesson Goals

- Read numbers up to 1,000.

GET READY

Introduction to Count and Represent Larger Numbers (B)

Students will get a glimpse of what they will learn about in the lesson. They will also read the lesson goals.

Subtracting 8 and 9 Math Facts

Students will practice subtracting 8 and 9.

LEARN AND TRY IT

LEARN Reading Numbers up to 1,000

Students will use place value to read numbers up to 1,000.

TIP Remind students not to say the word *and* when reading a number greater than 100. For example, 734 is read *seven hundred thirty-four*, not *seven hundred* **and** *thirty-four*.

TRY IT Read Numbers up to 1,000

Students will practice reading numbers up to 1,000. Support will be provided to help students overcome misconceptions.

TRY IT Practice Reading Numbers up to 1,000

Students will complete online practice problems. Then they will complete Practice Reading Numbers up to 1,000 from *Math 2 Activity Book*.

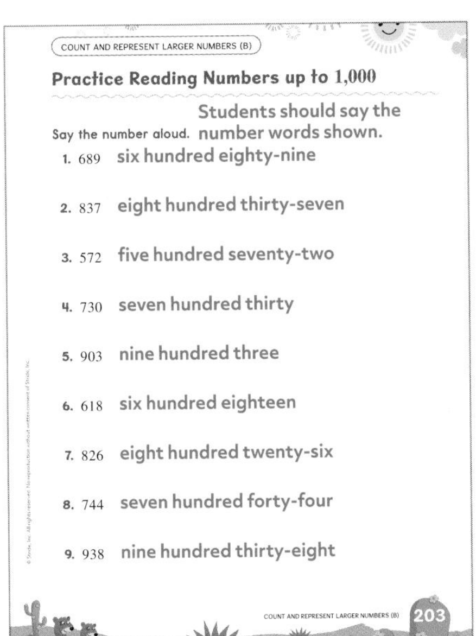

COUNT AND REPRESENT LARGER NUMBERS (B)

Practice Reading Numbers up to 1,000

Say the number aloud. Students should say the number words shown.

1. 689 six hundred eighty-nine
2. 837 eight hundred thirty-seven
3. 572 five hundred seventy-two
4. 730 seven hundred thirty
5. 903 nine hundred three
6. 618 six hundred eighteen
7. 826 eight hundred twenty-six
8. 744 seven hundred forty-four
9. 938 nine hundred thirty-eight

COUNT AND REPRESENT LARGER NUMBERS (B) 203

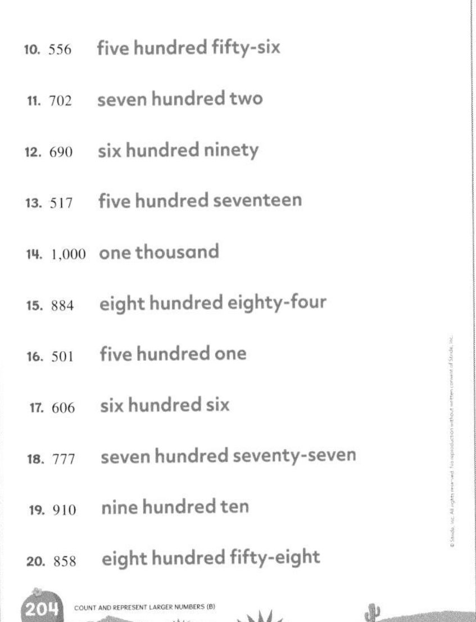

10. 556 five hundred fifty-six
11. 702 seven hundred two
12. 690 six hundred ninety
13. 517 five hundred seventeen
14. 1,000 one thousand
15. 884 eight hundred eighty-four
16. 501 five hundred one
17. 606 six hundred six
18. 777 seven hundred seventy-seven
19. 910 nine hundred ten
20. 858 eight hundred fifty-eight

204 COUNT AND REPRESENT LARGER NUMBERS (B)

WRAP-UP

Reading Numbers up to 1,000

Students will solve a problem to show that they understand how to read numbers up to 1,000.

Count and Represent Larger Numbers (C)

Lesson Overview

ACTIVITY	ACTIVITY TITLE	TIME	ONLINE/OFFLINE
GET READY	Introduction to Count and Represent Larger Numbers (C)	**2** minutes	online
	Subtracting 8 and 9 with Instant Recall	**7** minutes	online
LEARN AND TRY IT	Writing Larger Numbers as Number Words	**7** minutes	online
	Write Larger Numbers as Number Words	**7** minutes	online
ALL ABOUT ME	Brain Break	**1** minute	online or offline
LEARN AND TRY IT	Writing Larger Numbers from Number Words	**7** minutes	online
	Write Larger Numbers from Number Words	**7** minutes	online
	Practice Writing Larger Numbers	**20** minutes	online and offline
WRAP-UP	Writing Larger Numbers	**2** minutes	online

Content Background

Students will learn how to write number words to represent numbers up to 1,000. Students have experience with number words up to 500. Writing numbers from 500 to 999 is the same as writing numbers from 100 to 500. The number 1,000 has 1 thousand and no hundreds, tens, or ones. The number words for 1,000 are *one thousand*. Students will also learn to write numbers from number words using a place-value chart.

MATERIALS

Supplied

- *Math 2 Activity Book:* Practice Writing Larger Numbers

Lesson Goals

- Write number words for larger numbers.
- Write larger numbers from number words.

GET READY

Introduction to Count and Represent Larger Numbers (C)

Students will get a glimpse of what they will learn about in the lesson. They will also read the lesson goals.

Subtracting 8 and 9 with Instant Recall

Students will practice subtracting 8 and 9.

LEARN AND TRY IT

LEARN Writing Larger Numbers as Number Words

Students will write numbers through 1,000 as number words.

TIP Remind students to use place value for numbers that do not end in 00. They should write the number words for the tens and ones places using the patterns for numbers through 99. This includes putting a hyphen between the word for the tens and the word for the ones for numbers that end in 21 through 99 (and do not also end in 0).

TRY IT Write Larger Numbers as Number Words

Students will practice writing numbers through 1,000 as number words. Support will be provided to help students overcome misconceptions.

LEARN Writing Larger Numbers from Number Words

Students will learn how to use place value to write numbers through 1,000 from number words.

TRY IT Write Larger Numbers from Number Words

Students will practice writing numbers through 1,000 from number words. Support will be provided to help students overcome misconceptions.

TRY IT Practice Writing Larger Numbers

Students will complete online practice problems. Then they will complete Practice Writing Larger Numbers from *Math 2 Activity Book*.

SUPPORT For students having difficulty recalling or spelling number words, allow them to use the Number Words Chart on the first page of Practice Writing Numbers as Number Words in the activity book.

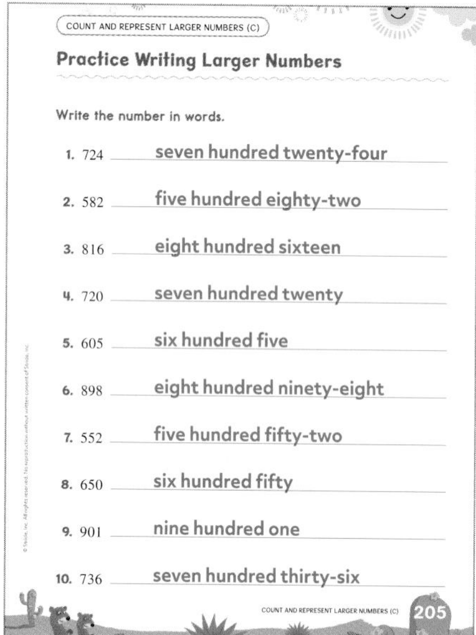

COUNT AND REPRESENT LARGER NUMBERS (C)

Practice Writing Larger Numbers

Write the number in words.

1. 724 seven hundred twenty-four
2. 582 five hundred eighty-two
3. 816 eight hundred sixteen
4. 720 seven hundred twenty
5. 605 six hundred five
6. 898 eight hundred ninety-eight
7. 552 five hundred fifty-two
8. 650 six hundred fifty
9. 901 nine hundred one
10. 736 seven hundred thirty-six

COUNT AND REPRESENT LARGER NUMBERS (C) 205

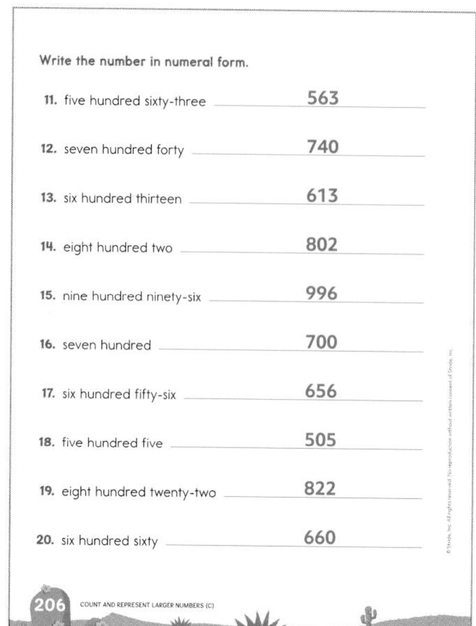

Write the number in numeral form.

11. five hundred sixty-three 563
12. seven hundred forty 740
13. six hundred thirteen 613
14. eight hundred two 802
15. nine hundred ninety-six 996
16. seven hundred 700
17. six hundred fifty-six 656
18. five hundred five 505
19. eight hundred twenty-two 822
20. six hundred sixty 660

206 COUNT AND REPRESENT LARGER NUMBERS (C)

WRAP-UP

Writing Larger Numbers

Students will solve problems to show that they understand how to write numbers through 1,000 as and from number words.

Count and Represent Larger Numbers (D)

Lesson Overview

ACTIVITY	ACTIVITY TITLE	TIME	ONLINE/OFFLINE
GET READY	Introduction to Count and Represent Larger Numbers (D)	2 minutes	
TRY IT	Review Count and Represent Larger Numbers	18 minutes	
QUIZ	Count and Represent Larger Numbers	25 minutes	
WRAP-UP	More Math Practice	15 minutes	

Lesson Goals

- Review counting, reading, and writing larger numbers.
- Take a quiz.

MATERIALS

There are no materials to gather for this lesson.

GET READY

Introduction to Count and Represent Larger Numbers (D)

Students will read the lesson goals.

TRY IT

Review Count and Represent Larger Numbers

Students will answer questions to review what they have learned about counting and representing larger numbers.

QUIZ

Count and Represent Larger Numbers

Students will complete the Count and Represent Larger Numbers quiz.

WRAP-UP

More Math Practice

Students will practice skills according to their individual needs.

Place Value of Larger Numbers (A)

Lesson Overview

ACTIVITY	ACTIVITY TITLE	TIME	ONLINE/OFFLINE
GET READY	Introduction to Place Value of Larger Numbers (A)	**2** minutes	online
	Look Back at Place Value in 3-Digit Numbers	**7** minutes	online
LEARN AND TRY IT	Identifying Place Value in Larger Numbers	**15** minutes	online
	Identify Place Value in Larger Numbers	**10** minutes	online
ALL ABOUT ME	Brain Break	**1** minute	online or offline
TRY IT	Practice Identifying Place Value in Larger Numbers	**20** minutes	online and offline
WRAP-UP	Identifying Place Value in Larger Numbers	**5** minutes	online

Content Background

Students will extend their understanding of place value and three-digit numbers to include numbers from 500 through 1,000. Students will also write numbers through 1,000 in unit form.

Base-10 Blocks

Students have experience representing numbers through 500 using hundreds flats, tens rods, and ones cubes. They have used base-10 blocks to learn that 10 ones is the same as 1 ten and that 10 tens is the same as 1 hundred. In this lesson, they will learn that 10 *hundreds* is the same as 1 *thousand*. They will also be introduced to a thousands cube. Students will not be expected to draw a representation of a thousands cube at this level.

Thousands	Hundreds	Tens	Ones
[thousands cube]			

MATERIALS

Supplied

- *Math 2 Activity Book:* Practice Identifying Place Value in Larger Numbers

KEYWORDS

place value – the value of a digit in a number

Example: The place value of the 2 in 23 is 20 or 2 tens.

unit form – a way to write a number by stating the place value of its digits

Example: The unit form of 415 is 4 hundreds, 1 ten, 5 ones.

Lesson Goals

- Find the place value of each digit in a larger number.
- Write larger numbers in unit form.

GET READY

Introduction to Place Value of Larger Numbers (A)

Students will get a glimpse of what they will learn about in the lesson. They will also read the lesson goals.

Look Back at Place Value in 3-Digit Numbers

Students will review and practice the prerequisite skill of identifying place value in three-digit numbers.

LEARN AND TRY IT

LEARN Identifying Place Value in Larger Numbers

Students will work with base-10 blocks to identify the place value of each digit in a larger number. They will also write numbers in unit form.

TRY IT Identify Place Value in Larger Numbers

Students will practice identifying the place value of each digit in a larger number and writing larger numbers in unit form. Support will be provided to help students overcome misconceptions.

TRY IT Practice Identifying Place Value in Larger Numbers

Students will complete online practice problems. Then they will complete Practice Identifying Place Value in Larger Numbers from *Math 2 Activity Book*.

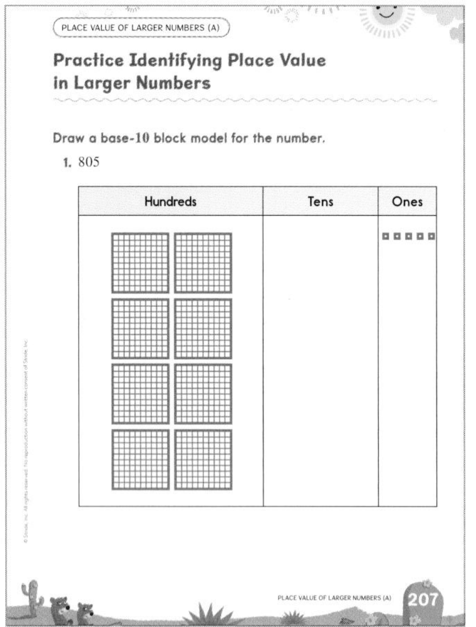
PLACE VALUE OF LARGER NUMBERS (A)

Practice Identifying Place Value in Larger Numbers

Draw a base-10 block model for the number.

1. 805

Hundreds	Tens	Ones

PLACE VALUE OF LARGER NUMBERS (A) 207

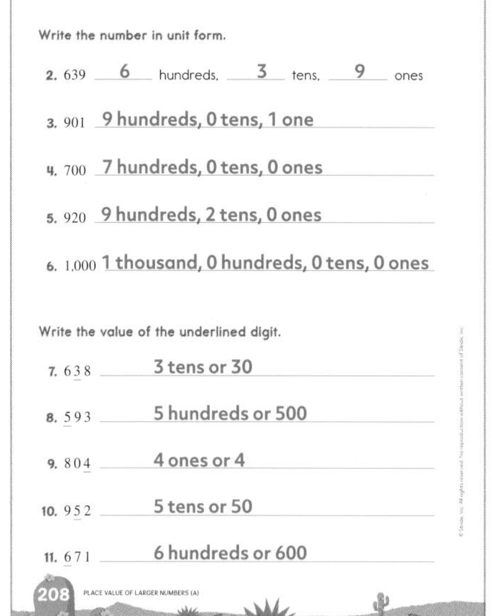
Write the number in unit form.

2. 639 6 hundreds, 3 tens, 9 ones
3. 901 9 hundreds, 0 tens, 1 one
4. 700 7 hundreds, 0 tens, 0 ones
5. 920 9 hundreds, 2 tens, 0 ones
6. 1,000 1 thousand, 0 hundreds, 0 tens, 0 ones

Write the value of the underlined digit.

7. 638 3 tens or 30
8. 593 5 hundreds or 500
9. 804 4 ones or 4
10. 952 5 tens or 50
11. 671 6 hundreds or 600

208 PLACE VALUE OF LARGER NUMBERS (A)

WRAP-UP

Identifying Place Value in Larger Numbers

Students will solve problems to show that they understand how to identify place value in larger numbers.

Place Value of Larger Numbers (B)

Lesson Overview

ACTIVITY	ACTIVITY TITLE	TIME	ONLINE/OFFLINE
GET READY	Introduction to Place Value of Larger Numbers (B)	**2** minutes	online
	Subtracting 8 and 9 Math Facts Game	**7** minutes	online
LEARN AND **TRY IT**	Writing Larger Numbers in Expanded Form	**7** minutes	online
	Write Larger Numbers in Expanded Form	**7** minutes	online
ALL ABOUT ME	Brain Break	**1** minute	online or offline
LEARN AND **TRY IT**	Writing Larger Numbers in Standard Form	**7** minutes	online
	Write Larger Numbers in Standard Form	**7** minutes	online
	Practice Writing Larger Numbers in Different Forms	**20** minutes	online and offline
WRAP-UP	Writing Larger Numbers in Different Forms	**2** minutes	online

Content Background

Students will extend their understanding of converting between expanded form and standard form to include numbers from 500 to 1,000. Students will continue to use models and an understanding of place value to determine the numbers of hundreds, tens, and ones in a three-digit number.

Lesson Goals

- Write larger numbers in expanded form.
- Write larger numbers in standard form.

MATERIALS

Supplied

- *Math 2 Activity Book:* Practice Writing Larger Numbers in Different Forms

KEYWORDS

expanded form – a way to write a number that shows the place value of each of its digits

Example: 428 = 400 + 20 + 8 or 4 hundreds + 2 tens + 8 ones

standard form – the usual way of writing a number using digits

Example: The standard form of 300 + 40 + 8 is 348.

GET READY

Introduction to Place Value of Larger Numbers (B)

Students will get a glimpse of what they will learn about in the lesson. They will also read the lesson goals.

Subtracting 8 and 9 Math Facts Game

Students will play a game to practice subtracting 8 and 9.

LEARN AND TRY IT

LEARN Writing Larger Numbers in Expanded Form

Students will learn how to write larger numbers in expanded form when given numbers in standard form.

SUPPORT If students have difficulty recognizing the value of each digit, encourage them to model the number using base-10 blocks.

TRY IT Write Larger Numbers in Expanded Form

Students will practice writing numbers in expanded form. Support will be provided to help students overcome misconceptions.

LEARN Writing Larger Numbers in Standard Form

Students will learn how to write larger numbers in standard form when given numbers in expanded form.

TRY IT Write Larger Numbers in Standard Form

Students will practice writing larger numbers in standard form. Support will be provided to help students overcome misconceptions.

TRY IT Practice Writing Larger Numbers in Different Forms

Students will complete online practice problems. Then they will complete Practice Writing Larger Numbers in Different Forms from *Math 2 Activity Book*.

PLACE VALUE OF LARGER NUMBERS (B)

Practice Writing Larger Numbers in Different Forms

Write the number in expanded form.

1. 736 = 7 hundreds + 3 tens + 6 ones
2. 549 = 5 hundreds + 4 tens + 9 ones
3. 630 = 6 hundreds + 3 tens + 0 ones
4. 893 = 800 + 90 + 3
5. 952 = 900 + 50 + 2
6. 790 = 700 + 90
7. 807 = 800 + 7
8. 682 600 + 80 + 2 or 6 hundreds + 8 tens + 2 ones
9. 926 900 + 20 + 6 or 9 hundreds + 2 tens + 6 ones

PLACE VALUE OF LARGER NUMBERS (B) 209

Write the number in standard form.

10. 5 hundreds + 7 tens + 2 ones = 572
11. 8 hundreds + 3 tens + 8 ones = 838
12. 6 hundreds + 3 tens + 6 ones = 636
13. 700 + 50 + 1 = 751
14. 900 + 30 + 2 = 932
15. 600 + 40 + 5 = 645
16. 500 + 0 + 5 = 505
17. 700 + 30 + 0 = 730
18. 900 + 60 + 6 = 966
19. 800 + 80 + 3 = 883

210 PLACE VALUE OF LARGER NUMBERS (B)

WRAP-UP

Writing Larger Numbers in Different Forms

Students will solve problems to show that they understand how to write larger numbers in standard form and expanded form.

Place Value of Larger Numbers (C)

Lesson Overview

ACTIVITY	ACTIVITY TITLE	TIME	ONLINE/OFFLINE
GET READY	Introduction to Place Value of Larger Numbers (C)	2 minutes	online
	Adding and Subtracting 1-Digit Numbers Math Facts	7 minutes	online
LEARN AND TRY IT	Composing and Decomposing Larger Numbers	15 minutes	online
	Compose and Decompose Larger Numbers	10 minutes	online
ALL ABOUT ME	Brain Break	1 minute	online or offline
TRY IT	Practice Composing and Decomposing Larger Numbers	20 minutes	online and offline
WRAP-UP	Composing and Decomposing Larger Numbers	5 minutes	online

Content Background

Students will extend their understanding of composing and decomposing numbers to include numbers from 500 through 1,000. They have learned to regroup 1 hundred as 10 tens and 1 ten as 10 ones. Students will continue to apply this knowledge as they compose and decompose larger numbers in multiple ways.

OPTIONAL Students can use physical base-10 blocks as they work through this lesson to help them solve problems. A printable version of base-10 blocks is linked in the lesson.

Lesson Goals

- Decompose a larger number in more than one way.
- Compose a larger number in more than one way.

MATERIALS

Supplied

- *Math 2 Activity Book:* Practice Composing and Decomposing Larger Numbers

KEYWORDS

compose a number – put a number together from smaller numbers

Example: $30 + 4 = 34$ and $20 + 14 = 34$

decompose a number – break a number into smaller numbers

Example: $53 = 50 + 3$ and $53 = 30 + 23$

regroup – use place-value concepts to rename numbers

Examples: 1 ten regroups into 10 ones; 1 hundred regroups into 10 tens

GET READY

Introduction to Place Value of Larger Numbers (C)

Students will get a glimpse of what they will learn about in the lesson. They will also read the lesson goals.

Adding and Subtracting 1-Digit Numbers Math Facts

Students will practice adding and subtracting one-digit numbers.

LEARN AND TRY IT

LEARN Composing and Decomposing Larger Numbers

Students will learn to compose and decompose larger numbers by regrouping.

TRY IT Compose and Decompose Larger Numbers

Students will practice composing and decomposing larger numbers. Support will be provided to help students overcome misconceptions.

TRY IT Practice Composing and Decomposing Larger Numbers

Students will complete online practice problems. Then they will complete Practice Composing and Decomposing Larger Numbers from *Math 2 Activity Book*.

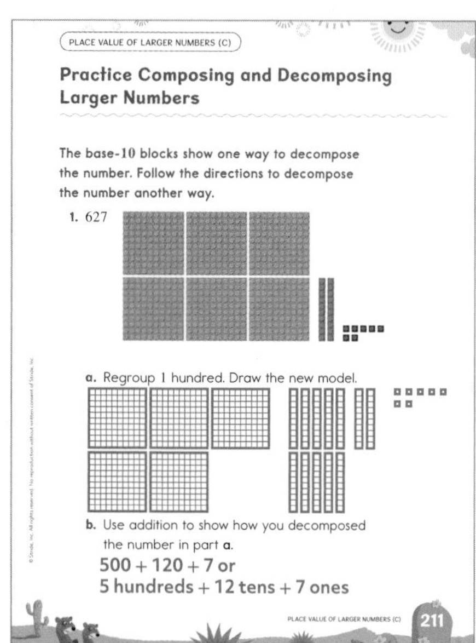
PLACE VALUE OF LARGER NUMBERS (C)

Practice Composing and Decomposing Larger Numbers

The base-10 blocks show one way to decompose the number. Follow the directions to decompose the number another way.

1. 627

a. Regroup 1 hundred. Draw the new model.

b. Use addition to show how you decomposed the number in part a.

500 + 120 + 7 or
5 hundreds + 12 tens + 7 ones

PLACE VALUE OF LARGER NUMBERS (C) 211

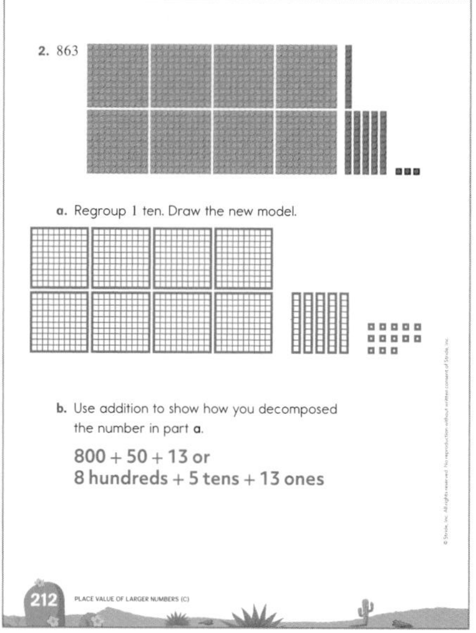
2. 863

a. Regroup 1 ten. Draw the new model.

b. Use addition to show how you decomposed the number in part a.

800 + 50 + 13 or
8 hundreds + 5 tens + 13 ones

212 PLACE VALUE OF LARGER NUMBERS (C)

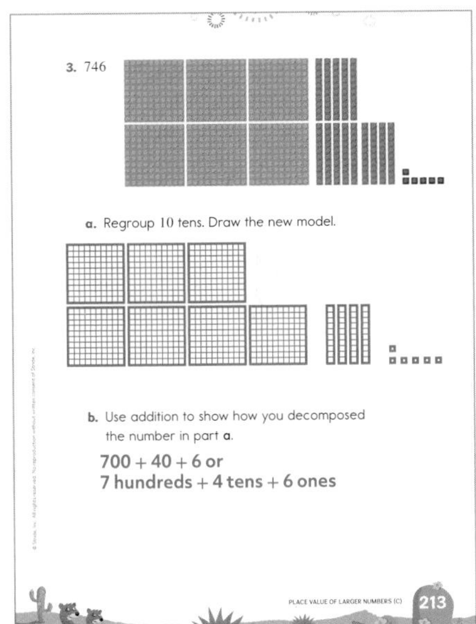

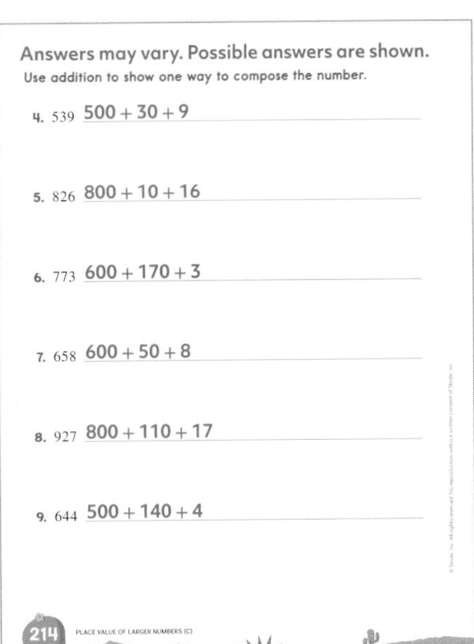

WRAP-UP

Composing and Decomposing Larger Numbers

Students will solve problems to show that they understand how to compose and decompose larger numbers.

Place Value of Larger Numbers (D)

Lesson Overview

ACTIVITY	ACTIVITY TITLE	TIME	ONLINE/OFFLINE
GET READY	Introduction to Place Value of Larger Numbers (D)	**2** minutes	
TRY IT	Review Place Value of Larger Numbers	**18** minutes	
QUIZ	Place Value of Larger Numbers	**25** minutes	
WRAP-UP	More Math Practice	**15** minutes	

Lesson Goals

- Review place value and expanded form of larger numbers.
- Review composing and decomposing larger numbers.
- Take a quiz.

MATERIALS

There are no materials to gather for this lesson.

GET READY

Introduction to Place Value of Larger Numbers (D)

Students will read the lesson goals.

TRY IT

Review Place Value of Larger Numbers

Students will answer questions to review what they have learned about place value of larger numbers.

QUIZ

Place Value of Larger Numbers

Students will complete the Place Value of Larger Numbers quiz.

WRAP-UP

More Math Practice

Students will practice skills according to their individual needs.

Compare and Order Larger Numbers (A)

Lesson Overview

ACTIVITY	ACTIVITY TITLE	TIME	ONLINE/OFFLINE
GET READY	Introduction to Compare and Order Larger Numbers (A)	**2** minutes	online
	Look Back at Ordering Numbers	**7** minutes	online
LEARN AND TRY IT	Using Models to Compare Larger Numbers	**15** minutes	online
	Use Models to Compare Larger Numbers	**10** minutes	online
ALL ABOUT ME	Brain Break	**1** minute	online or offline
TRY IT	Practice Using Models to Compare Larger Numbers	**20** minutes	online and offline
WRAP-UP	Using Models to Compare Larger Numbers	**5** minutes	online

Content Background

Students will expand their understanding of comparing three-digit numbers to numbers from 500 through 1,000. Both base-10 blocks and number lines will be used to model numbers. Students will continue to use symbols and words to express comparisons. Students will also be introduced to a new comparison symbol.

Not Equal Symbol

Students have experience using the symbols =, <, and > to compare numbers. When one number is greater than or less than another number, the numbers can also be compared using the ≠ symbol. For example, $652 < 699$ and $652 \neq 699$ are both comparison statements about the numbers 652 and 699. The statements convey different information, but they are both true.

Base-10 Blocks

Remind students to compare the hundreds first. If the hundreds are the same, compare the tens. If the tens are the same, compare the ones. The comparison is based on the first place value that differs.

Number Lines

Numbers on a number a line increase from left to right. When two numbers are plotted on a number line, the number on the left is less than the number on the right. In other words, the number on the right is greater than the number on the left.

MATERIALS

Supplied

- *Math 2 Activity Book:* Practice Using Models to Compare Larger Numbers

KEYWORDS

not equal symbol (≠) – symbol that means *not equal*

Example: "3 ≠ 5" means "3 is not equal to 5."

Lesson Goals

- Use models to compare larger numbers.

GET READY

Introduction to Compare and Order Larger Numbers (A)

Students will get a glimpse of what they will learn about in the lesson. They will also read the lesson goals.

Look Back at Ordering Numbers

Students will review and practice the prerequisite skill of ordering numbers up to 500.

LEARN AND TRY IT

LEARN Using Models to Compare Larger Numbers

Students will learn to use models to compare larger numbers.

TRY IT Use Models to Compare Larger Numbers

Students will practice using models to compare numbers. Support will be provided to help students overcome misconceptions.

TRY IT Practice Using Models to Compare Larger Numbers

Students will complete online practice problems. Then they will complete Practice Using Models to Compare Larger Numbers from *Math 2 Activity Book*.

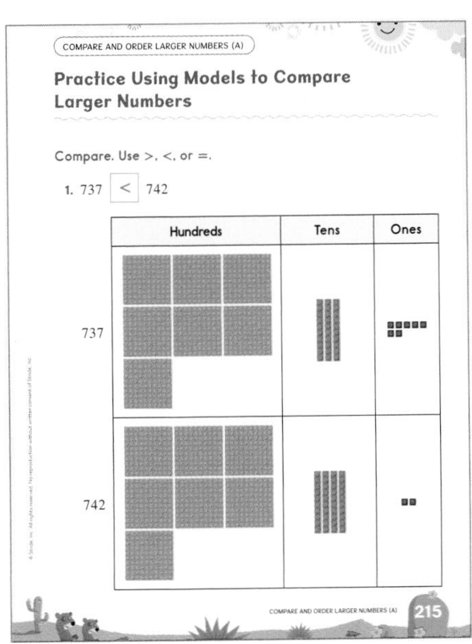

COMPARE AND ORDER LARGER NUMBERS (A)

Practice Using Models to Compare Larger Numbers

Compare. Use >, <, or =.

1. 737 [<] 742

	Hundreds	Tens	Ones
737			
742			

COMPARE AND ORDER LARGER NUMBERS (A) 215

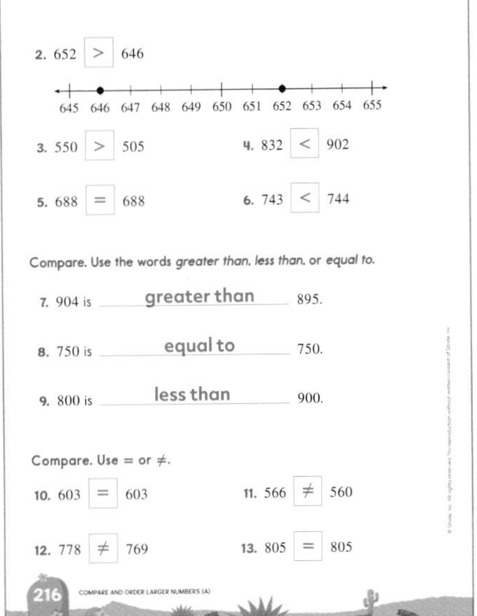

2. 652 [>] 646

3. 550 [>] 505
4. 832 [<] 902
5. 688 [=] 688
6. 743 [<] 744

Compare. Use the words *greater than*, *less than*, or *equal to*.

7. 904 is greater than 895.
8. 750 is equal to 750.
9. 800 is less than 900.

Compare. Use = or ≠.

10. 603 [=] 603
11. 566 [≠] 560
12. 778 [≠] 769
13. 805 [=] 805

216 COMPARE AND ORDER LARGER NUMBERS (A)

WRAP-UP

Using Models to Compare Larger Numbers

Students will solve problems to show that they understand how to compare numbers. Students may use base-10 block models to help them solve each problem.

Compare and Order Larger Numbers (B)

Lesson Overview

ACTIVITY	ACTIVITY TITLE	TIME	ONLINE/OFFLINE
GET READY	Introduction to Compare and Order Larger Numbers (B)	**2** minutes	online
	Adding and Subtracting 1-Digit Numbers with Instant Recall	**8** minutes	online
LEARN AND TRY IT	Using Place Value to Compare Larger Numbers	**15** minutes	online
	Use Place Value to Compare Larger Numbers	**10** minutes	online
	Practice Using Place Value to Compare Larger Numbers	**20** minutes	online and offline
WRAP-UP	Using Place Value to Compare Larger Numbers	**5** minutes	online

Content Background

Students will expand their understanding of using place value to compare numbers from 500 through 1,000. Students will continue to use place-value charts to compare the numbers of hundreds, tens, and ones. To compare numbers, students must find the greatest place value where the numbers are different.

MATERIALS

- *Math 2 Activity Book:* Practice Using Place Value to Compare Larger Numbers

Lesson Goals

- Use place value to compare larger numbers.

GET READY

Introduction to Compare and Order Larger Numbers (B)

Students will get a glimpse of what they will learn about in the lesson. They will also read the lesson goals.

Adding and Subtracting 1-Digit Numbers with Instant Recall

Students will practice adding and subtracting one-digit numbers.

LEARN AND TRY IT

LEARN Using Place Value to Compare Larger Numbers

Students will learn how to use place-value charts to compare larger numbers.

TIP Ask students to explain why one number is greater than or less than another number. The explanation should involve comparing the numbers of hundreds, tens, or ones.

TRY IT Use Place Value to Compare Larger Numbers

Students will practice using place-value charts to compare larger numbers. Support will be provided to help students overcome misconceptions.

TRY IT Practice Using Place Value to Compare Larger Numbers

Students will complete online practice problems. Then they will complete Practice Using Place Value to Compare Larger Numbers from *Math 2 Activity Book*.

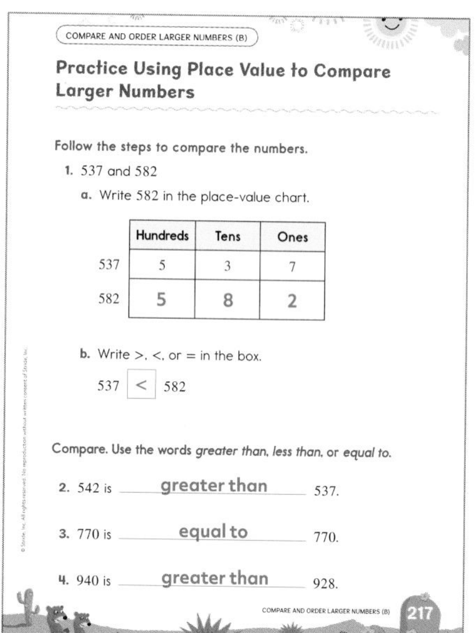
COMPARE AND ORDER LARGER NUMBERS (B)

Practice Using Place Value to Compare Larger Numbers

Follow the steps to compare the numbers.

1. 537 and 582
   a. Write 582 in the place-value chart.

	Hundreds	Tens	Ones
537	5	3	7
582	5	8	2

   b. Write $>$, $<$, or $=$ in the box.

   537 $<$ 582

Compare. Use the words *greater than*, *less than*, or *equal to*.

2. 542 is greater than 537.
3. 770 is equal to 770.
4. 940 is greater than 928.

COMPARE AND ORDER LARGER NUMBERS (B) 217

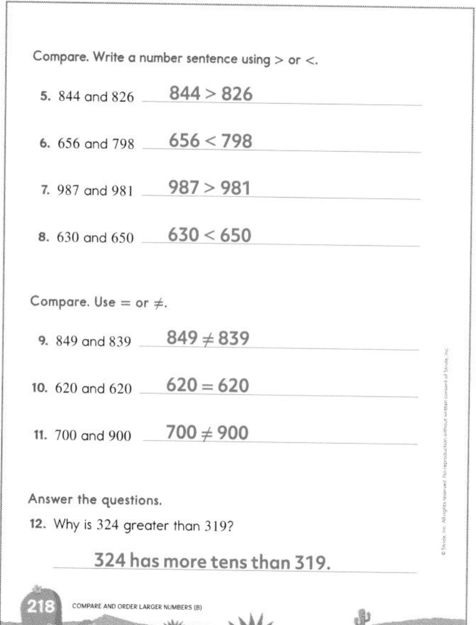
Compare. Write a number sentence using $>$ or $<$.

5. 844 and 826 $844 > 826$
6. 656 and 798 $656 < 798$
7. 987 and 981 $987 > 981$
8. 630 and 650 $630 < 650$

Compare. Use $=$ or $\neq$.

9. 849 and 839 $849 \neq 839$
10. 620 and 620 $620 = 620$
11. 700 and 900 $700 \neq 900$

Answer the questions.

12. Why is 324 greater than 319?
    324 has more tens than 319.

218 COMPARE AND ORDER LARGER NUMBERS (B)

WRAP-UP

Using Place Value to Compare Larger Numbers

Students will solve problems to show that they understand how to use place value to compare larger numbers.

Compare and Order Larger Numbers (C)

Lesson Overview

ACTIVITY	ACTIVITY TITLE	TIME	ONLINE/OFFLINE
GET READY	Introduction to Compare and Order Larger Numbers (C)	**2** minutes	online
	Adding and Subtracting 1-Digit Numbers Math Facts Game	**7** minutes	online
LEARN AND TRY IT	Ordering Larger Numbers from Least to Greatest	**7** minutes	online
	Order Larger Numbers from Least to Greatest	**7** minutes	online
ALL ABOUT ME	Brain Break	**1** minute	online or offline
LEARN AND TRY IT	Ordering Larger Numbers from Greatest to Least	**7** minutes	online
	Order Larger Numbers from Greatest to Least	**7** minutes	online
	Practice Ordering Larger Numbers	**20** minutes	online and offline
WRAP-UP	Ordering Larger Numbers	**2** minutes	online

Content Background

Students will expand their understanding of ordering numbers to include numbers from 500 through 1,000. They will order numbers from least to greatest and from greatest to least. Students will continue to use place-value charts and number lines to help them order numbers.

MATERIALS

Supplied

- *Math 2 Activity Book:* Practice Ordering Larger Numbers

Lesson Goals

- Order larger numbers from least to greatest.
- Order larger numbers from greatest to least.

GET READY

Introduction to Compare and Order Larger Numbers (C)

Students will get a glimpse of what they will learn about in the lesson. They will also read the lesson goals.

Adding and Subtracting 1-Digit Numbers Math Facts Game

Students will play a game to practice adding and subtracting one-digit numbers.

LEARN AND TRY IT

LEARN Ordering Larger Numbers from Least to Greatest

Students will use a place-value chart and a number line to order larger numbers from least to greatest.

TRY IT Order Larger Numbers from Least to Greatest

Students will practice ordering larger numbers from least to greatest. Support will be provided to help students overcome misconceptions.

LEARN Ordering Larger Numbers from Greatest to Least

Students will use a place-value chart and a number line to order larger numbers from greatest to least.

TRY IT Order Larger Numbers from Greatest to Least

Students will practice ordering larger numbers from greatest to least. Support will be provided to help students overcome misconceptions.

TRY IT Practice Ordering Larger Numbers

Students will complete online practice problems. Then they will complete Practice Ordering Larger Numbers from *Math 2 Activity Book.*

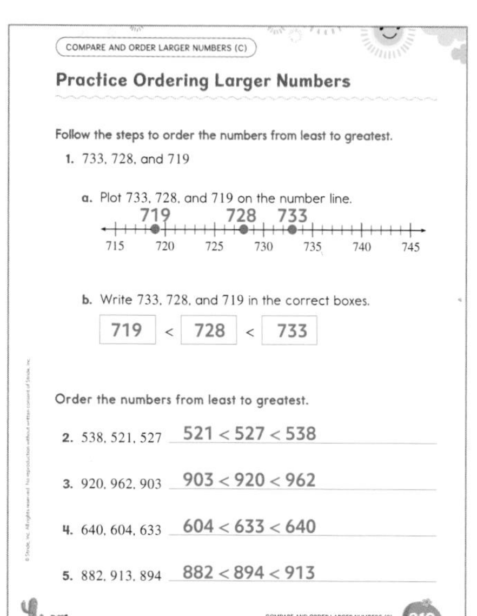

COMPARE AND ORDER LARGER NUMBERS (C)

Practice Ordering Larger Numbers

Follow the steps to order the numbers from least to greatest.

1. 733, 728, and 719

   a. Plot 733, 728, and 719 on the number line.

   b. Write 733, 728, and 719 in the correct boxes.

   719 < 728 < 733

Order the numbers from least to greatest.

2. 538, 521, 527 521 < 527 < 538
3. 920, 962, 903 903 < 920 < 962
4. 640, 604, 633 604 < 633 < 640
5. 882, 913, 894 882 < 894 < 913

COMPARE AND ORDER LARGER NUMBERS (C) 219

Follow the steps to order the numbers from greatest to least.

6. 858, 872, and 863

   a. Write 858, 872, and 863 in the place-value chart.

	Hundreds	Tens	Ones
858	8	5	8
872	8	7	2
863	8	6	3

   b. Write 858, 872, and 863 in the correct boxes.

   872 > 863 > 858

Order the numbers from greatest to least.

7. 673, 632, 646 673 > 646 > 632
8. 939, 902, 956 956 > 939 > 902
9. 527, 508, 516 527 > 516 > 508

220 COMPARE AND ORDER LARGER NUMBERS (C)

WRAP-UP

Ordering Larger Numbers

Students will solve problems to show that they understand how to order larger numbers from least to greatest and from greatest to least.

Compare and Order Larger Numbers (D)

Lesson Overview

ACTIVITY	ACTIVITY TITLE	TIME	ONLINE/OFFLINE
GET READY	Introduction to Compare and Order Larger Numbers (D)	**2** minutes	
TRY IT	Review Compare and Order Larger Numbers	**18** minutes	
QUIZ	Compare and Order Larger Numbers	**25** minutes	
WRAP-UP	More Math Practice	**15** minutes	

Lesson Goals

- Review comparing and ordering larger numbers.
- Take a quiz.

MATERIALS

There are no materials to gather for this lesson.

GET READY

Introduction to Compare and Order Larger Numbers (D)

Students will read the lesson goals.

TRY IT

Review Compare and Order Larger Numbers

Students will answer questions to review what they have learned about comparing and ordering larger numbers.

QUIZ

Compare and Order Larger Numbers

Students will complete the Compare and Order Larger Numbers quiz.

WRAP-UP

More Math Practice

Students will practice skills according to their individual needs.

Numbers Through 1,000 Wrap-Up

Lesson Overview

ACTIVITY	ACTIVITY TITLE	TIME	ONLINE/OFFLINE
GET READY	Introduction to Numbers Through 1,000 Wrap-Up	**2** minutes	online
TRY IT	Review Numbers Through 1,000	**23** minutes	online
UNIT CHECKPOINT	Numbers Through 1,000	**35** minutes	online

Lesson Goals

- Review numbers through 1,000.
- Show what you know about numbers through 1,000.

MATERIALS

There are no materials to gather for this lesson.

GET READY

Introduction to Numbers Through 1,000 Wrap-Up

Students will read the lesson goals.

TRY IT

Review Numbers Through 1,000

Students will answer questions to review what they have learned about numbers through 1,000.

UNIT CHECKPOINT

Numbers Through 1,000

Students will complete the Numbers Through 1,000 Unit Checkpoint.

LEARNING COACH CHECK-IN This is a graded assignment. Make sure students complete the online assessment.

Shapes

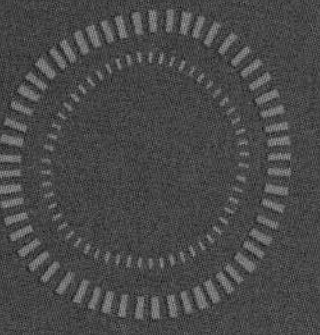

Identify and Draw Shapes (A)

Lesson Overview

ACTIVITY	ACTIVITY TITLE	TIME	ONLINE/OFFLINE
GET READY	Introduction to Identify and Draw Shapes (A)	**2** minutes	online
	Look Back at Counting Sides	**7** minutes	online
LEARN AND TRY IT	Identifying Shapes	**7** minutes	online
	Identify Shapes	**7** minutes	online
ALL ABOUT ME	Brain Break	**1** minute	online or offline
LEARN AND TRY IT	Drawing Shapes	**7** minutes	online
	Draw Shapes	**7** minutes	online
	Practice Identifying and Drawing Shapes	**20** minutes	online and offline
WRAP-UP	Identifying and Drawing Shapes	**2** minutes	online

Content Background

Students will learn to identify, name, and describe two-dimensional shapes. They will learn about some attributes of shapes, like the number of sides or vertices and the presence or absence of straight sides. Students will also learn to draw two-dimensional shapes to match a given description.

Parts of a Shape

Students will be asked to describe the sides and vertices of triangles, quadrilaterals, pentagons, and hexagons. The number of sides of a shape refers specifically to the number of *straight* sides. A curved figure, such as a circle or oval, is said to have no sides.

A vertex is formed exactly where two sides meet. The plural of vertex is *vertices*. Vertex is another name for corner. Students may notice that a shape has square corners, like a square or rectangle. But whether or not a shape has square corners is not an attribute that students are required to know or recognize in Math 2. A shape with straight sides always has the same number of sides and vertices.

MATERIALS

Supplied

- *Math 2 Activity Book:* Practice Identifying and Drawing Shapes

KEYWORDS

curve – a shape, or part of a shape, that is not straight

side – straight part that forms a shape

vertex of a shape – the place where two sides of a shape meet

Two-Dimensional Shapes

Here are some of the shapes students may encounter in this lesson.

Triangle	Quadrilateral	Pentagon
3 sides 3 vertices	4 sides 4 vertices *includes squares and rectangles*	5 sides 5 vertices
Hexagon	**Circle**	**Shape with Curved Parts**
6 sides 6 vertices	0 sides 0 vertices	3 straight sides 1 curved part

Lesson Goals

- Identify shapes.
- Draw shapes.

GET READY

Introduction to Identify and Draw Shapes (A)

Students will get a glimpse of what they will learn about in the lesson. They will also read the lesson goals.

Look Back at Counting Sides

Students will review and practice the prerequisite skill of counting the sides of a shape.

LEARN AND TRY IT

LEARN Identifying Shapes

Students will learn how to identify and name two-dimensional shapes.

TRY IT Identify Shapes

Students will practice identifying and naming two-dimensional shapes. Support will be provided to help students overcome misconceptions.

LEARN Drawing Shapes

Students will learn how to draw two-dimensional shapes.

TRY IT Draw Shapes

Students will practice drawing two-dimensional shapes. Support will be provided to help students overcome misconceptions.

TRY IT Practice Identifying and Drawing Shapes

Students will complete online practice problems. Then they will complete Practice Identifying and Drawing Shapes from *Math 2 Activity Book*.

NOTE Printable dot drawing paper is available online.

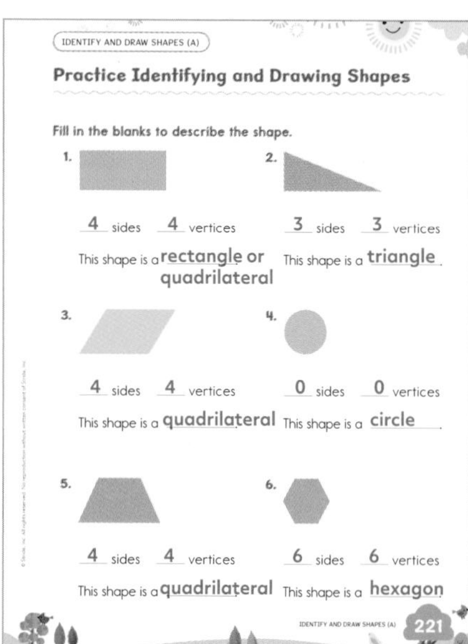

IDENTIFY AND DRAW SHAPES (A)

Practice Identifying and Drawing Shapes

Fill in the blanks to describe the shape.

1. 4 sides 4 vertices
   This shape is a rectangle or quadrilateral
2. 3 sides 3 vertices
   This shape is a triangle.
3. 4 sides 4 vertices
   This shape is a quadrilateral
4. 0 sides 0 vertices
   This shape is a circle
5. 4 sides 4 vertices
   This shape is a quadrilateral
6. 6 sides 6 vertices
   This shape is a hexagon

IDENTIFY AND DRAW SHAPES (A) 221

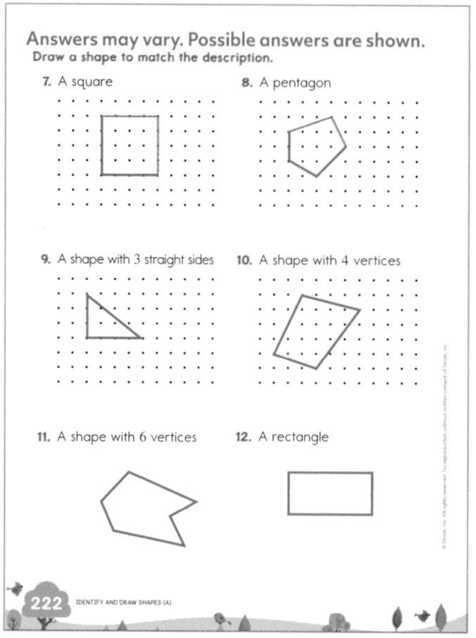

Answers may vary. Possible answers are shown.

Draw a shape to match the description.

7. A square
8. A pentagon
9. A shape with 3 straight sides
10. A shape with 4 vertices
11. A shape with 6 vertices
12. A rectangle

222 IDENTIFY AND DRAW SHAPES (A)

WRAP-UP

Identifying and Drawing Shapes

Students will solve problems to show that they understand how to identify shapes.

Identify and Draw Shapes (B)

Lesson Overview

ACTIVITY	ACTIVITY TITLE	TIME	ONLINE/OFFLINE
GET READY	Introduction to Identify and Draw Shapes (B)	**2** minutes	online
	Adding 10, 11, and 12 Math Facts	**8** minutes	online
LEARN AND TRY IT	Identifying and Drawing Shapes Using Angles	**15** minutes	online
	Identify and Draw Shapes Using Angles	**10** minutes	online
	Practice Identifying and Drawing Shapes Using Angles	**20** minutes	online and offline
WRAP-UP	Identifying and Drawing Shapes Using Angles	**5** minutes	online

Content Background

Students will first learn the definition of angle. Then they will learn to identify and draw two-dimensional shapes to match a given description of the angles in the shape.

Angles

An angle is formed by two sides and the included vertex of a shape. In other words, an angle is formed at *each* vertex of a shape. This means that a shape with straight sides always has the same number of sides, vertices, and angles. For example, a triangle has three sides, three vertices, and three angles.

MATERIALS

Supplied

- *Math 2 Activity Book:* Practice Identifying and Drawing Shapes Using Angles

KEYWORDS

angle – the part of a shape formed by two sides and the included vertex

Lesson Goals

- Identify shapes using angles.
- Draw shapes.

GET READY

Introduction to Identify and Draw Shapes (B)

Students will get a glimpse of what they will learn about in the lesson. They will also read the lesson goals.

Adding 10, 11, and 12 Math Facts

Students will practice adding 10, 11, and 12.

LEARN AND TRY IT

LEARN Identifying and Drawing Shapes Using Angles

Students will learn how to identify and draw two-dimensional shapes using angles.

TRY IT Identify and Draw Shapes Using Angles

Students will practice identifying and drawing shapes using angles. Support will be provided to help students overcome misconceptions.

TRY IT Practice Identifying and Drawing Shapes Using Angles

Students will complete online practice problems. Then they will complete Practice Identifying and Drawing Shapes Using Angles from *Math 2 Activity Book*.

NOTE Printable dot drawing paper is available online.

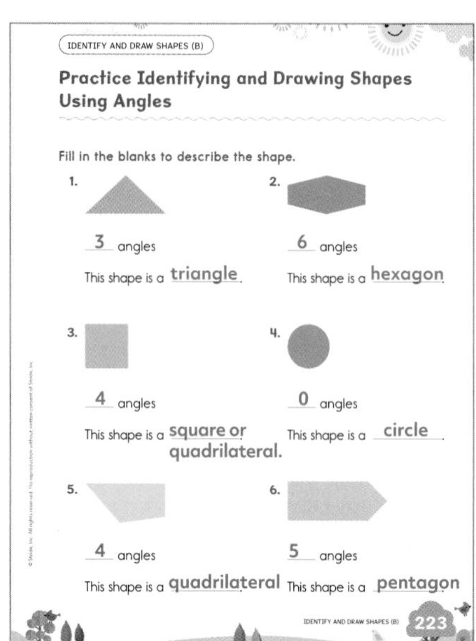

IDENTIFY AND DRAW SHAPES (B)

Practice Identifying and Drawing Shapes Using Angles

Fill in the blanks to describe the shape.

1. 3 angles
   This shape is a triangle.
2. 6 angles
   This shape is a hexagon.
3. 4 angles
   This shape is a square or quadrilateral.
4. 0 angles
   This shape is a circle.
5. 4 angles
   This shape is a quadrilateral
6. 5 angles
   This shape is a pentagon

IDENTIFY AND DRAW SHAPES (B) 223

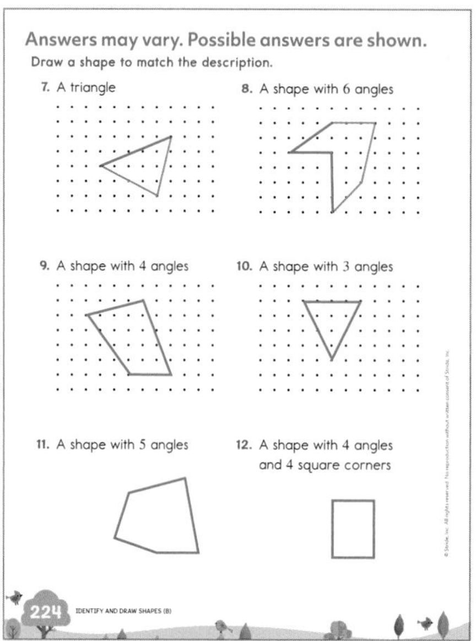

Answers may vary. Possible answers are shown.

Draw a shape to match the description.

7. A triangle
8. A shape with 6 angles
9. A shape with 4 angles
10. A shape with 3 angles
11. A shape with 5 angles
12. A shape with 4 angles and 4 square corners

224 IDENTIFY AND DRAW SHAPES (B)

WRAP-UP

Identifying and Drawing Shapes Using Angles

Students will solve a problem to show that they understand how to identify shapes using angles.

Identify and Draw Shapes (C)

Lesson Overview

ACTIVITY	ACTIVITY TITLE	TIME	ONLINE/OFFLINE
GET READY	Introduction to Identify and Draw Shapes (C)	2 minutes	online
	Adding 10, 11, and 12 with Instant Recall	7 minutes	online
LEARN AND TRY IT	Identifying and Making Solid Shapes	15 minutes	online
	Identify and Make Solid Shapes	10 minutes	online
ALL ABOUT ME	Brain Break	1 minute	online or offline
TRY IT	Practice Identifying and Making Solid Shapes	20 minutes	online and offline
WRAP-UP	Identifying and Making Solid Shapes	5 minutes	online

Content Background

Students will learn to identify, name, and describe three-dimensional solids. They will learn about some attributes of solids, like the number of faces, edges, or vertices and the presence or absence of flat faces. Students will also learn to make three-dimensional solids to match a given description.

Parts of a Solid

Students will be asked to describe the faces, edges, and vertices of solids. The number of faces of a solid refers specifically to the number of *flat* faces. A curved surface, such as a sphere, is said to have no faces. Students will also investigate the number of equal faces on a solid. For example, a cube has six square faces that are all the same size and a cylinder has two equal faces that are circles.

An edge is formed where two faces meet. Shapes and solids both have vertices. A vertex of a shape is the place where two *sides* meet, whereas a vertex of a solid is the place where two or more *edges* meet. Students will learn that a solid does not always have the same number of faces, vertices, and edges.

MATERIALS

Supplied

- *Math 2 Activity Book:* Practice Identifying and Making Solid Shapes

KEYWORDS

curve – a shape, or part of a shape, that is not straight

edge – the line where two faces of a solid meet

face – a flat surface on a solid

vertex of a solid – the place where two or more edges of a solid meet

Three-Dimensional Solids

Here are some of the solids students may encounter in this lesson.

Cube	Rectangular Prism	Square Pyramid
6 faces 12 edges 8 vertices	6 faces 12 edges 8 vertices	5 faces 8 edges 5 vertices
Sphere	**Cylinder**	**Cone**
0 faces 0 edges 0 vertices	2 flat faces 1 curved part	1 flat face 1 curved part

Lesson Goals

- Identify solid shapes.
- Make solid shapes.

GET READY

Introduction to Identify and Draw Shapes (C)

Students will get a glimpse of what they will learn about in the lesson. They will also read the lesson goals.

Adding 10, 11, and 12 with Instant Recall

Students will practice adding 10, 11, and 12.

LEARN AND TRY IT

LEARN Identifying and Making Solid Shapes

Students will learn how to identify and make solid shapes.

TRY IT **Identify and Make Solid Shapes**

Students will practice identifying and making solid shapes. Support will be provided to help students overcome misconceptions.

TRY IT **Practice Identifying and Making Solid Shapes**

Students will complete online practice problems. Then they will complete Practice Identifying and Making Solid Shapes from *Math 2 Activity Book*.

NOTE Printable dot drawing paper is available online.

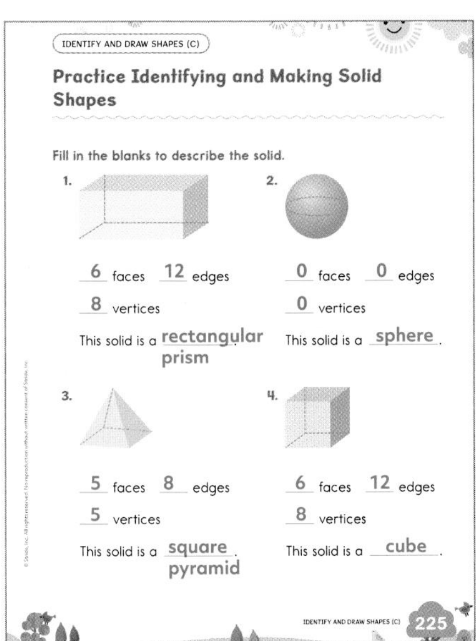

IDENTIFY AND DRAW SHAPES (C)

Practice Identifying and Making Solid Shapes

Fill in the blanks to describe the solid.

1. 6 faces 12 edges
8 vertices
This solid is a rectangular prism

2. 0 faces 0 edges
0 vertices
This solid is a sphere.

3. 5 faces 8 edges
5 vertices
This solid is a square pyramid

4. 6 faces 12 edges
8 vertices
This solid is a cube.

IDENTIFY AND DRAW SHAPES (C) 225

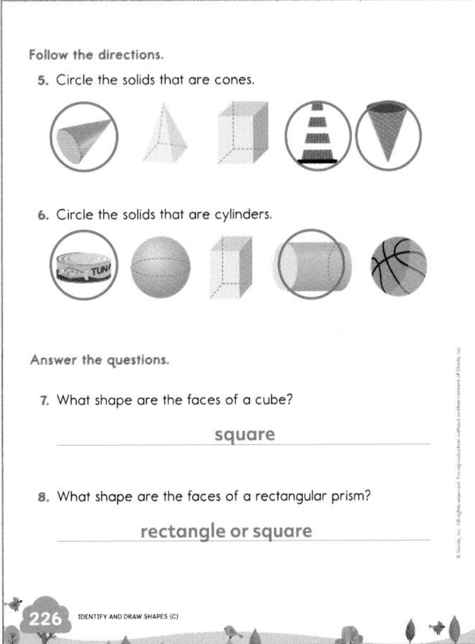

Follow the directions.

5. Circle the solids that are cones.

6. Circle the solids that are cylinders.

Answer the questions.

7. What shape are the faces of a cube?
square

8. What shape are the faces of a rectangular prism?
rectangle or square

226 IDENTIFY AND DRAW SHAPES (C)

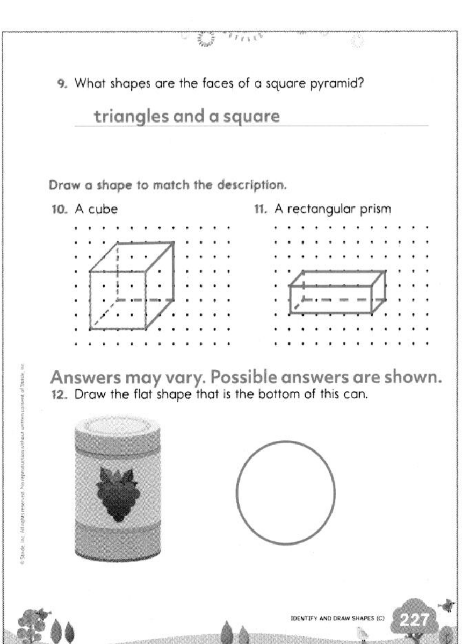

9. What shapes are the faces of a square pyramid?
triangles and a square

Draw a shape to match the description.

10. A cube

11. A rectangular prism

Answers may vary. Possible answers are shown.

12. Draw the flat shape that is the bottom of this can.

IDENTIFY AND DRAW SHAPES (C) 227

WRAP-UP

Identifying and Making Solid Shapes

Students will solve problems to show that they understand how to identify solid shapes.

Identify and Draw Shapes (D)

Lesson Overview

ACTIVITY	ACTIVITY TITLE	TIME	ONLINE/OFFLINE
GET READY	Introduction to Identify and Draw Shapes (D)	**2** minutes	
TRY IT	Review Identify and Draw Shapes	**18** minutes	
QUIZ	Identify and Draw Shapes	**25** minutes	
WRAP-UP	More Math Practice	**15** minutes	

Lesson Goals

- Review identifying and drawing shapes.
- Take a quiz.

MATERIALS

There are no materials to gather for this lesson.

GET READY

Introduction to Identify and Draw Shapes (D)

Students will read the lesson goals.

TRY IT

Review Identify and Draw Shapes

Students will answer questions to review what they have learned about how to identify and draw shapes.

QUIZ

Identify and Draw Shapes

Students will complete the Identify and Draw Shapes quiz.

WRAP-UP

More Math Practice

Students will practice skills according to their individual needs.

Partition Shapes (A)

Lesson Overview

ACTIVITY	ACTIVITY TITLE	TIME	ONLINE/OFFLINE
GET READY	Introduction to Partition Shapes (A)	**2** minutes	online
	Look Back at Using Terms to Describe Position	**7** minutes	online
LEARN AND **TRY IT**	Dividing Rectangles into Equal Squares	**15** minutes	online
	Divide Rectangles into Equal Squares	**10** minutes	online
ALL ABOUT ME	Brain Break	**1** minute	online or offline
TRY IT	Practice Dividing Rectangles into Equal Squares	**20** minutes	online and offline
WRAP-UP	Dividing Rectangles into Equal Squares	**5** minutes	online

Content Background

Students will learn to use a ruler to divide rectangles into equal squares, given the number of rows and the number of squares in each row. They will then count the number of squares that make up the whole rectangle. This work lays the foundation for learning about area in Math 3.

MATERIALS

Supplied
- *Math 2 Activity Book:* Practice Dividing Rectangles into Equal Squares

Also Needed
- ruler

Lesson Goals

- Divide a rectangle into equal squares.
- Count the number of equal squares.

GET READY

Introduction to Partition Shapes (A)

Students will get a glimpse of what they will learn about in the lesson. They will also read the lesson goals.

Look Back at Using Terms to Describe Position

Students will review and practice the prerequisite skill of using terms to describe the position of objects.

LEARN AND TRY IT

LEARN Dividing Rectangles into Equal Squares

Students will learn how to divide a rectangle into rows and columns of equal squares and how to count the number of squares.

TRY IT Divide Rectangles into Equal Squares

Students will practice dividing rectangles into equal squares. Support will be provided to help students overcome misconceptions.

TRY IT Practice Dividing Rectangles into Equal Squares

Students will complete online practice problems. Then they will complete Practice Dividing Rectangles into Equal Squares from *Math 2 Activity Book*.

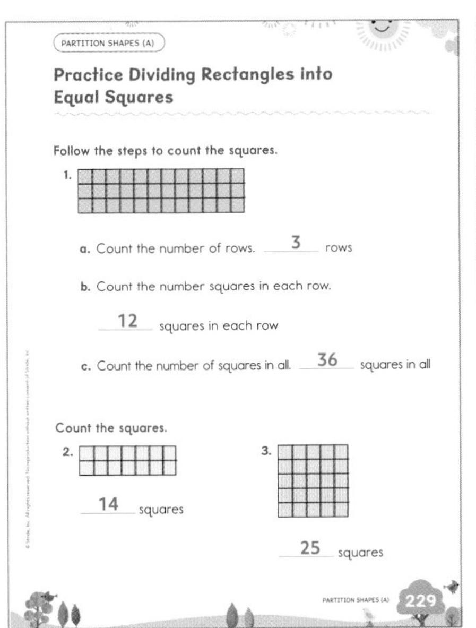

PARTITION SHAPES (A)

Practice Dividing Rectangles into Equal Squares

Follow the steps to count the squares.

1.

a. Count the number of rows. 3 rows

b. Count the number squares in each row.

12 squares in each row

c. Count the number of squares in all. 36 squares in all

Count the squares.

2. 14 squares

3. 25 squares

PARTITION SHAPES (A) 229

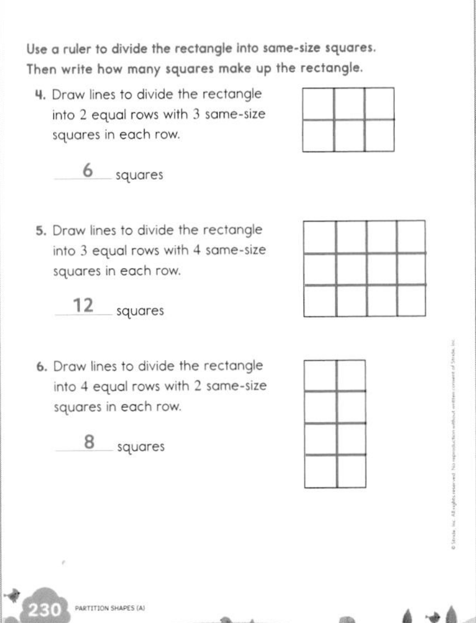

Use a ruler to divide the rectangle into same-size squares. Then write how many squares make up the rectangle.

4. Draw lines to divide the rectangle into 2 equal rows with 3 same-size squares in each row.

6 squares

5. Draw lines to divide the rectangle into 3 equal rows with 4 same-size squares in each row.

12 squares

6. Draw lines to divide the rectangle into 4 equal rows with 2 same-size squares in each row.

8 squares

230 PARTITION SHAPES (A)

WRAP-UP

Dividing Rectangles into Equal Squares

Students will solve a problem to show that they understand how to divide a rectangle into equal squares.

Partition Shapes (B)

Lesson Overview

ACTIVITY	ACTIVITY TITLE	TIME	ONLINE/OFFLINE
GET READY	Introduction to Partition Shapes (B)	**2** minutes	online
	Adding 10, 11, and 12 Math Facts Game	**8** minutes	online
LEARN AND TRY IT	Dividing Shapes into Equal Parts	**15** minutes	online
	Divide Shapes into Equal Parts	**10** minutes	online
	Practice Dividing Shapes into Equal Parts	**20** minutes	online and offline
WRAP-UP	Dividing Shapes into Equal Parts	**5** minutes	online

Content Background

Students will learn how to divide a whole into 2, 3, or 4 equal parts or shares. A whole will be represented as a circle or rectangle. They will learn the difference between equal parts and not-equal parts. Students will also learn that the parts become smaller as the number of parts increases when dividing a shape into equal parts.

MATERIALS

Supplied

- *Math 2 Activity Book:* Practice Dividing Shapes into Equal Parts

Lesson Goals

- Divide circles and rectangles into equal parts.
- Identify equal parts.

KEYWORDS

equal parts – portions of a shape that are equal in area

GET READY

Introduction to Partition Shapes (B)

Students will get a glimpse of what they will learn about in the lesson. They will also read the lesson goals.

Adding 10, 11, and 12 Math Facts Game

Students will play a game to practice adding 10, 11, and 12.

LEARN AND TRY IT

LEARN Dividing Shapes into Equal Parts

Students will learn how to divide circles and rectangles into 2, 3, or 4 equal parts.

TRY IT Divide Shapes into Equal Parts

Students will practice dividing circles and rectangles into equal parts. Support will be provided to help students overcome misconceptions.

TRY IT Practice Dividing Shapes into Equal Parts

Students will complete online practice problems. Then they will complete Practice Dividing Shapes into Equal Parts from *Math 2 Activity Book*.

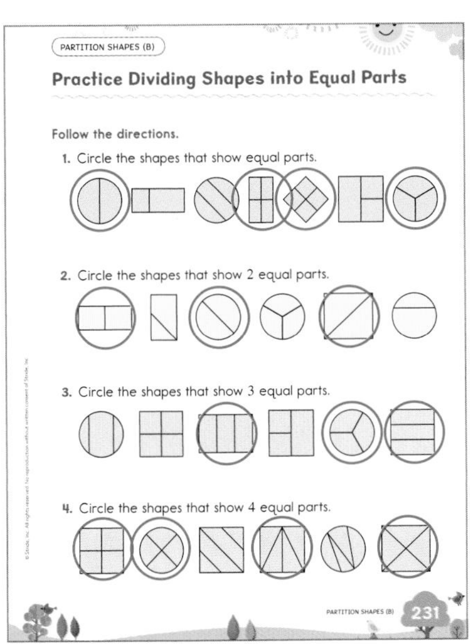
PARTITION SHAPES (B)

Practice Dividing Shapes into Equal Parts

Follow the directions.

1. Circle the shapes that show equal parts.
2. Circle the shapes that show 2 equal parts.
3. Circle the shapes that show 3 equal parts.
4. Circle the shapes that show 4 equal parts.

PARTITION SHAPES (B) 231

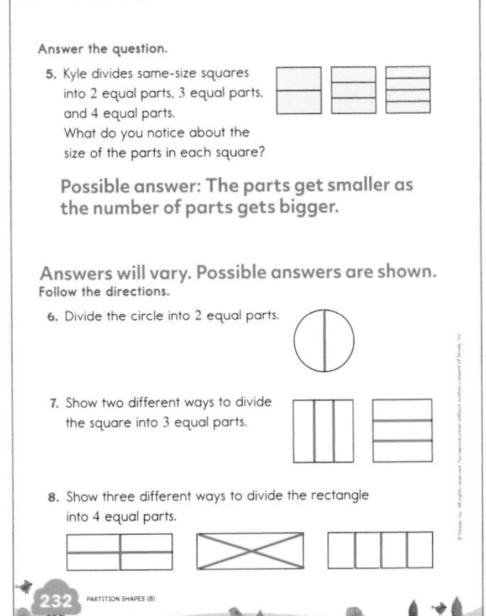
Answer the question.

5. Kyle divides same-size squares into 2 equal parts, 3 equal parts, and 4 equal parts. What do you notice about the size of the parts in each square?

Possible answer: The parts get smaller as the number of parts gets bigger.

Answers will vary. Possible answers are shown.

Follow the directions.

6. Divide the circle into 2 equal parts.
7. Show two different ways to divide the square into 3 equal parts.
8. Show three different ways to divide the rectangle into 4 equal parts.

232 PARTITION SHAPES (B)

WRAP-UP

Dividing Shapes into Equal Parts

Students will solve a problem to show that they understand how to divide shapes into equal parts.

Partition Shapes (C)

Lesson Overview

ACTIVITY	ACTIVITY TITLE	TIME	ONLINE/OFFLINE
GET READY	Introduction to Partition Shapes (C)	**2** minutes	online
	Adding 13, 14, 15, and 16 Math Facts	**7** minutes	online
LEARN AND TRY IT	Naming Equal Parts	**15** minutes	online
	Name Equal Parts	**10** minutes	online
ALL ABOUT ME	Brain Break	**1** minute	online or offline
TRY IT	Practice Naming Equal Parts	**20** minutes	online and offline
WRAP-UP	Naming Equal Parts	**5** minutes	online

Content Background

Students will learn the correct names for the equal parts of a shape that has been divided into 2, 3, or 4 equal parts. They will also learn how to describe a whole using those names. Finally, they will learn how to identify parts of identical wholes that are equal but have different shapes.

Names of Equal Parts

Students will learn the following names and relationships.

- When a shape is divided into 2 equal parts, each part is a *half.* Two *halves* make one whole.
- When a shape is divided into 3 equal parts, each part is a *third*. Three thirds make one whole.
- When a shape is divided into 4 equal parts, each part is a *fourth*. Four fourths make one whole.

Different Shape but Equal Parts

Here are three identical rectangles. Each is divided into 4 equal parts.

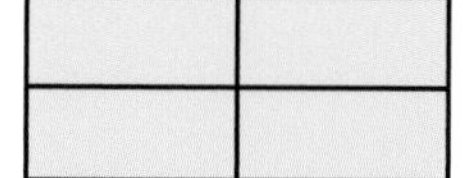

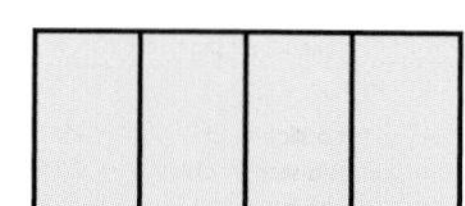

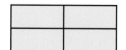

Although the parts in each rectangle have different shapes, each fourth is equal to every other fourth.

MATERIALS

Supplied

- *Math 2 Activity Book:* Practice Naming Equal Parts

Lesson Goals

- Name equal parts of a circle or rectangle.
- Describe a whole.

GET READY

Introduction to Partition Shapes (C)

Students will get a glimpse of what they will learn about in the lesson. They will also read the lesson goals.

Adding 13, 14, 15, and 16 Math Facts

Students will practice adding 13, 14, 15, and 16.

LEARN AND TRY IT

LEARN Naming Equal Parts

Students will learn how to name equal parts of a circle or rectangle.

TRY IT Name Equal Parts

Students will practice naming equal parts of a circle or rectangle. Support will be provided to help students overcome misconceptions.

TRY IT Practice Naming Equal Parts

Students will complete online practice problems. Then they will complete Practice Naming Equal Parts from *Math 2 Activity Book*.

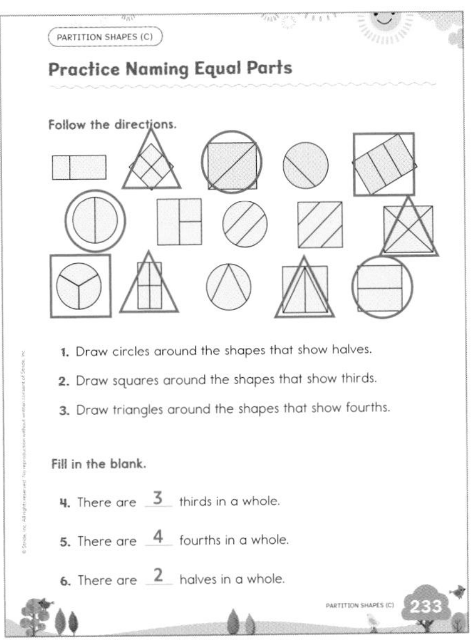

PARTITION SHAPES (C)

Practice Naming Equal Parts

Follow the directions.

1. Draw circles around the shapes that show halves.
2. Draw squares around the shapes that show thirds.
3. Draw triangles around the shapes that show fourths.

Fill in the blank.

4. There are 3 thirds in a whole.
5. There are 4 fourths in a whole.
6. There are 2 halves in a whole.

PARTITION SHAPES (C) 233

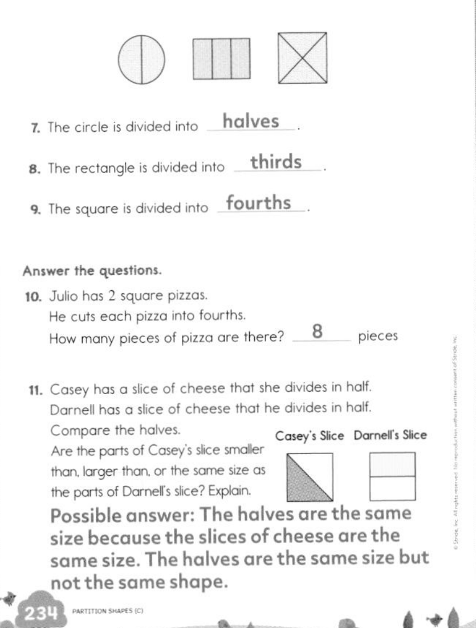

7. The circle is divided into halves.
8. The rectangle is divided into thirds.
9. The square is divided into fourths.

Answer the questions.

10. Julio has 2 square pizzas. He cuts each pizza into fourths. How many pieces of pizza are there? 8 pieces

11. Casey has a slice of cheese that she divides in half. Darnell has a slice of cheese that he divides in half. Compare the halves. Are the parts of Casey's slice smaller than, larger than, or the same size as the parts of Darnell's slice? Explain.

Casey's Slice | Darnell's Slice

Possible answer: The halves are the same size because the slices of cheese are the same size. The halves are the same size but not the same shape.

234 PARTITION SHAPES (C)

WRAP-UP

Naming Equal Parts

Students will solve a problem to show that they understand how to name equal parts of a shape.

Partition Shapes (D)

Lesson Overview

ACTIVITY	ACTIVITY TITLE	TIME	ONLINE/OFFLINE
GET READY	Introduction to Partition Shapes (D)	2 minutes	
TRY IT	Review Partition Shapes	18 minutes	
QUIZ	Partition Shapes	25 minutes	
WRAP-UP	More Math Practice	15 minutes	

Lesson Goals

- Review partitioning shapes.
- Take a quiz.

MATERIALS

There are no materials to gather for this lesson.

GET READY

Introduction to Partition Shapes (D)

Students will read the lesson goals.

TRY IT

Review Partition Shapes

Students will answer questions to review what they have learned about partitioning shapes.

QUIZ

Partition Shapes

Students will complete the Partition Shapes quiz.

WRAP-UP

More Math Practice

Students will practice skills according to their individual needs.

Shapes Wrap-Up

Lesson Overview

ACTIVITY	ACTIVITY TITLE	TIME	ONLINE/OFFLINE
GET READY	Introduction to Shapes Wrap-Up	**2** minutes	
TRY IT	Review Shapes	**18** minutes	
UNIT CHECKPOINT	Shapes Online Checkpoint	**18** minutes	
	Shapes Offline Checkpoint	**20** minutes	
WRAP-UP	Turn in Your Offline Checkpoint	**2** minutes	

Lesson Goals

- Review shapes.
- Show what you know about shapes.

MATERIALS

Supplied

- Shapes Offline Checkpoint (printout)

GET READY

Introduction to Shapes Wrap-Up

Students will read the lesson goals.

TRY IT

Review Shapes

Students will answer questions to review what they have learned about shapes.

UNIT CHECKPOINT

Shapes Online Checkpoint

Students will complete the Shapes Unit Checkpoint.

LEARNING COACH CHECK-IN This is a graded assignment. Make sure students complete the online assessment.

Shapes Offline Checkpoint

Students will complete multistep problems that go beyond the short answer and multiple choice problems in their regular lessons. These problems give students an opportunity to demonstrate problem solving, reasoning, communication, and modeling skills. Students will need to use paper and pencil and/or technology to show their work.

Materials are linked online. The materials are not provided in this lesson guide or the activity book.

LEARNING COACH CHECK-IN This is a graded assignment. Make sure students complete, review, and submit their assignment to the teacher. If you are unsure how to do this, ask students' teacher.

WRAP-UP

Turn in Your Offline Checkpoint

Students will turn in their graded assignment.

Add and Subtract within 1,000

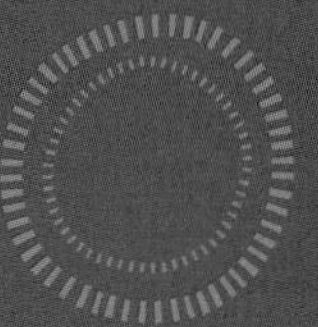

Use Place Value to Add (A)

Lesson Overview

ACTIVITY	ACTIVITY TITLE	TIME	ONLINE/OFFLINE
GET READY	Introduction to Use Place Value to Add (A)	2 minutes	online
	Look Back at Writing Numbers in Expanded Form	7 minutes	online
LEARN AND TRY IT	Adding 2 Numbers with Sums Greater Than 100	7 minutes	online
	Add 2 Numbers with Sums Greater Than 100	7 minutes	online
ALL ABOUT ME	Brain Break	1 minute	online or offline
LEARN AND TRY IT	Adding 3 and 4 Numbers with Sums Greater Than 100	7 minutes	online
	Add 3 and 4 Numbers with Sums Greater Than 100	7 minutes	online
	Practice Adding with Sums Greater Than 100	20 minutes	online and offline
WRAP-UP	Adding with Sums Greater Than 100	2 minutes	online

Content Background

Students will learn how to find sums that are greater than 100 when they have up to four 2-digit addends. Students have experience finding sums within 100 using strategies based on place value, such as open number lines, base-10 models, place-value charts, and expanded form. Students will learn to apply these strategies to sums that are greater than 100.

Sums Greater Than 100

Each addition problem in this lesson involves two-digit addends that result in a three-digit sum. In other words, each problem requires regrouping in the tens place. This regrouping step is based on the relationship that 10 tens equals 1 hundred. Some problems also require regrouping 10 ones into 1 ten.

NOTE Students learned strategies for adding within 100 to build fluency and ultimately add using mental math. Although students will use the same strategies in this unit, they are not expected to find sums greater than 100 using mental math. Encourage students to show their work or use models to find sums greater than 100. When a strategy is not specified, students may select the strategy that works best for them.

MATERIALS

Supplied

- *Math 2 Activity Book:* Practice Adding with Sums Greater Than 100

Lesson Goals

- Find a sum greater than 100 with two-digit addends.

GET READY

Introduction to Use Place Value to Add (A)

Students will get a glimpse of what they will learn about in the lesson. They will also read the lesson goals.

Look Back at Writing Numbers in Expanded Form

Students will review and practice the prerequisite skill of writing numbers in expanded form.

LEARN AND TRY IT

LEARN Adding 2 Numbers with Sums Greater Than 100

Students will learn how to add two 2-digit numbers with sums greater than 100 using strategies based on place value.

TRY IT Add 2 Numbers with Sums Greater Than 100

Students will practice adding two 2-digit numbers with sums greater than 100. Support will be provided to help students overcome misconceptions.

LEARN Adding 3 and 4 Numbers with Sums Greater Than 100

Students will learn how to add three or four 2-digit numbers with sums greater than 100 using strategies based on place value.

TRY IT Add 3 and 4 Numbers with Sums Greater Than 100

Students will practice adding three or four 2-digit numbers with sums greater than 100. Support will be provided to help students overcome misconceptions.

TRY IT Practice Adding with Sums Greater Than 100

Students will complete online practice problems. Then they will complete Practice Adding with Sums Greater Than 100 from *Math 2 Activity Book*.

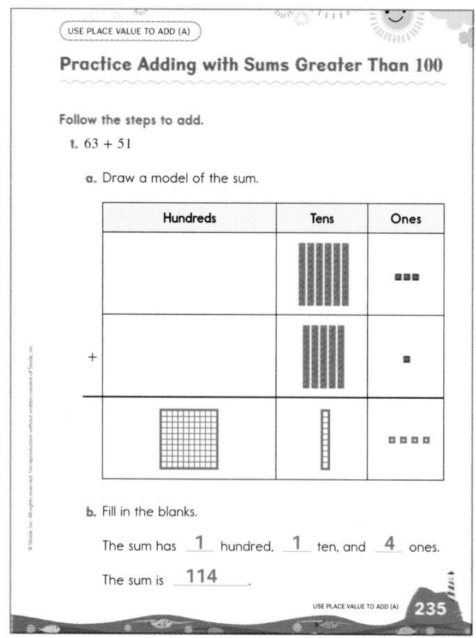

USE PLACE VALUE TO ADD (A)

Practice Adding with Sums Greater Than 100

Follow the steps to add.

1. 63 + 51

a. Draw a model of the sum.

	Hundreds	Tens	Ones
+			

b. Fill in the blanks.

The sum has 1 hundred, 1 ten, and 4 ones.

The sum is 114.

USE PLACE VALUE TO ADD (A) 235

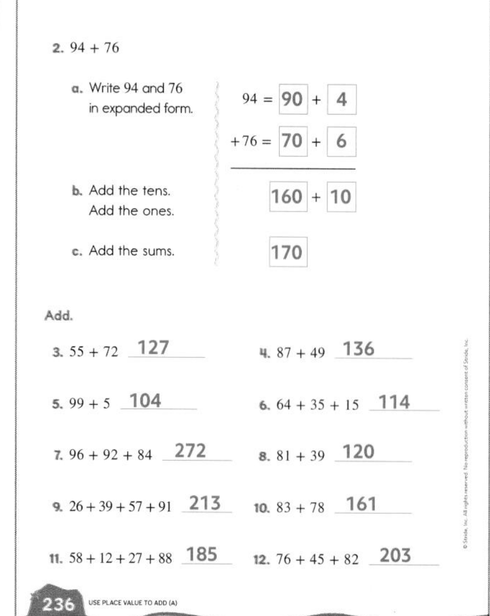

2. 94 + 76

a. Write 94 and 76 in expanded form.

94 = 90 + 4

+76 = 70 + 6

b. Add the tens. Add the ones.

160 + 10

c. Add the sums.

170

Add.

3. 55 + 72 127
4. 87 + 49 136
5. 99 + 5 104
6. 64 + 35 + 15 114
7. 96 + 92 + 84 272
8. 81 + 39 120
9. 26 + 39 + 57 + 91 213
10. 83 + 78 161
11. 58 + 12 + 27 + 88 185
12. 76 + 45 + 82 203

236 USE PLACE VALUE TO ADD (A)

WRAP-UP

Adding with Sums Greater Than 100

Students will solve problems to show that they understand how to add with sums greater than 100.

Use Place Value to Add (B)

Lesson Overview

ACTIVITY	ACTIVITY TITLE	TIME	ONLINE/OFFLINE
GET READY	Introduction to Use Place Value to Add (B)	2 minutes	online
	Adding 13, 14, 15, and 16 with Instant Recall	7 minutes	online
LEARN AND TRY IT	Adding 3-Digit and 1-Digit Numbers	7 minutes	online
	Add 3-Digit and 1-Digit Numbers	7 minutes	online
ALL ABOUT ME	Brain Break	1 minute	online or offline
LEARN AND TRY IT	Adding 3-Digit and 2-Digit Numbers	7 minutes	online
	Add 3-Digit and 2-Digit Numbers	7 minutes	online
	Practice Adding to a 3-Digit Number	20 minutes	online and offline
WRAP-UP	Adding to a 3-Digit Number	2 minutes	online

Content Background

Students will learn how to find sums of a three-digit addend and a one- or two-digit addend. They will encounter problems with and without regrouping, and regrouping problems may require regrouping once or twice. Students have experience finding sums of two-digit addends using strategies based on place value, such as open number lines, base-10 models, place-value charts, and expanded form. Students will learn to apply these strategies to sums with one 3-digit addend.

MATERIALS

Supplied

- *Math 2 Activity Book:* Practice Adding to a 3-Digit Number

Lesson Goals

- Find a sum greater than 100 with one 3-digit addend.

GET READY

Introduction to Use Place Value to Add (B)

Students will get a glimpse of what they will learn about in the lesson. They will also read the lesson goals.

Adding 13, 14, 15, and 16 with Instant Recall

Students will practice adding 13, 14, 15, and 16.

LEARN AND TRY IT

LEARN Adding 3-Digit and 1-Digit Numbers

Students will add a three-digit number and a one-digit number using strategies based on place value.

TRY IT Add 3-Digit and 1-Digit Numbers

Students will practice adding three-digit and one-digit numbers. Support will be provided to help students overcome misconceptions.

LEARN Adding 3-Digit and 2-Digit Numbers

Students will add a three-digit number and a two-digit number using strategies based on place value.

TRY IT Add 3-Digit and 2-Digit Numbers

Students will practice adding three-digit and two-digit numbers. Support will be provided to help students overcome misconceptions.

TRY IT Practice Adding to a 3-Digit Number

Students will complete online practice problems. Then they will complete Practice Adding to a 3-Digit Number from *Math 2 Activity Book*.

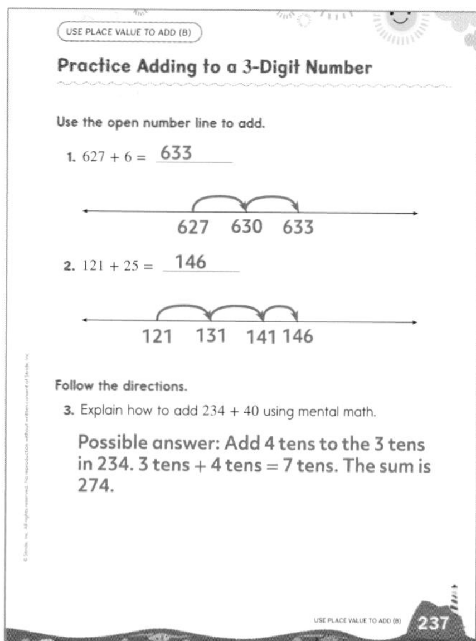

USE PLACE VALUE TO ADD (B)

Practice Adding to a 3-Digit Number

Use the open number line to add.

1. 627 + 6 = 633

   627 630 633

2. 121 + 25 = 146

   121 131 141 146

Follow the directions.

3. Explain how to add 234 + 40 using mental math.

   Possible answer: Add 4 tens to the 3 tens in 234. 3 tens + 4 tens = 7 tens. The sum is 274.

USE PLACE VALUE TO ADD (B) 237

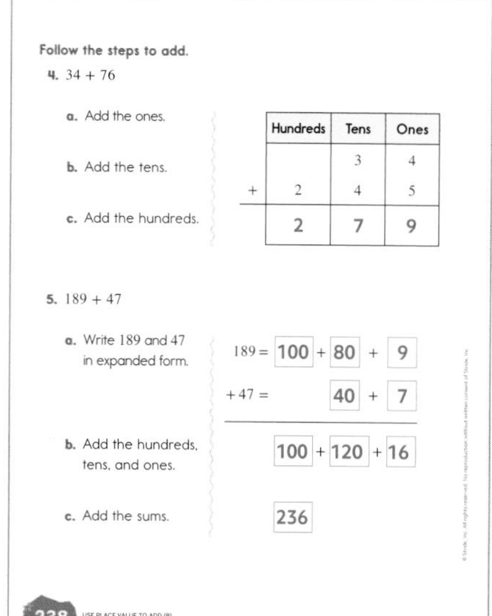

Follow the steps to add.

4. 34 + 76

   a. Add the ones.

   b. Add the tens.

   c. Add the hundreds.

	Hundreds	Tens	Ones
		3	4
+	2	4	5
	2	7	9

5. 189 + 47

   a. Write 189 and 47 in expanded form.

   189 = 100 + 80 + 9

   + 47 = 40 + 7

   b. Add the hundreds, tens, and ones.

   100 + 120 + 16

   c. Add the sums.

   236

238 USE PLACE VALUE TO ADD (B)

Add.

6. 825 + 4 829
7. 476 + 12 488
8. 84 + 162 246
9. 9 + 849 858
10. 294 + 67 361
11. 362 + 44 406
12. 190 + 83 273
13. 18 + 457 475
14. 468 + 7 475
15. 258 + 43 301

Answer the questions.

16. Deanna has 109 pennies. She finds 32 more pennies. How many pennies does Deanna have now? 141 pennies

17. There are 287 people on a plane. Then 55 more people get on the plane. How many people are on the plane now? 342 people

USE PLACE VALUE TO ADD (B) 239

WRAP-UP

Adding to a 3-Digit Number

Students will solve problems to show that they understand how to add to a three-digit number.

Use Place Value to Add (C)

Lesson Overview

ACTIVITY	ACTIVITY TITLE	TIME	ONLINE/OFFLINE
GET READY	Introduction to Use Place Value to Add (C)	**2** minutes	online
	Adding 13, 14, 15, and 16 Math Facts Game	**7** minutes	online
LEARN AND TRY IT	Adding Two 3-Digit Numbers	**15** minutes	online
	Add Two 3-Digit Numbers	**10** minutes	online
ALL ABOUT ME	Brain Break	**1** minute	online or offline
TRY IT	Practice Adding Two 3-Digit Numbers	**20** minutes	online and offline
WRAP-UP	Adding Two 3-Digit Numbers	**5** minutes	online

Content Background

Students will learn how to find sums of two 3-digit addends. They will encounter problems with and without regrouping, and regrouping problems may require regrouping once or twice. Students will continue to apply strategies based on place value to sums with two 3-digit addends.

MATERIALS

Supplied

- *Math 2 Activity Book:* Practice Adding Two 3-Digit Numbers

Lesson Goals

- Find a sum greater than 100 with two 3-digit addends.

GET READY

Introduction to Use Place Value to Add (C)

Students will get a glimpse of what they will learn about in the lesson. They will also read the lesson goals.

Adding 13, 14, 15, and 16 Math Facts Game

Students will play a game to practice adding 13, 14, 15, and 16.

LEARN AND TRY IT

LEARN Adding Two 3-Digit Numbers

Students will learn how to add two 3-digit numbers using strategies based on place value.

TRY IT Add Two 3-Digit Numbers

Students will practice adding two 3-digit numbers. Support will be provided to help students overcome misconceptions.

TRY IT Practice Adding Two 3-Digit Numbers

Students will complete online practice problems. Then they will complete Practice Adding Two 3-Digit Numbers from *Math 2 Activity Book*.

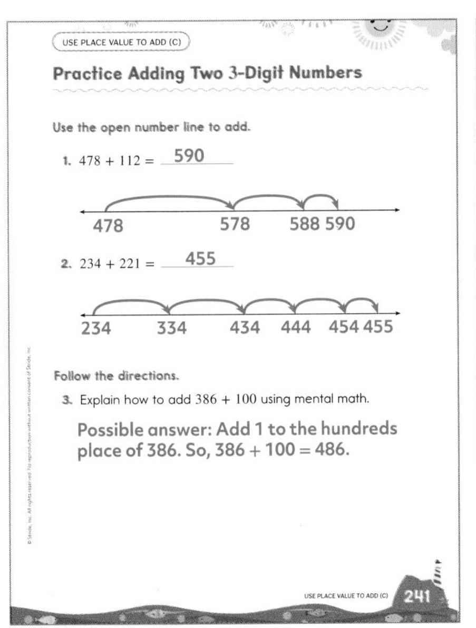

USE PLACE VALUE TO ADD (C)

Practice Adding Two 3-Digit Numbers

Use the open number line to add.

1. 478 + 112 = 590

478 578 588 590

2. 234 + 221 = 455

234 334 434 444 454 455

Follow the directions.

3. Explain how to add 386 + 100 using mental math.

Possible answer: Add 1 to the hundreds place of 386. So, 386 + 100 = 486.

USE PLACE VALUE TO ADD (C) 241

Follow the steps to add.

4. 136 + 523

a. Write 136 and 523 in expanded form.

136 = 100 + 30 + 6
+ 523 = 500 + 20 + 3

b. Add the hundreds, tens, and ones.

600 + 50 + 9

c. Add the sums.

659

5. 457 + 276

a. Add the ones. Regroup.

b. Add the tens. Regroup.

c. Add the hundreds.

	Hundreds	Tens	Ones
	1	1	
	4	5	7
+	2	7	6
	7	3	3

242 USE PLACE VALUE TO ADD (C)

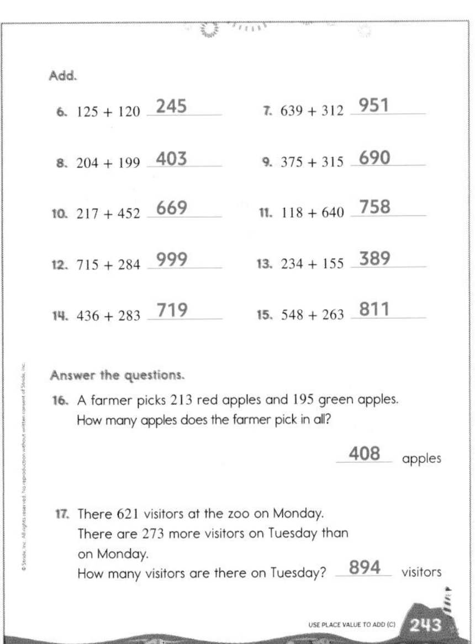

Add.

6. 125 + 120 245
7. 639 + 312 951
8. 204 + 199 403
9. 375 + 315 690
10. 217 + 452 669
11. 118 + 640 758
12. 715 + 284 999
13. 234 + 155 389
14. 436 + 283 719
15. 548 + 263 811

Answer the questions.

16. A farmer picks 213 red apples and 195 green apples. How many apples does the farmer pick in all? 408 apples

17. There 621 visitors at the zoo on Monday. There are 273 more visitors on Tuesday than on Monday. How many visitors are there on Tuesday? 894 visitors

USE PLACE VALUE TO ADD (C) 243

WRAP-UP

Adding Two 3-Digit Numbers

Students will solve problems to show that they understand how to add two 3-digit numbers.

Use Place Value to Add (D)

Lesson Overview

ACTIVITY	ACTIVITY TITLE	TIME	ONLINE/OFFLINE
GET READY	Introduction to Use Place Value to Add (D)	**2** minutes	Online
TRY IT	Review Use Place Value to Add	**18** minutes	Online
QUIZ	Use Place Value to Add	**25** minutes	Online
WRAP-UP	More Math Practice	**15** minutes	Online

Lesson Goals

- Review finding sums greater than 100.
- Take a quiz.

MATERIALS

There are no materials to gather for this lesson.

GET READY

Introduction to Use Place Value to Add (D)

Students will read the lesson goals.

TRY IT

Review Use Place Value to Add

Students will answer questions to review what they have learned about using place value to add.

QUIZ

Use Place Value to Add

Students will complete the Use Place Value to Add quiz.

WRAP-UP

More Math Practice

Students will practice skills according to their individual needs.

Use Place Value to Subtract (A)

Lesson Overview

ACTIVITY	ACTIVITY TITLE	TIME	ONLINE/OFFLINE
GET READY	Introduction to Use Place Value to Subtract (A)	**2** minutes	online
	Look Back at Expanded Form	**7** minutes	online
LEARN AND TRY IT	Subtracting 1-Digit from 3-Digit Numbers	**15** minutes	online
	Subtract 1-Digit from 3-Digit Numbers	**10** minutes	online
ALL ABOUT ME	Brain Break	**1** minute	online or offline
TRY IT	Practice Subtracting 1-Digit from 3-Digit Numbers	**20** minutes	online and offline
WRAP-UP	Subtracting 1-Digit from 3-Digit Numbers	**5** minutes	online

Content Background

Students will learn how to subtract a one-digit number from a three-digit number. They will encounter problems with and without regrouping, and regrouping problems may require regrouping once or twice. Students have experience finding differences of numbers with two digits using strategies based on place value, such as open number lines, base-10 models, place-value charts, and expanded form. Students will learn to apply these strategies to differences with a three-digit minuend and a one-digit subtrahend.

Minuends Greater Than 100

Each subtraction problem in this concept has a minuend that is greater than 100. In other words, each minuend is a three-digit number. Some problems require regrouping 1 ten into 10 ones so that there are enough ones to subtract. Some problems require regrouping 1 hundred into 10 tens so that there are enough tens to subtract. Other problems require regrouping *both* a ten and a hundred.

MATERIALS

Supplied

- *Math 2 Activity Book:* Practice Subtracting 1-Digit from 3-Digit Numbers

Lesson Goals

- Subtract a one-digit number from a three-digit number.

GET READY

Introduction to Use Place Value to Subtract (A)

Students will get a glimpse of what they will learn about in the lesson. They will also read the lesson goals.

Look Back at Expanded Form

Students will review and practice the prerequisite skill of writing numbers in expanded form.

LEARN AND TRY IT

LEARN Subtracting 1-Digit from 3-Digit Numbers

Students will learn how to subtract one-digit numbers from three-digit numbers using strategies based on place value.

TRY IT Subtract 1-Digit from 3-Digit Numbers

Students will practice subtracting one-digit numbers from three-digit numbers. Support will be provided to help students overcome misconceptions.

TRY IT Practice Subtracting 1-Digit from 3-Digit Numbers

Students will complete online practice problems. Then they will complete Practice Subtracting 1-Digit from 3-Digit Numbers from *Math 2 Activity Book.*

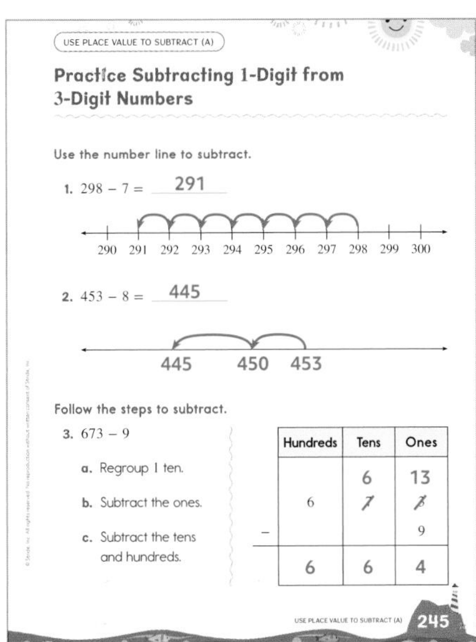

USE PLACE VALUE TO SUBTRACT (A)

Practice Subtracting 1-Digit from 3-Digit Numbers

Use the number line to subtract.

1. 298 – 7 = 291

290 291 292 293 294 295 296 297 298 299 300

2. 453 – 8 = 445

445 450 453

Follow the steps to subtract.

3. 673 – 9

a. Regroup 1 ten.

b. Subtract the ones.

c. Subtract the tens and hundreds.

	Hundreds	Tens	Ones
	6	6 7	13 3
–			9
	6	6	4

USE PLACE VALUE TO SUBTRACT (A) 245

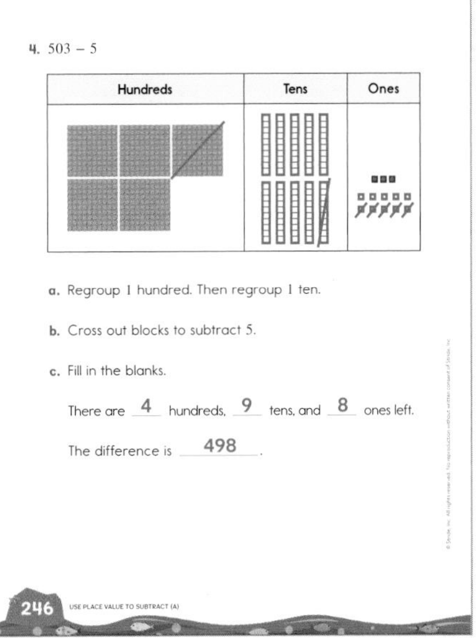

4. 503 – 5

Hundreds	Tens	Ones

a. Regroup 1 hundred. Then regroup 1 ten.

b. Cross out blocks to subtract 5.

c. Fill in the blanks.

There are 4 hundreds, 9 tens, and 8 ones left.

The difference is 498.

246 USE PLACE VALUE TO SUBTRACT (A)

5. 507 – 8

a. Regroup 1 hundred. Then regroup 1 ten.

b. Subtract the ones.

c. Subtract the tens and hundreds.

	Hundreds	Tens	Ones
	4 5	9 10 0	17 7
–			8
	4	9	9

Subtract.

6. 374 – 2 372

7. 167 – 4 163

8. 640 – 6 634

9. 319 – 7 312

10. 100 – 6 94

11. 398 – 9 389

12. 415 – 8 407

13. 253 – 2 251

14. 483 – 7 476

15. 188 – 6 182

USE PLACE VALUE TO SUBTRACT (A) 247

WRAP-UP

Subtracting 1-Digit from 3-Digit Numbers

Students will solve a problem to show that they understand how to subtract a one-digit number from a three-digit number.

Use Place Value to Subtract (B)

Lesson Overview

ACTIVITY	ACTIVITY TITLE	TIME	ONLINE/OFFLINE
GET READY	Introduction to Use Place Value to Subtract (B)	**2** minutes	online
	Adding 17, 18, 19, and 20 Math Facts	**7** minutes	online
LEARN AND **TRY IT**	Subtracting 2-Digit from 3-Digit Numbers without Regrouping	**7** minutes	online
	Subtract 2-Digit from 3-Digit Numbers without Regrouping	**7** minutes	online
ALL ABOUT ME	Brain Break	**1** minute	online or offline
LEARN AND **TRY IT**	Subtracting 2-Digit from 3-Digit Numbers with Regrouping	**7** minutes	online
	Subtract 2-Digit from 3-Digit Numbers with Regrouping	**7** minutes	online
	Practice Subtracting 2-Digit from 3-Digit Numbers	**20** minutes	online and offline
WRAP-UP	Subtracting 2-Digit from 3-Digit Numbers	**2** minutes	online

Content Background

Students will learn how to subtract a two-digit number from a three-digit number using strategies based on place value. They will encounter problems with and without regrouping, and regrouping problems may require regrouping once or twice. Subtraction strategies include open number lines, base-10 models, place-value charts, and expanded form.

MATERIALS

Supplied

- *Math 2 Activity Book:* Practice Subtracting 2-Digit from 3-Digit Numbers

Lesson Goals

- Subtract a two-digit number from a three-digit number.

GET READY

Introduction to Use Place Value to Subtract (B)

Students will get a glimpse of what they will learn about in the lesson. They will also read the lesson goals.

Adding 17, 18, 19, and 20 Math Facts

Students will practice adding 17, 18, 19, and 20.

LEARN AND TRY IT

LEARN Subtracting 2-Digit from 3-Digit Numbers without Regrouping

Students will learn how to subtract two-digit numbers from three-digit numbers without regrouping. Students will apply subtraction strategies based on place value.

TRY IT Subtract 2-Digit from 3-Digit Numbers without Regrouping

Students will practice subtracting two-digit numbers from three-digit numbers without regrouping. Support will be provided to help students overcome misconceptions.

LEARN Subtracting 2-Digit from 3-Digit Numbers with Regrouping

Students will learn how to subtract two-digit numbers from three-digit numbers with regrouping. Students will apply subtraction strategies based on place value.

TRY IT Subtract 2-Digit from 3-Digit Numbers with Regrouping

Students will practice subtracting two-digit numbers from three-digit numbers with regrouping. Support will be provided to help students overcome misconceptions.

TRY IT Practice Subtracting 2-Digit from 3-Digit Numbers

Students will complete online practice problems. Then they will complete Practice Subtracting 2-Digit from 3-Digit Numbers from *Math 2 Activity Book*.

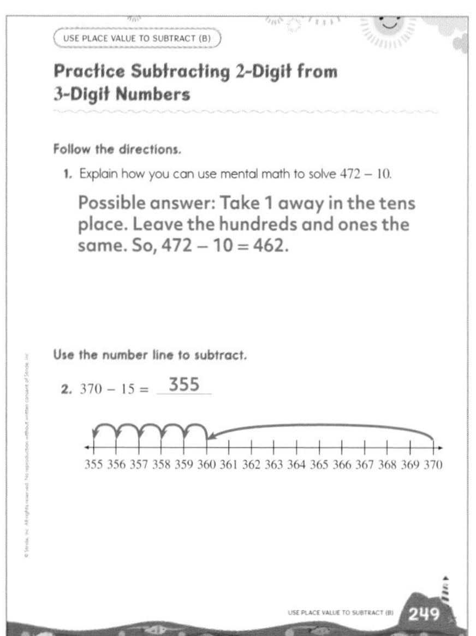

USE PLACE VALUE TO SUBTRACT (B)

Practice Subtracting 2-Digit from 3-Digit Numbers

Follow the directions.

1. Explain how you can use mental math to solve 472 – 10.

Possible answer: Take 1 away in the tens place. Leave the hundreds and ones the same. So, 472 – 10 = 462.

Use the number line to subtract.

2. 370 – 15 = 355

355 356 357 358 359 360 361 362 363 364 365 366 367 368 369 370

USE PLACE VALUE TO SUBTRACT (B) 249

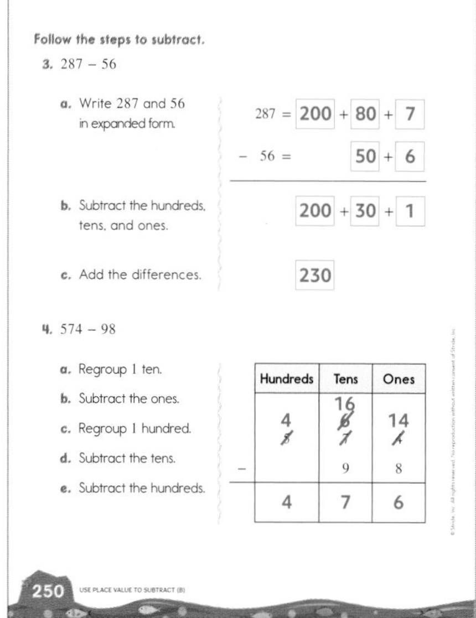

Follow the steps to subtract.

3. 287 – 56

a. Write 287 and 56 in expanded form. 287 = 200 + 80 + 7; – 56 = 50 + 6

b. Subtract the hundreds, tens, and ones. 200 + 30 + 1

c. Add the differences. 230

4. 574 – 98

a. Regroup 1 ten.
b. Subtract the ones.
c. Regroup 1 hundred.
d. Subtract the tens.
e. Subtract the hundreds.

	Hundreds	Tens	Ones
	4 (5 crossed out)	16 (6, 7 crossed out)	14 (4 crossed out)
–		9	8
	4	7	6

250 USE PLACE VALUE TO SUBTRACT (B)

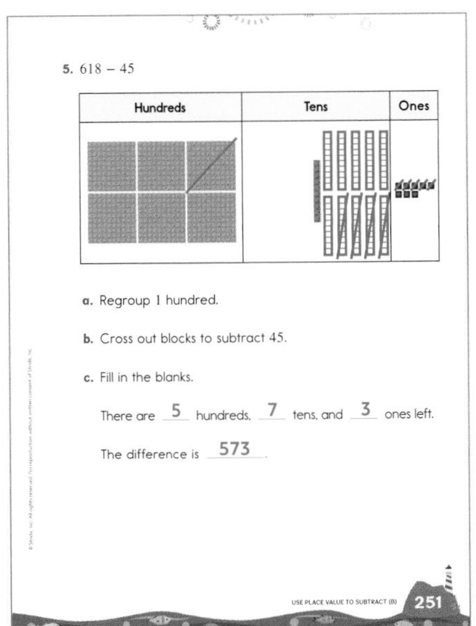

5. 618 − 45

Hundreds	Tens	Ones

a. Regroup 1 hundred.

b. Cross out blocks to subtract 45.

c. Fill in the blanks.

There are 5 hundreds, 7 tens, and 3 ones left.

The difference is 573.

USE PLACE VALUE TO SUBTRACT (B) 251

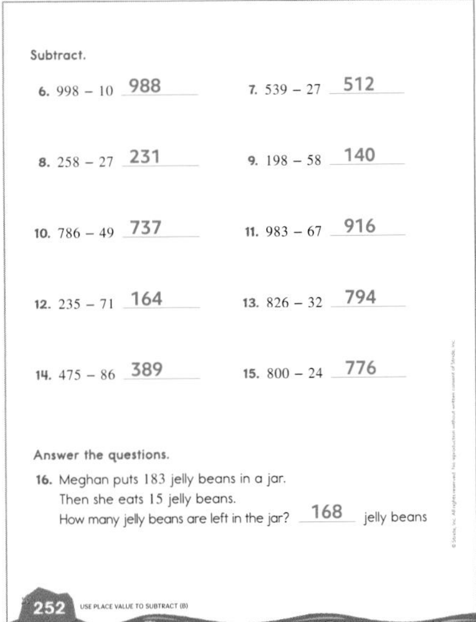

Subtract.

6. 998 − 10 988

7. 539 − 27 512

8. 258 − 27 231

9. 198 − 58 140

10. 786 − 49 737

11. 983 − 67 916

12. 235 − 71 164

13. 826 − 32 794

14. 475 − 86 389

15. 800 − 24 776

Answer the questions.

16. Meghan puts 183 jelly beans in a jar.
Then she eats 15 jelly beans.
How many jelly beans are left in the jar? 168 jelly beans

252 USE PLACE VALUE TO SUBTRACT (B)

WRAP-UP

Subtracting 2-Digit from 3-Digit Numbers

Students will solve problems to show that they understand how to subtract a two-digit number from a three-digit number.

Use Place Value to Subtract (C)

Lesson Overview

ACTIVITY	ACTIVITY TITLE	TIME	ONLINE/OFFLINE
GET READY	Introduction to Use Place Value to Subtract (C)	**2** minutes	online
	Adding 17, 18, 19, and 20 with Instant Recall	**7** minutes	online
LEARN AND TRY IT	Subtracting 3-Digit from 3-Digit Numbers without Regrouping	**7** minutes	online
	Subtract 3-Digit from 3-Digit Numbers without Regrouping	**7** minutes	online
ALL ABOUT ME	Brain Break	**1** minute	online or offline
LEARN AND TRY IT	Subtracting 3-Digit from 3-Digit Numbers with Regrouping	**7** minutes	online
	Subtract 3-Digit from 3-Digit Numbers with Regrouping	**7** minutes	online
	Practice Subtracting 3-Digit from 3-Digit Numbers	**20** minutes	online and offline
WRAP-UP	Subtracting 3-Digit from 3-Digit Numbers	**2** minutes	online

Content Background

Students will learn how to subtract a three-digit number from a three-digit number using strategies based on place value. They will encounter problems with and without regrouping, and regrouping problems may require regrouping once or twice. Subtraction strategies include open number lines, base-10 models, place-value charts, and expanded form.

MATERIALS

Supplied

- *Math 2 Activity Book:* Practice Subtracting 3-Digit from 3-Digit Numbers

Lesson Goals

- Subtract a three-digit number from a three-digit number.

GET READY

Introduction to Use Place Value to Subtract (C)

Students will get a glimpse of what they will learn about in the lesson. They will also read the lesson goals.

Adding 17, 18, 19, and 20 with Instant Recall

Students will practice adding 17 18, 19, and 20.

LEARN AND TRY IT

LEARN Subtracting 3-Digit from 3-Digit Numbers without Regrouping

Students will learn how to subtract three-digit numbers from three-digit numbers without regrouping. Students will apply subtraction strategies based on place value.

TRY IT Subtract 3-Digit from 3-Digit Numbers without Regrouping

Students will practice subtracting three-digit numbers from three-digit numbers without regrouping. Support will be provided to help students overcome misconceptions.

LEARN Subtracting 3-Digit from 3-Digit Numbers with Regrouping

Students will learn how to subtract three-digit numbers from three-digit numbers with regrouping. Students will apply subtraction strategies based on place value.

TRY IT Subtract 3-Digit from 3-Digit Numbers with Regrouping

Students will practice subtracting three-digit numbers from three-digit numbers with regrouping. Support will be provided to help students overcome misconceptions.

TRY IT Practice Subtracting 3-Digit from 3-Digit Numbers

Students will complete online practice problems. Then they will complete Practice Subtracting 3-Digit from 3-Digit Numbers from *Math 2 Activity Book.*

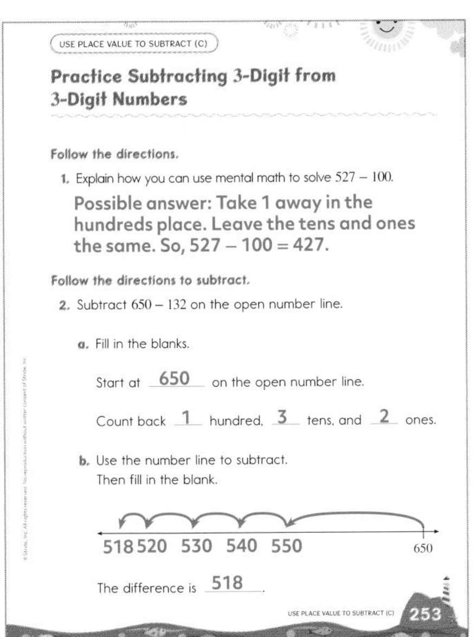

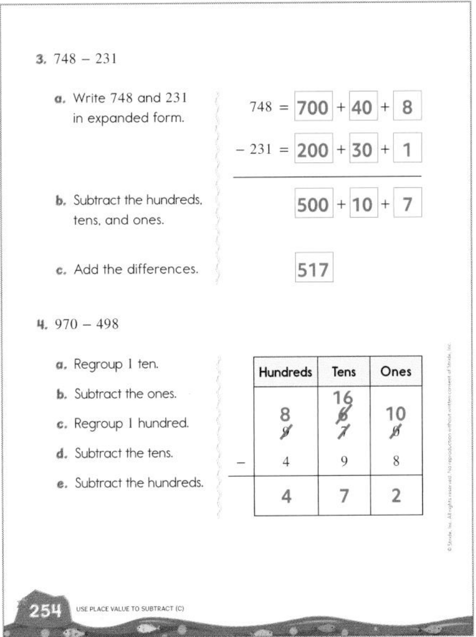

5. 429 − 243

Hundreds	Tens	Ones

a. Regroup 1 hundred.

b. Cross out blocks to subtract 243.

c. Fill in the blanks.

There are 1 hundred, 8 tens, and 6 ones left.

The difference is 186.

USE PLACE VALUE TO SUBTRACT (C) 255

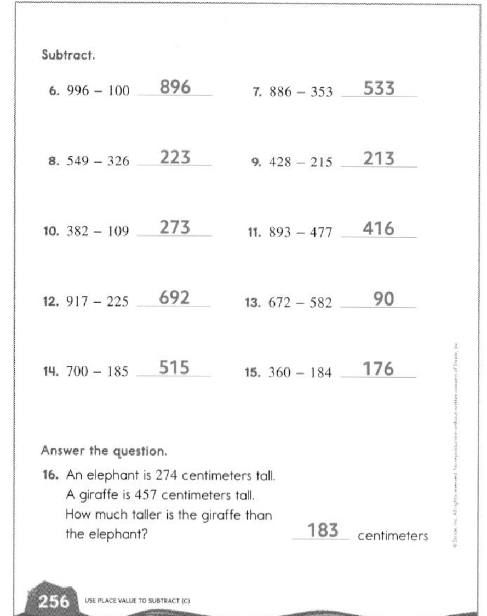

Subtract.

6. 996 − 100 896

7. 886 − 353 533

8. 549 − 326 223

9. 428 − 215 213

10. 382 − 109 273

11. 893 − 477 416

12. 917 − 225 692

13. 672 − 582 90

14. 700 − 185 515

15. 360 − 184 176

Answer the question.

16. An elephant is 274 centimeters tall. A giraffe is 457 centimeters tall. How much taller is the giraffe than the elephant? 183 centimeters

256 USE PLACE VALUE TO SUBTRACT (C)

WRAP-UP

Subtracting 3-Digit from 3-Digit Numbers

Students will solve problems to show that they understand how to subtract a three-digit number from a three-digit number.

Use Place Value to Subtract (D)

Lesson Overview

ACTIVITY	ACTIVITY TITLE	TIME	ONLINE/OFFLINE
GET READY	Introduction to Use Place Value to Subtract (D)	**2** minutes	
TRY IT	Review Use Place Value to Subtract	**18** minutes	
QUIZ	Use Place Value to Subtract	**25** minutes	
WRAP-UP	More Math Practice	**15** minutes	

Lesson Goals

- Review subtracting from a three-digit number.
- Take a quiz.

MATERIALS

There are no materials to gather for this lesson.

GET READY

Introduction to Use Place Value to Subtract (D)

Students will read the lesson goals.

TRY IT

Review Use Place Value to Subtract

Students will answer questions to review what they have learned about using place value to subtract.

QUIZ

Use Place Value to Subtract

Students will complete the Use Place Value to Subtract quiz.

WRAP-UP

More Math Practice

Students will practice skills according to their individual needs.

Use Properties to Add and Subtract (A)

Lesson Overview

ACTIVITY	ACTIVITY TITLE	TIME	ONLINE/OFFLINE
GET READY	Introduction to Use Properties to Add and Subtract (A)	2 minutes	online
	Look Back at 3-Digit Numbers	7 minutes	online
LEARN AND TRY IT	Grouping Addends to Add Larger Numbers	15 minutes	online
	Group Addends to Add Larger Numbers	10 minutes	online
ALL ABOUT ME	Brain Break	1 minute	online or offline
TRY IT	Practice Grouping Addends to Add Larger Numbers	20 minutes	online and offline
WRAP-UP	Grouping Addends to Add Larger Numbers	5 minutes	online

Content Background

Students will learn how to apply the associative property to add larger numbers. The associative property states that grouping numbers in different ways does not change their sum. First, students will learn how to break apart one addend and regroup the addends to make it easier to add. Then they will group addends in problems with three or four addends to make a ten or a hundred.

MATERIALS

Supplied

- *Math 2 Activity Book:* Practice Grouping Addends to Add Larger Numbers

Lesson Goals

- Add larger numbers by grouping addends to make a ten.
- Add larger numbers by grouping addends to make a hundred.

GET READY

Introduction to Use Properties to Add and Subtract (A)

Students will get a glimpse of what they will learn about in the lesson. They will also read the lesson goals.

Look Back at 3-Digit Numbers

Students will review and practice the prerequisite skill of using models and expanded form to show a three-digit number.

LEARN AND TRY IT

LEARN Grouping Addends to Add Larger Numbers

Students will learn how to group addends to add larger numbers.

TRY IT Group Addends to Add Larger Numbers

Students will practice grouping addends to add larger numbers. Support will be provided to help students overcome misconceptions.

TRY IT Practice Grouping Addends to Add Larger Numbers

Students will complete online practice problems. Then they will complete Practice Grouping Addends to Add Larger Numbers from *Math 2 Activity Book*.

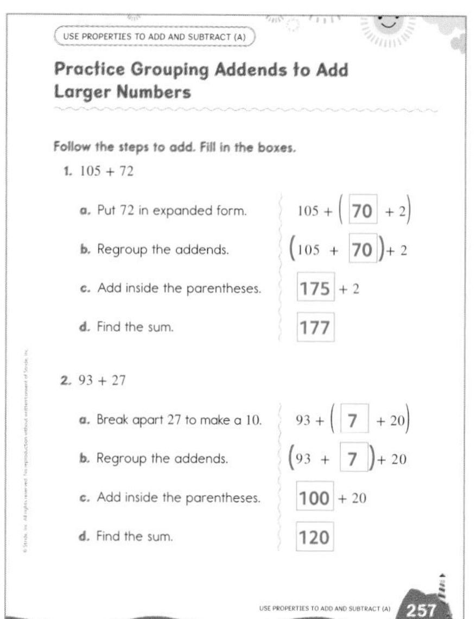

USE PROPERTIES TO ADD AND SUBTRACT (A)

Practice Grouping Addends to Add Larger Numbers

Follow the steps to add. Fill in the boxes.

1. 105 + 72
   - a. Put 72 in expanded form. 105 + (70 + 2)
   - b. Regroup the addends. (105 + 70) + 2
   - c. Add inside the parentheses. 175 + 2
   - d. Find the sum. 177

2. 93 + 27
   - a. Break apart 27 to make a 10. 93 + (7 + 20)
   - b. Regroup the addends. (93 + 7) + 20
   - c. Add inside the parentheses. 100 + 20
   - d. Find the sum. 120

USE PROPERTIES TO ADD AND SUBTRACT (A) 257

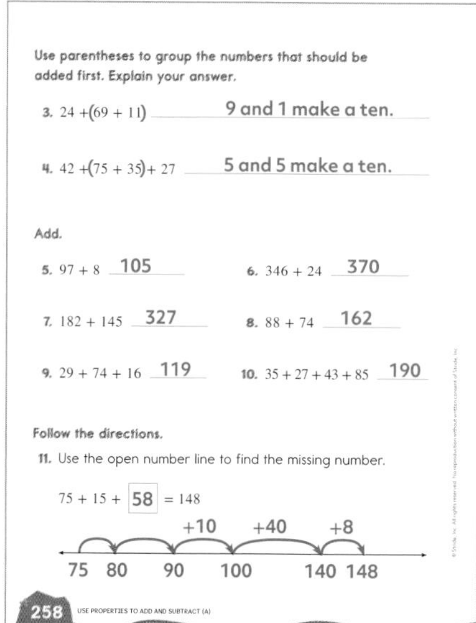

Use parentheses to group the numbers that should be added first. Explain your answer.

3. 24 + (69 + 11) 9 and 1 make a ten.
4. 42 + (75 + 35) + 27 5 and 5 make a ten.

Add.

5. 97 + 8 105
6. 346 + 24 370
7. 182 + 145 327
8. 88 + 74 162
9. 29 + 74 + 16 119
10. 35 + 27 + 43 + 85 190

Follow the directions.

11. Use the open number line to find the missing number.

75 + 15 + 58 = 148

+10 +40 +8

75 80 90 100 140 148

258 USE PROPERTIES TO ADD AND SUBTRACT (A)

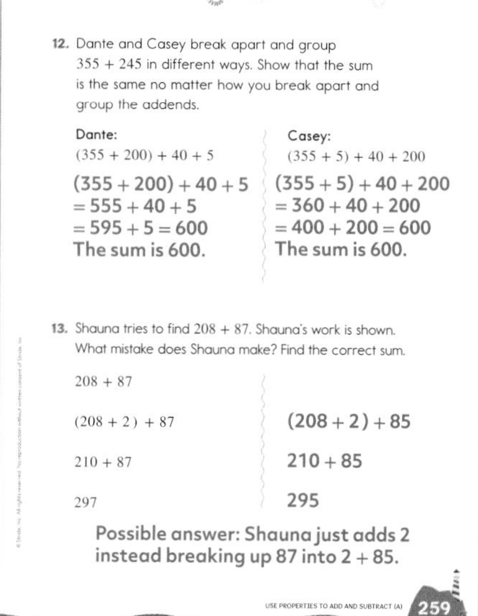

12. Dante and Casey break apart and group 355 + 245 in different ways. Show that the sum is the same no matter how you break apart and group the addends.

Dante: (355 + 200) + 40 + 5	Casey: (355 + 5) + 40 + 200
(355 + 200) + 40 + 5 = 555 + 40 + 5 = 595 + 5 = 600 The sum is 600.	(355 + 5) + 40 + 200 = 360 + 40 + 200 = 400 + 200 = 600 The sum is 600.

13. Shauna tries to find 208 + 87. Shauna's work is shown. What mistake does Shauna make? Find the correct sum.

208 + 87	
(208 + 2) + 87	(208 + 2) + 85
210 + 87	210 + 85
297	295

Possible answer: Shauna just adds 2 instead breaking up 87 into 2 + 85.

USE PROPERTIES TO ADD AND SUBTRACT (A) 259

WRAP-UP

Grouping Addends to Add Larger Numbers

Students will solve a problem to show that they understand how to group addends to add larger numbers.

Use Properties to Add and Subtract (B)

Lesson Overview

ACTIVITY	ACTIVITY TITLE	TIME	ONLINE/OFFLINE
GET READY	Introduction to Use Properties to Add and Subtract (B)	**2** minutes	online
	Adding 17, 18, 19, and 20 Math Facts Game	**8** minutes	online
LEARN AND TRY IT	Moving Addends to Add Larger Numbers	**15** minutes	online
	Move Addends to Add Larger Numbers	**10** minutes	online
	Practice Moving Addends to Add Larger Numbers	**20** minutes	online and offline
WRAP-UP	Moving Addends to Add Larger Numbers	**5** minutes	online

Content Background

Students will learn how to apply the commutative property to add larger numbers. The commutative property states that moving numbers to add them in different orders does not change their sum. First, students will learn how to break apart one addend and move the addends to make it easier to add. Then they will move addends in problems with three or four addends to make a ten or a hundred.

MATERIALS

Supplied

- *Math 2 Activity Book:* Practice Moving Addends to Add Larger Numbers

Lesson Goals

- Add larger numbers by moving addends to change their order.

GET READY

Introduction to Use Properties to Add and Subtract (B)

Students will get a glimpse of what they will learn about in the lesson. They will also read the lesson goals.

Adding 17, 18, 19, and 20 Math Facts Game

Students will play a game to practice adding 17, 18, 19, and 20.

LEARN AND TRY IT

LEARN Moving Addends to Add Larger Numbers

Students will learn how to move addends to add larger numbers.

TRY IT Move Addends to Add Larger Numbers

Students will practice moving addends to add larger numbers. Support will be provided to help students overcome misconceptions.

TRY IT Practice Moving Addends to Add Larger Numbers

Students will complete online practice problems. Then they will complete Practice Moving Addends to Add Larger Numbers from *Math 2 Activity Book*.

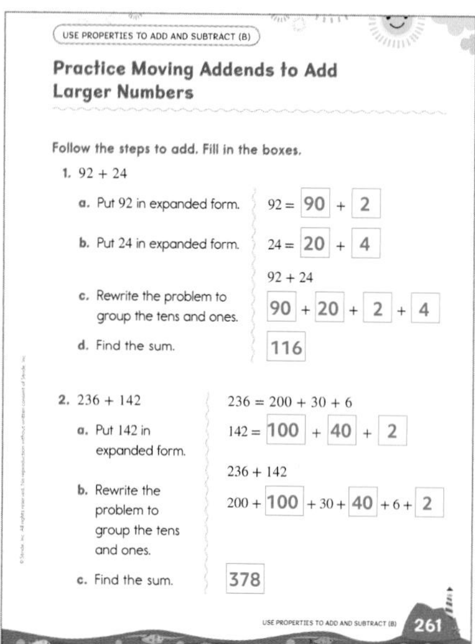

USE PROPERTIES TO ADD AND SUBTRACT (B)

Practice Moving Addends to Add Larger Numbers

Follow the steps to add. Fill in the boxes.

1. 92 + 24
   a. Put 92 in expanded form. 92 = 90 + 2
   b. Put 24 in expanded form. 24 = 20 + 4
   c. Rewrite the problem to group the tens and ones. 92 + 24 = 90 + 20 + 2 + 4
   d. Find the sum. 116

2. 236 + 142
   236 = 200 + 30 + 6
   a. Put 142 in expanded form. 142 = 100 + 40 + 2
   b. Rewrite the problem to group the tens and ones. 236 + 142 = 200 + 100 + 30 + 40 + 6 + 2
   c. Find the sum. 378

USE PROPERTIES TO ADD AND SUBTRACT (B) 261

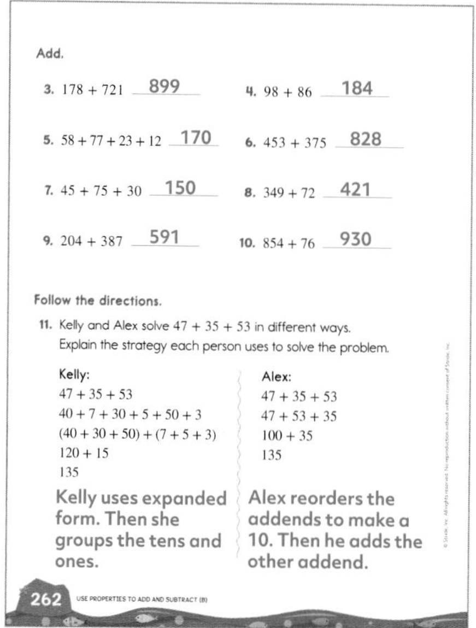

Add.

3. 178 + 721 899
4. 98 + 86 184
5. 58 + 77 + 23 + 12 170
6. 453 + 375 828
7. 45 + 75 + 30 150
8. 349 + 72 421
9. 204 + 387 591
10. 854 + 76 930

Follow the directions.

11. Kelly and Alex solve 47 + 35 + 53 in different ways. Explain the strategy each person uses to solve the problem.

Kelly:	Alex:
47 + 35 + 53	47 + 35 + 53
40 + 7 + 30 + 5 + 50 + 3	47 + 53 + 35
(40 + 30 + 50) + (7 + 5 + 3)	100 + 35
120 + 15	135
135	
Kelly uses expanded form. Then she groups the tens and ones.	Alex reorders the addends to make a 10. Then he adds the other addend.

262 USE PROPERTIES TO ADD AND SUBTRACT (B)

WRAP-UP

Moving Addends to Add Larger Numbers

Students will solve a problem to show that they understand how to move addends to add larger numbers.

Use Properties to Add and Subtract (C)

Lesson Overview

ACTIVITY	ACTIVITY TITLE	TIME	ONLINE/OFFLINE
GET READY	Introduction to Use Properties to Add and Subtract (C)	**2** minutes	
	Subtracting 10, 11, and 12 Math Facts	**7** minutes	
LEARN AND **TRY IT**	Breaking Apart Larger Numbers to Subtract	**15** minutes	
	Break Apart Larger Numbers to Subtract	**10** minutes	
ALL ABOUT ME	Brain Break	**1** minute	or
TRY IT	Practice Breaking Apart Larger Numbers to Subtract	**20** minutes	and
WRAP-UP	Breaking Apart Larger Numbers to Subtract	**5** minutes	

Content Background

Students will learn how breaking apart numbers can make it easier to subtract larger numbers. Some problems become easier when you break apart the subtrahend and then subtract both parts from the minuend. Other problems become easier when you break apart the minuend using addition and then subtract the subtrahend from one of those parts. Students will learn both strategies.

MATERIALS

Supplied

- *Math 2 Activity Book:* Practice Breaking Apart Larger Numbers to Subtract

Lesson Goals

- Break apart larger numbers to subtract.

GET READY

Introduction to Use Properties to Add and Subtract (C)

Students will get a glimpse of what they will learn about in the lesson. They will also read the lesson goals.

Subtracting 10, 11, and 12 Math Facts

Students will practice subtracting 10, 11, and 12.

LEARN AND TRY IT

LEARN Breaking Apart Larger Numbers to Subtract

Students will learn how to break apart larger numbers to make subtracting easier.

TRY IT Break Apart Larger Numbers to Subtract

Students will practice breaking apart larger numbers to subtract. Support will be provided to help students overcome misconceptions.

TRY IT Practice Breaking Apart Larger Numbers to Subtract

Students will complete online practice problems. Then they will complete Practice Breaking Apart Larger Numbers to Subtract from *Math 2 Activity Book*.

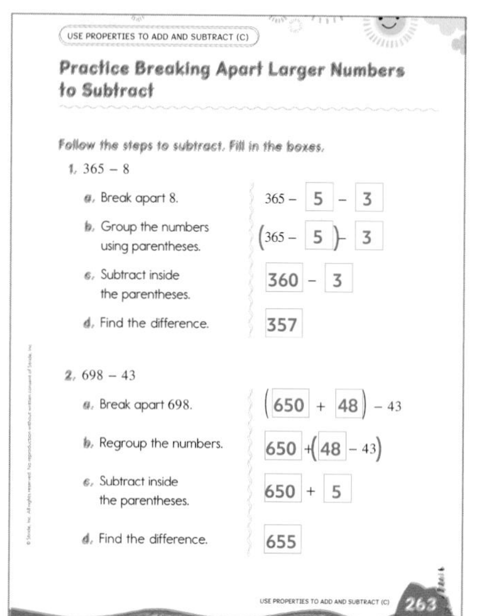

USE PROPERTIES TO ADD AND SUBTRACT (C)

Practice Breaking Apart Larger Numbers to Subtract

Follow the steps to subtract. Fill in the boxes.

1. 365 − 8
   a. Break apart 8. 365 − 5 − 3
   b. Group the numbers using parentheses. (365 − 5) − 3
   c. Subtract inside the parentheses. 360 − 3
   d. Find the difference. 357
2. 698 − 43
   a. Break apart 698. (650 + 48) − 43
   b. Regroup the numbers. 650 + (48 − 43)
   c. Subtract inside the parentheses. 650 + 5
   d. Find the difference. 655

USE PROPERTIES TO ADD AND SUBTRACT (C) 263

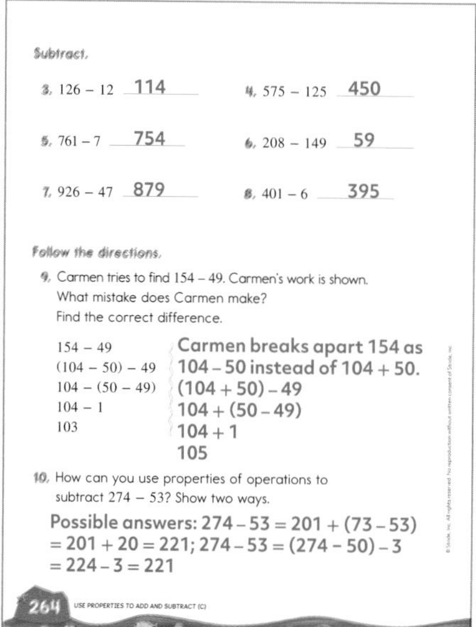

Subtract.

3. 126 − 12 114
4. 575 − 125 450
5. 761 − 7 754
6. 208 − 149 59
7. 926 − 47 879
8. 401 − 6 395

Follow the directions.

9. Carmen tries to find 154 − 49. Carmen's work is shown. What mistake does Carmen make? Find the correct difference.

   154 − 49
   (104 − 50) − 49
   104 − (50 − 49)
   104 − 1
   103

   Carmen breaks apart 154 as 104 − 50 instead of 104 + 50.
   (104 + 50) − 49
   104 + (50 − 49)
   104 + 1
   105

10. How can you use properties of operations to subtract 274 − 53? Show two ways.

    Possible answers: 274 − 53 = 201 + (73 − 53) = 201 + 20 = 221; 274 − 53 = (274 − 50) − 3 = 224 − 3 = 221

264 USE PROPERTIES TO ADD AND SUBTRACT (C)

WRAP-UP

Breaking Apart Larger Numbers to Subtract

Students will solve a problem to show that they understand how to break apart larger numbers to subtract.

Use Properties to Add and Subtract (D)

Lesson Overview

ACTIVITY	ACTIVITY TITLE	TIME	ONLINE/OFFLINE
GET READY	Introduction to Use Properties to Add and Subtract (D)	**2** minutes	
TRY IT	Review Use Properties to Add and Subtract	**18** minutes	
QUIZ	Use Properties to Add and Subtract	**25** minutes	
WRAP-UP	More Math Practice	**15** minutes	

Lesson Goals

- Review adding and subtracting larger numbers using properties.
- Take a quiz.

MATERIALS

There are no materials to gather for this lesson.

GET READY

Introduction to Use Properties to Add and Subtract (D)

Students will read the lesson goals.

TRY IT

Review Use Properties to Add and Subtract

Students will answer questions to review what they have learned about using properties to add and subtract.

QUIZ

Use Properties to Add and Subtract

Students will complete the Use Properties to Add and Subtract quiz.

WRAP-UP

More Math Practice

Students will practice skills according to their individual needs.

Use Relationships to Add and Subtract (A)

Lesson Overview

ACTIVITY	ACTIVITY TITLE	TIME	ONLINE/OFFLINE
GET READY	Introduction to Use Relationships to Add and Subtract (A)	**2** minutes	online
	Look Back at Using Friendly Numbers	**7** minutes	online
LEARN AND **TRY IT**	Adding Using Relationships	**15** minutes	online
	Add Using Relationships	**10** minutes	online
ALL ABOUT ME	Brain Break	**1** minute	online or offline
TRY IT	Practice Adding Using Relationships	**20** minutes	online and offline
WRAP-UP	Adding Using Relationships	**5** minutes	online

Content Background

Students will learn how to use the relationship between addition and subtraction to make addition problems with larger numbers easier to solve. They will learn how to make friendly numbers.

Making Friendly Numbers

Numbers are *friendly* when they are easier to add. Students can make one addend friendly, add, then adjust the result. They can also make both addends friendly by moving an amount from one addend to the other. Here are some examples.

Change One Addend	Change Both Addends
$327 + 3 = 330$ $+\ 186 \quad = 186$ $516 - 3 = 513$	$327 - 14 = 313$ $+\ 186 + 14 = 200$ 513

MATERIALS

Supplied

- *Math 2 Activity Book:* Practice Adding Using Relationships

Lesson Goals

- Add larger numbers using friendly numbers.

GET READY

Introduction to Use Relationships to Add and Subtract (A)

Students will get a glimpse of what they will learn about in the lesson. They will also read the lesson goals.

Look Back at Using Friendly Numbers

Students will review and practice the prerequisite skill of using friendly numbers to add and subtract two-digit numbers.

LEARN AND TRY IT

LEARN Adding Using Relationships

Students will learn how to add larger numbers using the relationship between addition and subtraction.

TRY IT Add Using Relationships

Students will practice adding using relationships. Support will be provided to help students overcome misconceptions.

TRY IT Practice Adding Using Relationships

Students will complete online practice problems. Then they will complete Practice Adding Using Relationships from *Math 2 Activity Book*.

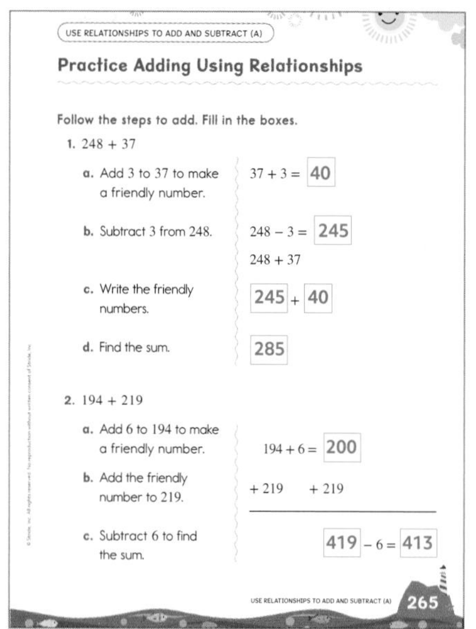

USE RELATIONSHIPS TO ADD AND SUBTRACT (A)

Practice Adding Using Relationships

Follow the steps to add. Fill in the boxes.

1. 248 + 37
   - a. Add 3 to 37 to make a friendly number. 37 + 3 = 40
   - b. Subtract 3 from 248. 248 − 3 = 245; 248 + 37
   - c. Write the friendly numbers. 245 + 40
   - d. Find the sum. 285
2. 194 + 219
   - a. Add 6 to 194 to make a friendly number. 194 + 6 = 200
   - b. Add the friendly number to 219. + 219 + 219
   - c. Subtract 6 to find the sum. 419 − 6 = 413

USE RELATIONSHIPS TO ADD AND SUBTRACT (A) 265

Add.

3. 755 + 9 764
4. 186 + 22 208
5. 658 + 239 897
6. 416 + 92 508
7. 322 + 43 365
8. 236 + 189 425
9. 167 + 145 312
10. 843 + 28 871

Follow the directions.

11. Ian uses friendly numbers to add 164 + 16. What is another way to add using friendly numbers? Show your work.

164 + 16
− 4 + 4
160 + 20 = 180

Possible answers:

164 + 16
+ 1 − 1
165 + 15 = 180

266 USE RELATIONSHIPS TO ADD AND SUBTRACT (A)

WRAP-UP

Adding Using Relationships

Students will solve a problem to show that they understand how to add using relationships.

Use Relationships to Add and Subtract (B)

Lesson Overview

ACTIVITY	ACTIVITY TITLE	TIME	ONLINE/OFFLINE
GET READY	Introduction to Use Relationships to Add and Subtract (B)	**2** minutes	online
	Subtracting 10, 11, and 12 with Instant Recall	**7** minutes	online
LEARN AND TRY IT	Subtracting Using Relationships	**15** minutes	online
	Subtract Using Relationships	**10** minutes	online
ALL ABOUT ME	Brain Break	**1** minute	online or offline
TRY IT	Practice Subtracting Using Relationships	**20** minutes	online and offline
WRAP-UP	Subtracting Using Relationships	**5** minutes	online

Content Background

Students will learn how to use the relationship between addition and subtraction to make subtraction problems with larger numbers easier to solve. They will learn how to count on with a number line and make friendly numbers.

Making Friendly Numbers

Numbers are *friendly* when they are easier to subtract. Students can make one number friendly, subtract, then adjust the result. They can also make both numbers friendly by adding or subtracting the same amount to both numbers. Here are some examples.

Change One Number	Change Both Numbers
$709 + 1 = 710$ $-\ 55 \quad = 55$ $655 - 1 = 654$	$709 - 5 = 704$ $-\ 55 - 5 = 50$ 654

MATERIALS

Supplied

- *Math 2 Activity Book:* Practice Subtracting Using Relationships

Lesson Goals

- Subtract larger numbers using friendly numbers.
- Subtract larger numbers by adding.

GET READY

Introduction to Use Relationships to Add and Subtract (B)

Students will get a glimpse of what they will learn about in the lesson. They will also read the lesson goals.

Subtracting 10, 11, and 12 with Instant Recall

Students will practice subtracting 10, 11, and 12.

LEARN AND TRY IT

LEARN Subtracting Using Relationships

Students will learn how to subtract larger numbers using the relationship between addition and subtraction.

TRY IT Subtract Using Relationships

Students will practice subtracting using relationships. Support will be provided to help students overcome misconceptions.

TRY IT Practice Subtracting Using Relationships

Students will complete online practice problems. Then they will complete Practice Subtracting Using Relationships from *Math 2 Activity Book*.

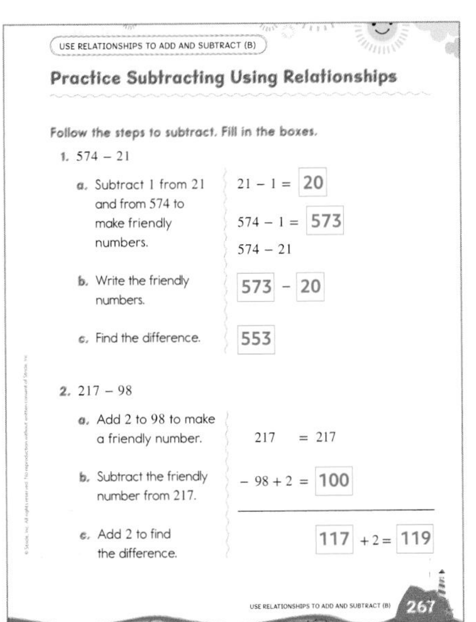

USE RELATIONSHIPS TO ADD AND SUBTRACT (B)

Practice Subtracting Using Relationships

Follow the steps to subtract. Fill in the boxes.

1. 574 – 21
   a. Subtract 1 from 21 and from 574 to make friendly numbers. 21 – 1 = 20; 574 – 1 = 573; 574 – 21
   b. Write the friendly numbers. 573 – 20
   c. Find the difference. 553

2. 217 – 98
   a. Add 2 to 98 to make a friendly number. 217 = 217
   b. Subtract the friendly number from 217. – 98 + 2 = 100
   c. Add 2 to find the difference. 117 + 2 = 119

USE RELATIONSHIPS TO ADD AND SUBTRACT (B) 267

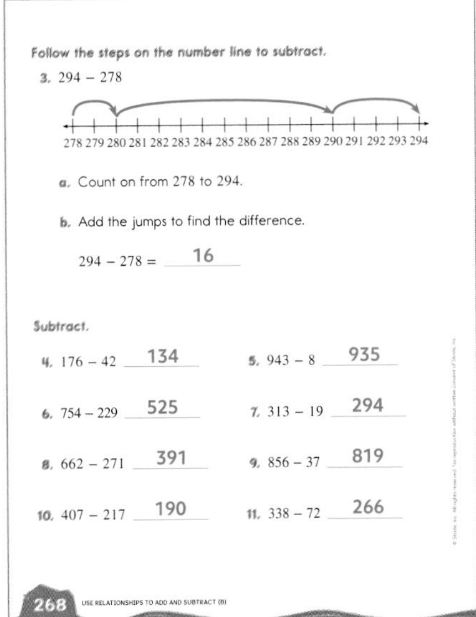

Follow the steps on the number line to subtract.

3. 294 – 278

   a. Count on from 278 to 294.
   b. Add the jumps to find the difference.

   294 – 278 = 16

Subtract.

4. 176 – 42 = 134
5. 943 – 8 = 935
6. 754 – 229 = 525
7. 313 – 19 = 294
8. 662 – 271 = 391
9. 856 – 37 = 819
10. 407 – 217 = 190
11. 338 – 72 = 266

268 USE RELATIONSHIPS TO ADD AND SUBTRACT (B)

WRAP-UP

Subtracting Using Relationships

Students will solve problems to show that they understand how to subtract using relationships.

Use Relationships to Add and Subtract (C)

Lesson Overview

ACTIVITY	ACTIVITY TITLE	TIME	ONLINE/OFFLINE
GET READY	Introduction to Use Relationships to Add and Subtract (C)	**2** minutes	
TRY IT	Review Use Relationships to Add and Subtract	**18** minutes	
QUIZ	Use Relationships to Add and Subtract	**25** minutes	
WRAP-UP	More Math Practice	**15** minutes	

Lesson Goals

- Review using relationships to add and subtract.
- Take a quiz.

MATERIALS

There are no materials to gather for this lesson.

GET READY

Introduction to Use Relationships to Add and Subtract (C)

Students will read the lesson goals.

TRY IT

Review Use Relationships to Add and Subtract

Students will answer questions to review what they have learned about using relationships to add and subtract.

QUIZ

Use Relationships to Add and Subtract

Students will complete the Use Relationships to Add and Subtract quiz.

WRAP-UP

More Math Practice

Students will practice skills according to their individual needs.

Add and Subtract within 1,000 Wrap-Up

Lesson Overview

ACTIVITY	ACTIVITY TITLE	TIME	ONLINE/OFFLINE
GET READY	Introduction to Add and Subtract within 1,000 Wrap-Up	2 minutes	
TRY IT	Review Add and Subtract within 1,000	23 minutes	
UNIT CHECKPOINT	Add and Subtract within 1,000	35 minutes	

Lesson Goals

- Review adding and subtracting within 1,000.
- Show what you know about adding and subtracting within 1,000.

MATERIALS

There are no materials to gather for this lesson.

GET READY

Introduction to Add and Subtract within 1,000 Wrap-Up

Students will read the lesson goals.

TRY IT

Review Add and Subtract within 1,000

Students will answer questions to review what they have learned about adding and subtracting within 1,000.

UNIT CHECKPOINT

Add and Subtract within 1,000

Students will complete the Add and Subtract within 1,000 Unit Checkpoint.

LEARNING COACH CHECK-IN This is a graded assignment. Make sure students complete the online assessment.

Skip Counting (A)

Lesson Overview

ACTIVITY	ACTIVITY TITLE	TIME	ONLINE/OFFLINE
GET READY	Introduction to Skip Counting (A)	**2** minutes	online
	Look Back at Counting by 10s to 100	**7** minutes	online
LEARN AND TRY IT	Skip Counting by 10s	**7** minutes	online
	Skip Count by 10s	**7** minutes	online
ALL ABOUT ME	Brain Break	**1** minute	online or offline
LEARN AND TRY IT	Skip Counting by 100s	**7** minutes	online
	Skip Count by 100s	**7** minutes	online
	Practice Skip Counting by 10s and 100s	**20** minutes	online and offline
WRAP-UP	Skip Counting by 10s and 100s	**2** minutes	online

Content Background

Students will learn to skip count by 10s and 100s to 1,000. They will use a hundred chart and a number line to help them skip count. Skip counting can help students count to greater numbers more quickly than if they counted by ones. It also prepares students to learn about multiplication in Math 3.

Skip Counting

Skip counting means to count by a number other than 1. Students will only practice counting by 10s from numbers that end in zero, which are called multiples of 10. They will only practice counting by 100s from numbers that end in two zeros, which are called multiples of 100.

MATERIALS

Supplied

- *Math 2 Activity Book:* Practice Skip Counting by 10s and 100s

KEYWORDS

skip count – to count by a number other than 1

Lesson Goals

- Skip count by 10s.
- Skip count by 100s.

GET READY

Introduction to Skip Counting (A)

Students will get a glimpse of what they will learn about in the lesson. They will also read the lesson goals.

Look Back at Counting by 10s to 100

Students will review and practice the prerequisite skill of counting by 10s to 100.

LEARN AND TRY IT

LEARN Skip Counting by 10s

Students will learn how to skip count by 10s up to 1,000.

OPTIONAL Allow students to count objects in groups of 10 or that represent 10. For example, they can count by 10s to find the value of a group of dimes.

TRY IT Skip Count by 10s

Students will practice skip counting by 10s. Support will be provided to help students overcome misconceptions.

LEARN Skip Counting by 100s

Students will learn how to skip count by 100s up to 1,000.

TIP Have students count aloud from 1 to 9 and then skip count aloud by 100s from 100 to 900. Then ask what sounded the same or different. Help students recognize that they say each number from 1 to 9 when they skip count by 100s. The difference is that students also say the word *hundred* for each number as they skip count.

TRY IT Skip Count by 100s

Students will practice skip counting by 100s. Support will be provided to help students overcome misconceptions.

TRY IT Practice Skip Counting by 10s and 100s

Students will complete online practice problems. Then they will complete Practice Skip Counting by 10s and 100s from *Math 2 Activity Book*.

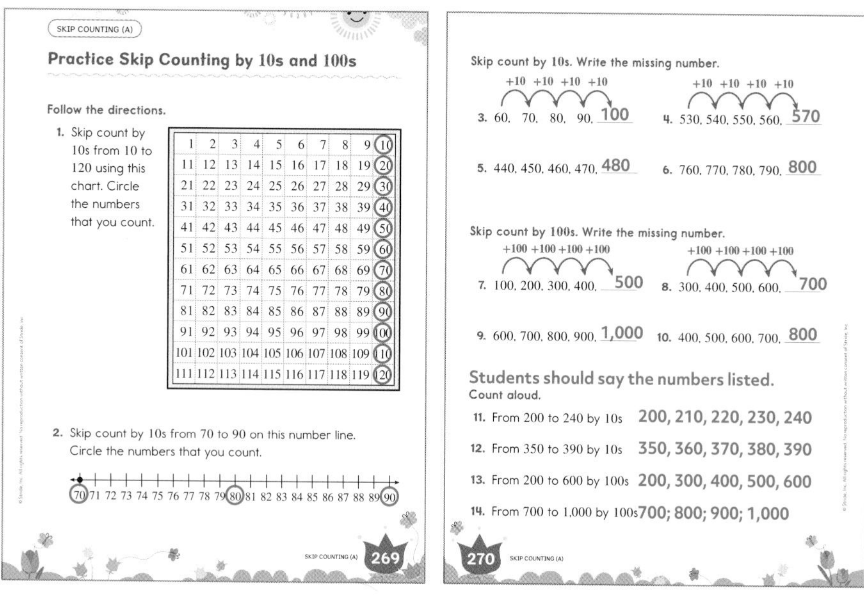

SKIP COUNTING (A)

Practice Skip Counting by 10s and 100s

Follow the directions.

1. Skip count by 10s from 10 to 120 using this chart. Circle the numbers that you count.

1	2	3	4	5	6	7	8	9	(10)
11	12	13	14	15	16	17	18	19	(20)
21	22	23	24	25	26	27	28	29	(30)
31	32	33	34	35	36	37	38	39	(40)
41	42	43	44	45	46	47	48	49	(50)
51	52	53	54	55	56	57	58	59	(60)
61	62	63	64	65	66	67	68	69	(70)
71	72	73	74	75	76	77	78	79	(80)
81	82	83	84	85	86	87	88	89	(90)
91	92	93	94	95	96	97	98	99	(100)
101	102	103	104	105	106	107	108	109	(110)
111	112	113	114	115	116	117	118	119	(120)

2. Skip count by 10s from 70 to 90 on this number line. Circle the numbers that you count.

(70) 71 72 73 74 75 76 77 78 79 (80) 81 82 83 84 85 86 87 88 89 (90)

SKIP COUNTING (A) 269

Skip count by 10s. Write the missing number.

3. 60, 70, 80, 90, 100 (+10 +10 +10 +10)
4. 530, 540, 550, 560, 570 (+10 +10 +10 +10)
5. 440, 450, 460, 470, 480
6. 760, 770, 780, 790, 800

Skip count by 100s. Write the missing number.

7. 100, 200, 300, 400, 500 (+100 +100 +100 +100)
8. 300, 400, 500, 600, 700 (+100 +100 +100 +100)
9. 600, 700, 800, 900, 1,000
10. 400, 500, 600, 700, 800

Students should say the numbers listed.

Count aloud.

11. From 200 to 240 by 10s 200, 210, 220, 230, 240
12. From 350 to 390 by 10s 350, 360, 370, 380, 390
13. From 200 to 600 by 100s 200, 300, 400, 500, 600
14. From 700 to 1,000 by 100s 700; 800; 900; 1,000

270 SKIP COUNTING (A)

WRAP-UP

Skip Counting by 10s and 100s

Students will solve problems to show that they understand how to skip count by 10s and 100s.

Skip Counting (B)

Lesson Overview

ACTIVITY	ACTIVITY TITLE	TIME	ONLINE/OFFLINE
GET READY	Introduction to Skip Counting (B)	**2** minutes	
	Subtracting 10, 11, and 12 Math Facts Game	**8** minutes	
LEARN AND **TRY IT**	Skip Counting by 5s	**15** minutes	
	Skip Count by 5s	**10** minutes	
	Practice Skip Counting by 5s	**20** minutes	and
WRAP-UP	Skip Counting by 5s	**5** minutes	

Content Background

Students will learn to skip count by 5s up to 1,000. They will use a hundred chart and a number line to help them skip count. Students will only practice counting by 5s from numbers that end in 0 or 5, which are called multiples of 5.

MATERIALS

Supplied

- *Math 2 Activity Book:* Practice Skip Counting by 5s

Lesson Goals

- Skip count by 5s.

GET READY

Introduction to Skip Counting (B)

Students will get a glimpse of what they will learn about in the lesson. They will also read the lesson goals.

Subtracting 10, 11, and 12 Math Facts Game

Students will play a game to practice subtracting 10, 11, and 12.

Collect and Display Data (C)

Lesson Overview

ACTIVITY	ACTIVITY TITLE	TIME	ONLINE/OFFLINE
GET READY	Introduction to Collect and Display Data (C)	**2** minutes	
TRY IT	Review Collect and Display Data	**18** minutes	
QUIZ	Collect and Display Data	**25** minutes	
WRAP-UP	More Math Practice	**15** minutes	

Lesson Goals

- Review collecting and displaying data.
- Take a quiz.

MATERIALS

There are no materials to gather for this lesson.

GET READY

Introduction to Collect and Display Data (C)

Students will read the lesson goals.

TRY IT

Review Collect and Display Data

Students will answer questions to review what they have learned about collecting and displaying data.

QUIZ

Collect and Display Data

Students will complete the Collect and Display Data quiz.

WRAP-UP

More Math Practice

Students will practice skills according to their individual needs.

Picture Graphs (A)

Lesson Overview

ACTIVITY	ACTIVITY TITLE	TIME	ONLINE/OFFLINE
GET READY	Introduction to Picture Graphs (A)	**2** minutes	online
	Look Back at Organizing Data	**7** minutes	online
LEARN AND **TRY IT**	Interpreting Picture Graphs	**15** minutes	online
	Interpret Picture Graphs	**10** minutes	online
ALL ABOUT ME	Brain Break	**1** minute	online or offline
TRY IT	Practice Interpreting Picture Graphs	**20** minutes	online and offline
WRAP-UP	Interpreting Picture Graphs	**5** minutes	online

Content Background

Students will learn how to interpret data shown in a picture graph. In a picture graph, data is separated into categories and each picture represents one data value. Students will answer questions about how many data values are in certain categories, which categories have the most or fewest data values, and which categories have the same number of data values. Students will also interpret picture graphs by stating their own observations about a picture graph.

MATERIALS

Supplied

- *Math 2 Activity Book:* Practice Interpreting Picture Graphs

KEYWORDS

picture graph – a graph that uses pictures to represent data

Lesson Goals

- Answer questions about data shown in a picture graph.

GET READY

Introduction to Picture Graphs (A)

Students will get a glimpse of what they will learn about in the lesson. They will also read the lesson goals.

Look Back at Organizing Data

Students will review and practice the prerequisite skill of organizing data into two or three categories.

LEARN AND TRY IT

LEARN Interpreting Picture Graphs

Students will learn how to interpret picture graphs by answering questions about data shown in a picture graph.

TRY IT Interpret Picture Graphs

Students will practice interpreting picture graphs. Support will be provided to help students overcome misconceptions.

TRY IT Practice Interpreting Picture Graphs

Students will complete online practice problems. Then they will complete Practice Interpreting Picture Graphs from *Math 2 Activity Book*.

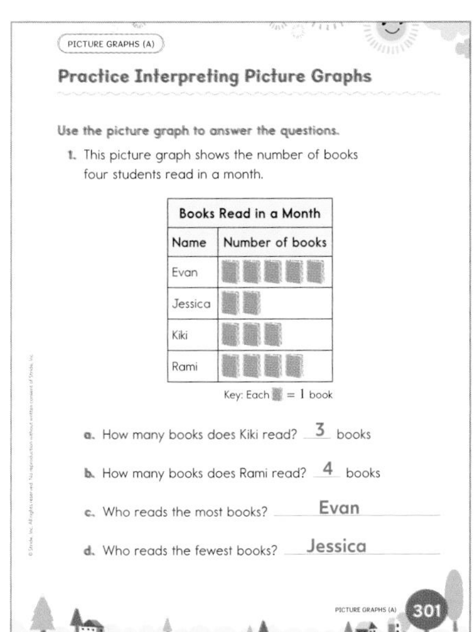

PICTURE GRAPHS (A)

Practice Interpreting Picture Graphs

Use the picture graph to answer the questions.

1. This picture graph shows the number of books four students read in a month.

Books Read in a Month	
Name	Number of books
Evan	
Jessica	
Kiki	
Rami	

Key: Each = 1 book

a. How many books does Kiki read? 3 books

b. How many books does Rami read? 4 books

c. Who reads the most books? Evan

d. Who reads the fewest books? Jessica

PICTURE GRAPHS (A) 301

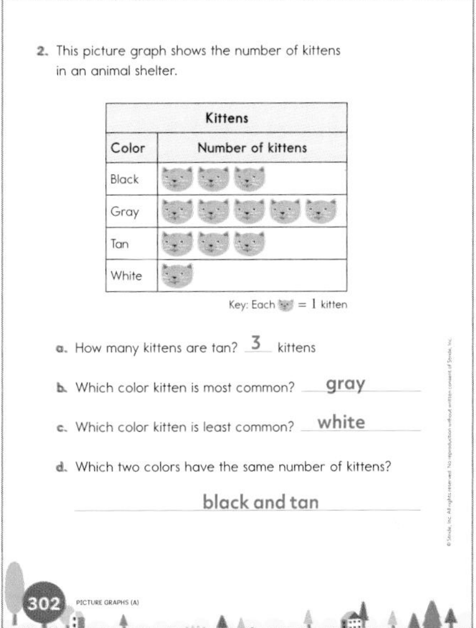

2. This picture graph shows the number of kittens in an animal shelter.

Kittens	
Color	Number of kittens
Black	
Gray	
Tan	
White	

Key: Each = 1 kitten

a. How many kittens are tan? 3 kittens

b. Which color kitten is most common? gray

c. Which color kitten is least common? white

d. Which two colors have the same number of kittens?

black and tan

302 PICTURE GRAPHS (A)

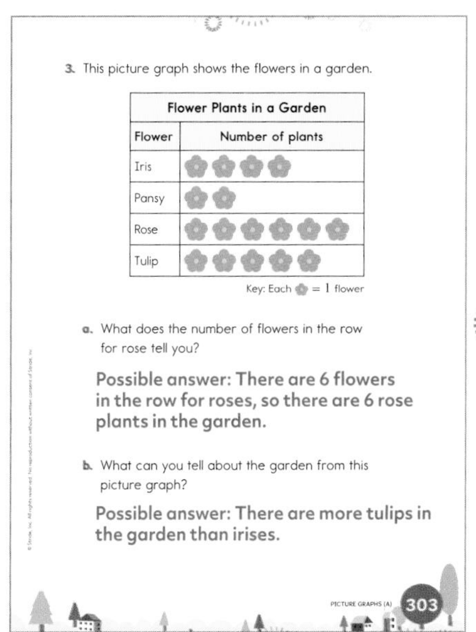

3. This picture graph shows the flowers in a garden.

Flower Plants in a Garden	
Flower	Number of plants
Iris	
Pansy	
Rose	
Tulip	

Key: Each = 1 flower

a. What does the number of flowers in the row for rose tell you?

Possible answer: There are 6 flowers in the row for roses, so there are 6 rose plants in the garden.

b. What can you tell about the garden from this picture graph?

Possible answer: There are more tulips in the garden than irises.

PICTURE GRAPHS (A) 303

WRAP-UP

Interpreting Picture Graphs

Students will solve a problem to show that they understand how to interpret picture graphs.

Picture Graphs (B)

Lesson Overview

ACTIVITY	ACTIVITY TITLE	TIME	ONLINE/OFFLINE
GET READY	Introduction to Picture Graphs (B)	**2** minutes	online
	Subtracting 17, 18, 19, and 20 Math Facts Game	**7** minutes	online
LEARN AND TRY IT	Making Picture Graphs	**15** minutes	online
	Make Picture Graphs	**10** minutes	online
ALL ABOUT ME	Brain Break	**1** minute	online or offline
TRY IT	Practice Making Picture Graphs	**20** minutes	online and offline
WRAP-UP	Making Picture Graphs	**5** minutes	online

Content Background

Students will learn how to represent data by making a picture graph. Some data sets will be given in a tally chart. Other data sets may be given as images or in a list that students must organize into a tally chart. Ultimately, students must draw one picture to represent each data value in a picture graph.

MATERIALS

Supplied

- *Math 2 Activity Book:* Practice Making Picture Graphs

Lesson Goals

- Show data in a picture graph.

GET READY

Introduction to Picture Graphs (B)

Students will get a glimpse of what they will learn about in the lesson. They will also read the lesson goals.

Subtracting 17, 18, 19, and 20 Math Facts Game

Students will play a game to practice subtracting 17, 18, 19, and 20.

LEARN AND TRY IT

LEARN Making Picture Graphs

Students will learn how to make picture graphs to represent data.

TRY IT Make Picture Graphs

Students will practice making picture graphs. Support will be provided to help students overcome misconceptions.

TRY IT Practice Making Picture Graphs

Students will complete online practice problems. Then they will complete Practice Making Picture Graphs from *Math 2 Activity Book*.

NOTE Pictures that students draw when they make a picture graph can be as simple or elaborate as they desire. However, each picture within one graph should be the same.

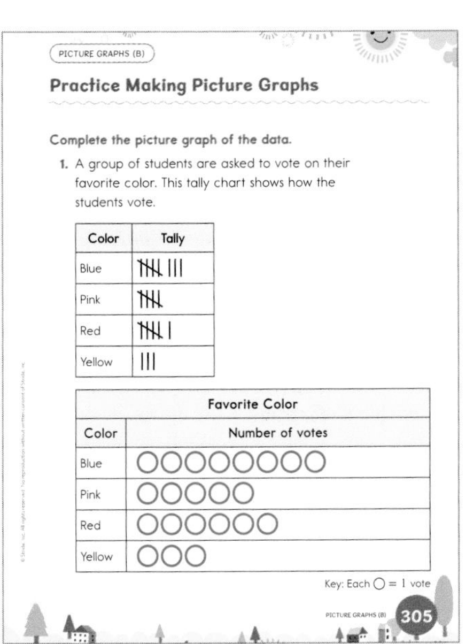

PICTURE GRAPHS (B)

Practice Making Picture Graphs

Complete the picture graph of the data.

1. A group of students are asked to vote on their favorite color. This tally chart shows how the students vote.

Color	Tally
Blue	𝍸 III
Pink	𝍸
Red	𝍸 I
Yellow	III

Favorite Color	
Color	Number of votes
Blue	○○○○○○○○
Pink	○○○○○
Red	○○○○○○
Yellow	○○○

Key: Each ○ = 1 vote

PICTURE GRAPHS (B) 305

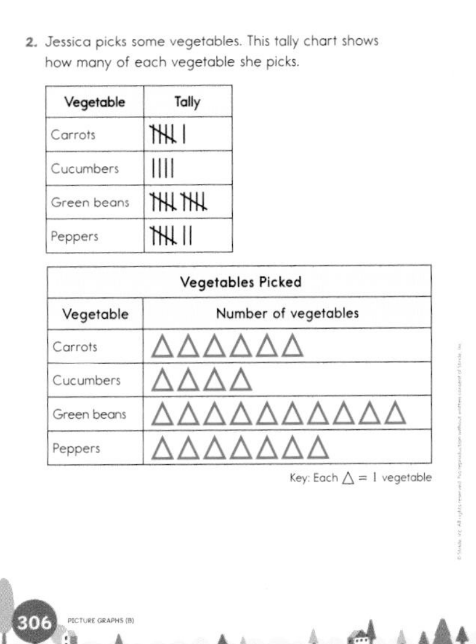

2. Jessica picks some vegetables. This tally chart shows how many of each vegetable she picks.

Vegetable	Tally
Carrots	𝍸 I
Cucumbers	IIII
Green beans	𝍸 𝍸
Peppers	𝍸 II

Vegetables Picked	
Vegetable	Number of vegetables
Carrots	△△△△△△
Cucumbers	△△△△
Green beans	△△△△△△△△△△
Peppers	△△△△△△△

Key: Each △ = 1 vegetable

306 PICTURE GRAPHS (B)

Follow the steps.

3. Jessica has a box of crayons. These are the crayons in the box.

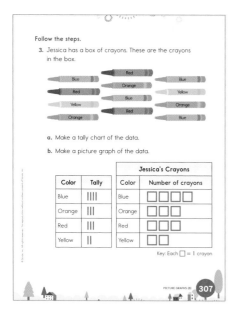

Blue Red Blue
Orange Red Yellow
Yellow Blue Orange
Orange Red Blue

a. Make a tally chart of the data.

b. Make a picture graph of the data.

Color	Tally
Blue	||||
Orange	|||
Red	|||
Yellow	||

Jessica's Crayons	
Color	Number of crayons
Blue	□□□□
Orange	□□□
Red	□□□
Yellow	□□

Key: Each □ = 1 crayon

PICTURE GRAPHS (B) 307

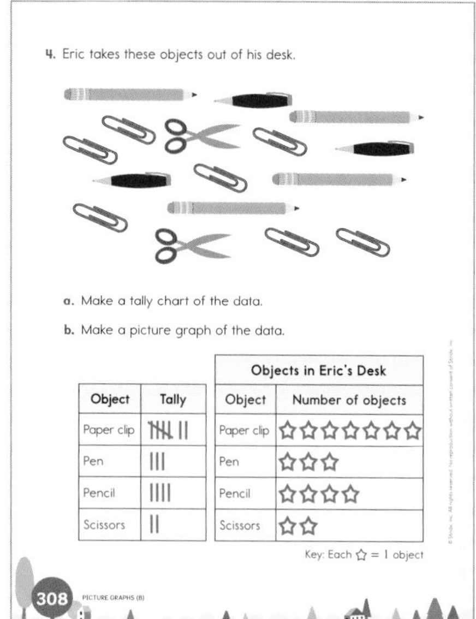
4. Eric takes these objects out of his desk.

a. Make a tally chart of the data.

b. Make a picture graph of the data.

Object	Tally
Paper clip	𝍸 ||
Pen	|||
Pencil	||||
Scissors	||

Objects in Eric's Desk	
Object	Number of objects
Paper clip	☆☆☆☆☆☆☆
Pen	☆☆☆
Pencil	☆☆☆☆
Scissors	☆☆

Key: Each ☆ = 1 object

308 PICTURE GRAPHS (B)

WRAP-UP

Making Picture Graphs

Students will solve a problem to show that they understand how to make picture graphs.

Picture Graphs (C)

Lesson Overview

ACTIVITY	ACTIVITY TITLE	TIME	ONLINE/OFFLINE
GET READY	Introduction to Picture Graphs (C)	**2** minutes	
TRY IT	Review Picture Graphs	**18** minutes	
QUIZ	Picture Graphs	**25** minutes	
WRAP-UP	More Math Practice	**15** minutes	

Lesson Goals

- Review picture graphs.
- Take a quiz.

MATERIALS

There are no materials to gather for this lesson.

GET READY

Introduction to Picture Graphs (C)

Students will read the lesson goals.

TRY IT

Review Picture Graphs

Students will answer questions to review what they have learned about picture graphs.

QUIZ

Picture Graphs

Students will complete the Picture Graphs quiz.

WRAP-UP

More Math Practice

Students will practice skills according to their individual needs.

Bar Graphs (A)

Lesson Overview

ACTIVITY	ACTIVITY TITLE	TIME	ONLINE/OFFLINE
GET READY	Introduction to Bar Graphs (A)	**2** minutes	online
	Look Back at Representing Data	**7** minutes	online
LEARN AND TRY IT	Interpreting Bar Graphs	**15** minutes	online
	Interpret Bar Graphs	**10** minutes	online
ALL ABOUT ME	Brain Break	**1** minute	online or offline
TRY IT	Practice Interpreting Bar Graphs	**20** minutes	online and offline
WRAP-UP	Interpreting Bar Graphs	**5** minutes	online

Content Background

Students will learn how to interpret data shown in a bar graph. In a bar graph, data is separated into categories and the height of each bar represents the number of data values in that category. Students will encounter both vertical and horizontal bar graphs in this concept. They will answer questions about how many data values are in certain categories, which categories have the most or fewest data values, and which categories have the same number of data values. Students will also interpret bar graphs by stating their own observations about a bar graph.

MATERIALS

Supplied

- *Math 2 Activity Book:* Practice Interpreting Bar Graphs

KEYWORDS

bar graph – a graph that uses bars of different lengths to represent data

Lesson Goals

- Answer questions about data shown in bar graphs.

GET READY

Introduction to Bar Graphs (A)

Students will get a glimpse of what they will learn about in the lesson. They will also read the lesson goals.

Look Back at Representing Data

Students will review and practice the prerequisite skill of representing data in three categories.

LEARN AND TRY IT

LEARN Interpreting Bar Graphs

Students will learn how to interpret bar graphs by answering questions about data shown in a bar graph.

overcome misconceptions.

TRY IT Practice Interpreting Bar Graphs

Students will complete online practice problems. Then they will complete Practice Interpreting Bar Graphs from *Math 2 Activity Book*.

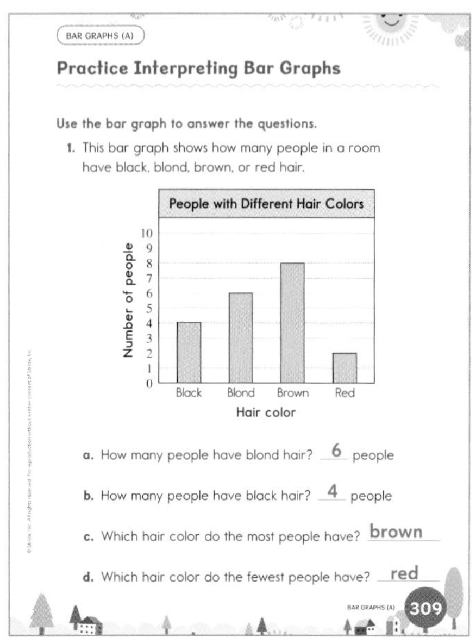

BAR GRAPHS (A)

Practice Interpreting Bar Graphs

Use the bar graph to answer the questions.

1. This bar graph shows how many people in a room have black, blond, brown, or red hair.

a. How many people have blond hair? 6 people

b. How many people have black hair? 4 people

c. Which hair color do the most people have? brown

d. Which hair color do the fewest people have? red

BAR GRAPHS (A) 309

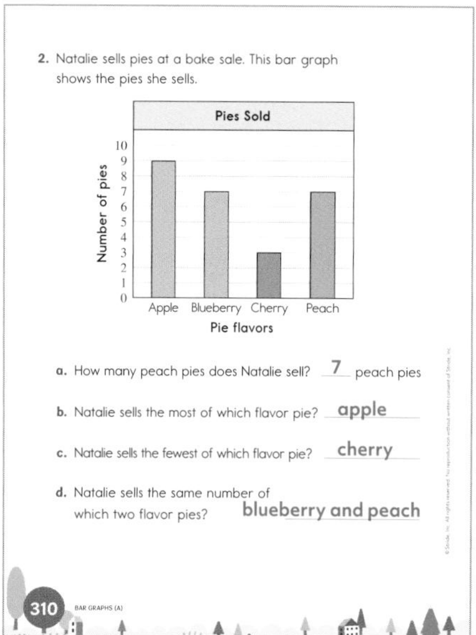

2. Natalie sells pies at a bake sale. This bar graph shows the pies she sells.

a. How many peach pies does Natalie sell? 7 peach pies

b. Natalie sells the most of which flavor pie? apple

c. Natalie sells the fewest of which flavor pie? cherry

d. Natalie sells the same number of which two flavor pies? blueberry and peach

310 BAR GRAPHS (A)

3. A shelf holds cans of vegetables. This bar graph shows the number of each type of can on the shelf.

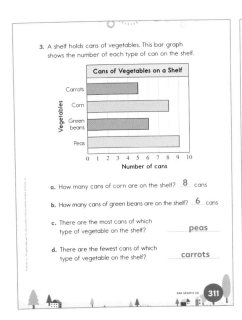

Cans of Vegetables on a Shelf

Vegetables: Carrots, Corn, Green beans, Peas

Number of cans: 0 1 2 3 4 5 6 7 8 9 10

a. How many cans of corn are on the shelf? 8 cans

b. How many cans of green beans are on the shelf? 6 cans

c. There are the most cans of which type of vegetable on the shelf? peas

d. There are the fewest cans of which type of vegetable on the shelf? carrots

BAR GRAPHS (A) 311

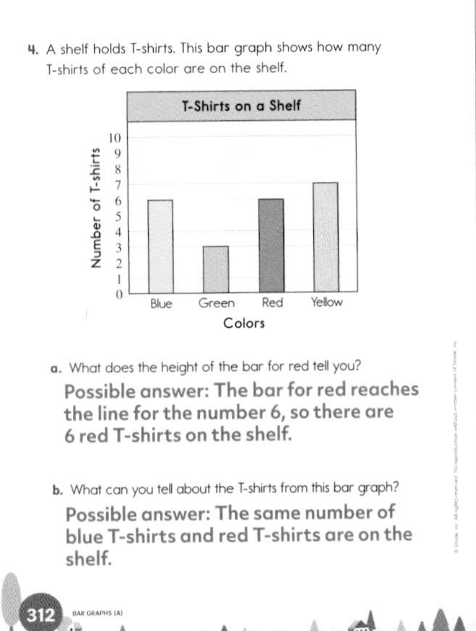

4. A shelf holds T-shirts. This bar graph shows how many T-shirts of each color are on the shelf.

a. What does the height of the bar for red tell you?
Possible answer: The bar for red reaches the line for the number 6, so there are 6 red T-shirts on the shelf.

b. What can you tell about the T-shirts from this bar graph?
Possible answer: The same number of blue T-shirts and red T-shirts are on the shelf.

312 BAR GRAPHS (A)

WRAP-UP

Interpreting Bar Graphs

Students will solve a problem to show that they understand how to interpret bar graphs.

Bar Graphs (B)

Lesson Overview

	Adding and Subtracting within 20 Math Facts	**8** minutes	
LEARN AND **TRY IT**	Making Bar Graphs	**15** minutes	
	Make Bar Graphs	**10** minutes	
	Practice Making Bar Graphs	**20** minutes	and
WRAP-UP	Making Bar Graphs	**5** minutes	

Content Background

Students will learn how to represent data by making a bar graph. Some data sets will be given in a tally chart. Other data sets may be given as images or in a list that students must organize into a tally chart. Ultimately, they must draw bars at the correct heights or lengths to represent the data values in a bar graph. Students will learn how to make vertical and horizontal bar graphs.

MATERIALS

Supplied

- *Math 2 Activity Book:* Practice Making Bar Graphs

Lesson Goals

- Show data in a bar graph.

GET READY

Introduction to Bar Graphs (B)

Students will get a glimpse of what they will learn about in the lesson. They will also read the lesson goals.

Adding and Subtracting within 20 Math Facts

Students will practice adding and subtracting within 20.

LEARN AND TRY IT

LEARN Making Bar Graphs

Students will learn how to make vertical and horizontal bar graphs.

TRY IT Make Bar Graphs

Students will practice making bar graphs. Support will be provided to help students overcome misconceptions.

TRY IT Practice Making Bar Graphs

Students will complete online practice problems. Then they will complete Practice Making Bar Graphs from *Math 2 Activity Book*.

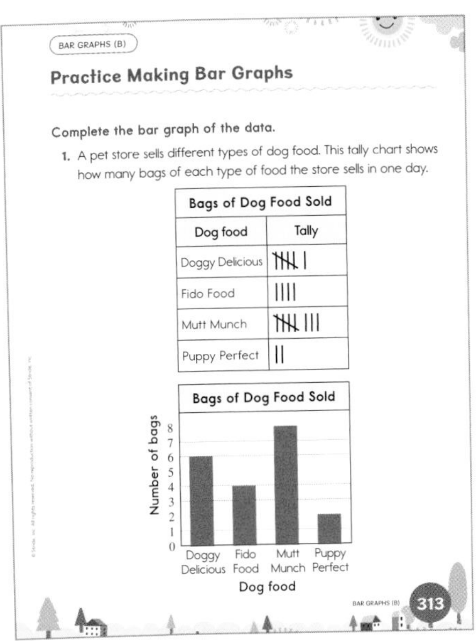
BAR GRAPHS (B)

Practice Making Bar Graphs

Complete the bar graph of the data.

1. A pet store sells different types of dog food. This tally chart shows how many bags of each type of food the store sells in one day.

Bags of Dog Food Sold	
Dog food	Tally
Doggy Delicious	𝍸 I
Fido Food	IIII
Mutt Munch	𝍸 III
Puppy Perfect	II

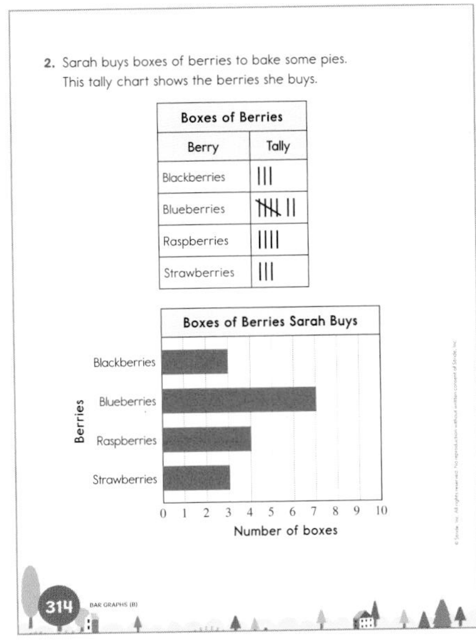
2. Sarah buys boxes of berries to bake some pies. This tally chart shows the berries she buys.

Boxes of Berries	
Berry	Tally
Blackberries	III
Blueberries	𝍸 II
Raspberries	IIII
Strawberries	III

Follow the steps.

3. Jordan takes these toys out of his toy box.

Toys	Tally
Balls	𝍸 I
Cars	IIII
Robots	I
Teddy bears	II

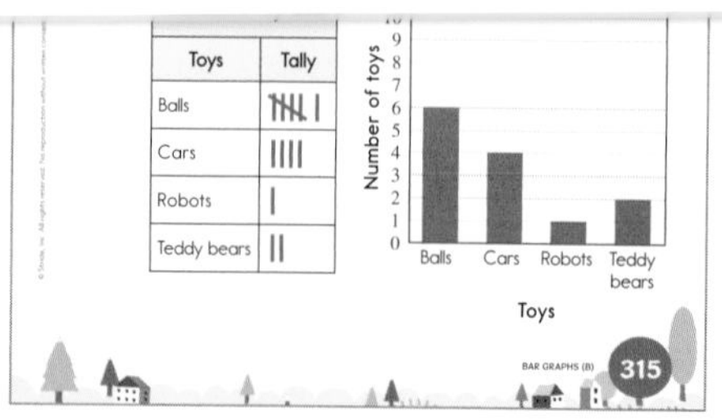

4. A group of people vote for their favorite snack food. This table shows the foods they choose.

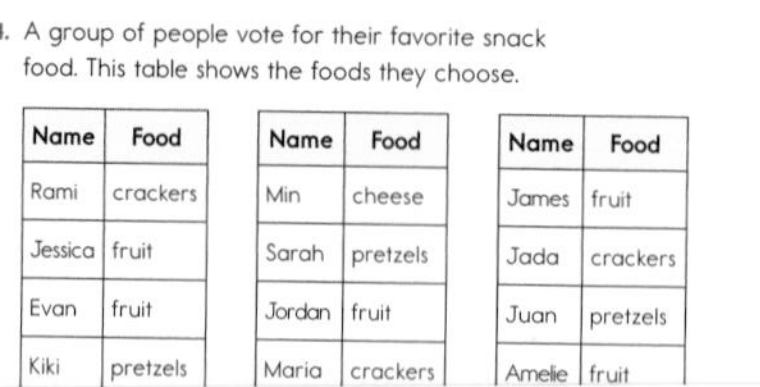

Name	Food
Rami	crackers
Jessica	fruit
Evan	fruit
Kiki	pretzels

Name	Food
Min	cheese
Sarah	pretzels
Jordan	fruit
Maria	crackers

Name	Food
James	fruit
Jada	crackers
Juan	pretzels
Amelie	fruit

Snack Food

Food	Tally
Cheese	I
Crackers	III
Fruit	𝍸
Pretzels	III

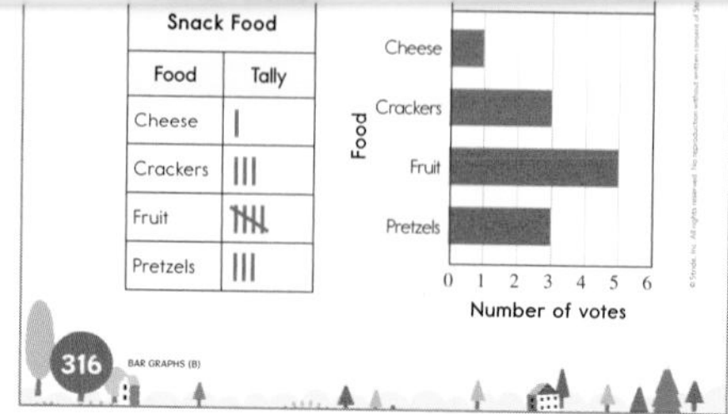

WRAP-UP

Making Bar Graphs

Students will solve a problem to show that they understand how to make bar graphs.

Bar Graphs (C)

Lesson Overview

ACTIVITY	ACTIVITY TITLE	TIME	ONLINE/OFFLINE
GET READY	Introduction to Bar Graphs (C)	**2** minutes	online
	Adding and Subtracting within 20 with Instant Recall	**7** minutes	online
LEARN AND **TRY IT**	Solving Problems Using Bar Graphs	**15** minutes	online
	Solve Problems Using Bar Graphs	**10** minutes	online
ALL ABOUT ME	Brain Break	**1** minute	online or offline
TRY IT	Practice Solving Problems Using Bar Graphs	**20** minutes	online and offline
WRAP-UP	Solving Problems Using Bar Graphs	**5** minutes	online

Content Background

Students will learn how to solve simple compare, put-together, and take-apart problems using data shown in bar graphs. Students have experience using the three problem-solving steps to solve one-step story problems. To solve problems presented in this lesson, students must find numbers in a bar graph. Data will be presented in both vertical and horizontal bar graphs.

MATERIALS

Supplied

- *Math 2 Activity Book:* Practice Solving Problems Using Bar Graphs

Lesson Goals

- Solve problems about data shown in bar graphs.

GET READY

Introduction to Bar Graphs (C)

Students will get a glimpse of what they will learn about in the lesson. They will also read the lesson goals.

Adding and Subtracting within 20 with Instant Recall

Students will practice adding and subtracting within 20.

LEARN AND TRY IT

LEARN Solving Problems Using Bar Graphs

Students will learn how to solve problems using data shown in bar graphs.

TRY IT Solve Problems Using Bar Graphs

TRY IT Practice Solving Problems Using Bar Graphs

Students will complete online practice problems. Then they will complete Practice Solving Problems Using Bar Graphs from *Math 2 Activity Book*.

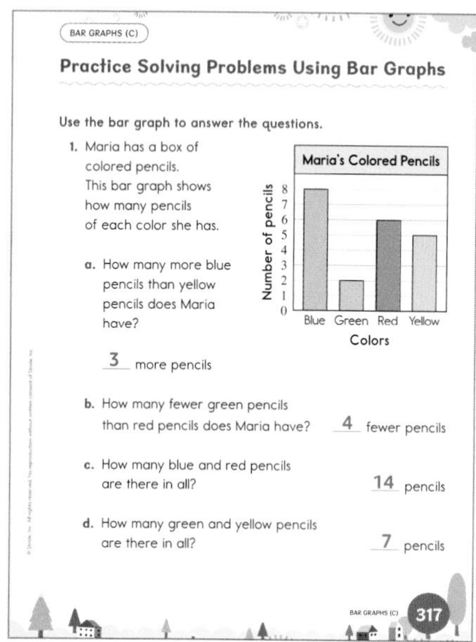

BAR GRAPHS (C)

Practice Solving Problems Using Bar Graphs

Use the bar graph to answer the questions.

1. Maria has a box of colored pencils. This bar graph shows how many pencils of each color she has.

a. How many more blue pencils than yellow pencils does Maria have?

3 more pencils

b. How many fewer green pencils than red pencils does Maria have? 4 fewer pencils

c. How many blue and red pencils are there in all? 14 pencils

d. How many green and yellow pencils are there in all? 7 pencils

BAR GRAPHS (C) 317

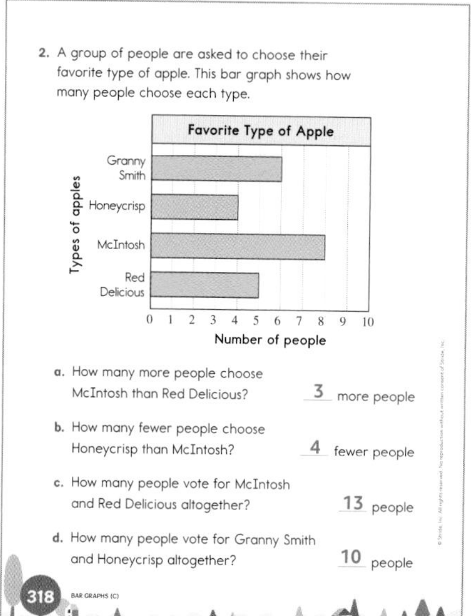

2. A group of people are asked to choose their favorite type of apple. This bar graph shows how many people choose each type.

a. How many more people choose McIntosh than Red Delicious? 3 more people

b. How many fewer people choose Honeycrisp than McIntosh? 4 fewer people

c. How many people vote for McIntosh and Red Delicious altogether? 13 people

d. How many people vote for Granny Smith and Honeycrisp altogether? 10 people

318 BAR GRAPHS (C)

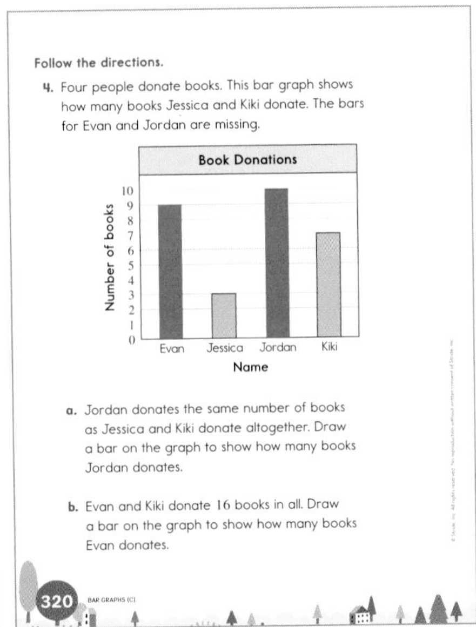

3. Four people make paper snowflakes. This bar graph shows how many snowflakes Amelie, Eloise, and Min make. The bar for Matthew is missing.

a. How many more snowflakes does Min make than Amelie? 4 more snowflakes

b. How many snowflakes do Eloise and Min make altogether? 15 snowflakes

c. Matthew and Amelie make 13 snowflakes in all. How many snowflakes does Matthew make? 10 snowflakes

BAR GRAPHS (C) 319

Follow the directions.

4. Four people donate books. This bar graph shows how many books Jessica and Kiki donate. The bars for Evan and Jordan are missing.

a. Jordan donates the same number of books as Jessica and Kiki donate altogether. Draw a bar on the graph to show how many books Jordan donates.

b. Evan and Kiki donate 16 books in all. Draw a bar on the graph to show how many books Evan donates.

320 BAR GRAPHS (C)

WRAP-UP

Solving Problems Using Bar Graphs

Students will solve problems to show that they understand how to solve problems using bar graphs.

Bar Graphs (D)

Lesson Overview

TRY IT	Review Bar Graphs	**18** minutes	
QUIZ	Bar Graphs	**25** minutes	
WRAP-UP	More Math Practice	**15** minutes	

Lesson Goals

- Review bar graphs.
- Take a quiz.

MATERIALS

There are no materials to gather for this lesson.

GET READY

Introduction to Bar Graphs (D)

Students will read the lesson goals.

TRY IT

Review Bar Graphs

Students will answer questions to review what they have learned about bar graphs.

QUIZ

Bar Graphs

Students will complete the Bar Graphs quiz.

WRAP-UP

More Math Practice

Students will practice skills according to their individual needs.

Data Displays Wrap-Up

Lesson Overview

TRY IT	Review Data Displays	**18** minutes	
UNIT CHECKPOINT	Data Displays Online Checkpoint	**18** minutes	
	Data Displays Offline Checkpoint	**20** minutes	
WRAP-UP	Turn in Your Offline Checkpoint	**2** minutes	

Lesson Goals

- Review data displays.
- Show what you know about data displays.

MATERIALS

Supplied

- Data Displays Offline Checkpoint (printout)

GET READY

Introduction to Data Displays Wrap-Up

Students will read the lesson goals.

TRY IT

Review Data Displays

Students will answer questions to review what they have learned about data displays.

UNIT CHECKPOINT

Data Displays Online Checkpoint

Students will complete the Data Displays Unit Checkpoint.

LEARNING COACH CHECK-IN This is a graded assignment. Make sure students complete the online assessment.

Data Displays Offline Checkpoint

Students will complete multistep problems that go beyond the short answer and multiple choice problems in their regular lessons. These problems give students an opportunity to demonstrate problem solving, reasoning, communication, and modeling skills. Students will need to use paper and pencil and/or technology to show their work.

Materials are linked online. The materials are not provided in this lesson guide or the activity book.

LEARNING COACH CHECK-IN This is a graded assignment. Make sure students complete, review, and submit their assignment to the teacher. If you are unsure how to do this, ask students' teacher.

WRAP-UP

Turn in Your Offline Checkpoint

Students will turn in their graded assignment.

End-of-Year Project

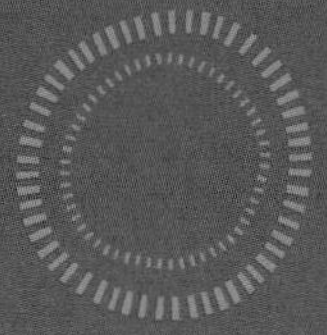

End-of-Year Project

Project Overview

1. **Learn and Try It:** Students learn more about selected topics.

2. **Putting It All Together:** Students complete a small, creative project designed to extend concepts and skills they have encountered across units. This project is designed to emphasize a real-world application that connects mathematics to everyday life. Students will need to use pencil and paper and/or technology to show their work.

   LEARNING COACH CHECK-IN This is a graded assignment. Make sure students complete, review, and submit the assignment to their teacher.

Students will be presented with two project options. They will choose and complete one project. All materials needed for this lesson are linked online. The materials are not provided in this lesson guide or the activity book.

MATERIALS

(printout)

- Sticker Graph Project (printout)